Buddleia Dance on the Asylum:

A Nurse's Journey through a Mental Hospital

Stephen Burrow

Published by

MELROSE BOOKS

An Imprint of Melrose Press Limited
St Thomas Place, Ely
Cambridgeshire
CB7 4GG, UK
www.melrosebooks.com

FIRST EDITION

Copyright © Stephen Burrow 2010

The Author asserts his moral right to
be identified as the author of this work

Cover designed by Catherinne McIntyre

ISBN 978 1 907040 01 6

Printed and bound in Great Britain by:
The MPG Books Group. King's Lynn
and Bodmin

Mixed Sources

Product group from well-managed
forests, controlled sources and
recycled wood or fiber
www.fsc.org Cert no. TT-COC-002303
© 1996 Forest Stewardship Council

CONTENTS

This book is dedicated to my two daughters,
Rachel and Heather.

ABSTRACTS

"When we step into the family, by the act of being born, we do step into a world which has its own strange laws, into a world which could do without us, into a world which we have not made."
G.K. Chesterton: *Heretics*.

"We live not only our own lives but, whether we know it or not, also the life of our time."
Laurens Van Der Post: *The Dark Eye in Africa*.

"I will not serve that in which I no longer believe whether it call itself my home, my fatherland or my church: and I will try to express myself in some mode of life or art as freely as I can and as wholly as I can, using for my defence the only arms I allow myself to use – silence, exile, and cunning."
James Joyce: *A Portrait of the Artist as a Young Man*.

"And I have found both freedom and safety in my madness; the freedom of loneliness and the safety from being understood, for those who understand us enslave something in us."
Khalil Gibran: *A Spiritual Treasure*.

INTRODUCTION

THIS BOOK COVERS IN THE REGION OF a 30 year period, beginning in the early 1970s, and ending in the year 2005. When I started out, those of us in our profession were called "mental nurses". This is a record of a personal, occupational journey that brought me into contact with the life of a large English State institution which, like its counterparts, was designed and commissioned for the isolation of mental disorder. These institutions were termed Mental Hospitals. Not so very long before they had been designated as Asylums, places where mental disorder was demarcated from mainstream society just as any other health alert had demarcated people infected with, say, tuberculosis or scarlet fever. Asylums meant that one size fitted all. Whatever the patients' problems, whatever their diagnosis, whether an acute episode or chronic debility, the hospital could take all comers. With their sprawling dimensions and influence they prevailed like hardy monasteries until financial stringency, loss of faith, and reforming policy stripped the lead from their roofs and left them in a state of dissolution. The few remaining hospitals were protected with a "listed" status, maintained in order to save their essential structure, and sold off as private sector accommodation which survives today as semi-historical dwellings for those who have such an interest.

There is a bountiful literature associated with the asylum, the mental hospital, community care, and other specialist units managing the mentally disordered patient. This includes historical records of individual institutions, historical research, documentary films, archive films, formal investigative inquiries, sociological studies, fictional films and books, patient biographies, their poems and paintings, employee reminiscences and their retrospective appreciations, and the journalism of freelance writers. Some fall into the category of obscure academia, others inform the interested lay reader, while others haunt and entertain the collective imagination. But each contribution to this disparate montage enables a conceptual and intellectual archaeology of the world of the mental hospital – its architecture, routines, treatments, staff and patient relations, and evolution. My justification for writing this book lies in the belief that my account, though a personal appreciation of the working life of a mental health nurse as I experienced and perceived it over an extended period, will interest the lay reader as well as fellow professionals in the field. Although I do not pretend to be objective or impartial I hope that the attempt to examine some of the issues makes for a relatively inclusive and balanced account, as well as making for a good and realistic story. I particularly trust that it is sufficiently informed to bring to life some of the manifestations of mental disorder, its institutionalization, and other tactical efforts at management, for it is about real people, actual events, relevant discourse and real establishments. It could be said that a veritable tsunami whipped across the Health Service, including the Mental Health Service, over this period. In attempting to capture some of this change my record is intended to be more than a partial record. So, whilst this confinement to one mental asylum necessarily must treat the institution as an isolated, historical artefact, it has not been forgotten that its existence is embedded in a garland of wider historical, developmental, and professional contexts. I have attempted to indicate some of the more crucial themes of the developing role of the mental health nurse though I cannot pretend that it is an exhaustive history as this was not my intention. Nor do I approach the story as the detached, unblemished observer who casts judgements to left and right with impunity. I recognise the place for my own biographical context which I draw upon sufficiently, I hope, to give credence to the whole raison d'être for my ever being, and continuing, in this profession of mental health care without it being over-intrusive. Hence, the ensuing pages combine personal biography, experiential observation, retrospective reflection, historical record and inference, and professional discourse.

I have confined my portrayal to one traditional mental institution at which I commenced employment, subsequently departed from, and returned to for two further stints. I have especially wanted to recall cameos that portray the general working life, individual members of staff and patients, and specific incidents that are indelibly etched into my memory. Most mental nurses who experienced these hospitals will identify with such material even if they may interpret them differently.

I did not spend my entire nursing career in this one institution, my time there being divided into three separate spells: (1973–1977); (1984–1986); (1998–2005). In the interim periods of the three spells working in the hospital of this tale, my time was spent in General Nursing, a Community Psychiatric Unit, a General Hospital Psychiatric Unit, and London University. However, the mainstay of my nursing career was the forensic mental health service and the establishments of the high security "Special Hospitals", the Prison Service, and the medium security forensic units that abound today. I have only hinted at those experiences which occurred beyond this one hospital on which I have concentrated, as there is a separate place for these elsewhere. The predominant mode, then, was of a career spent in institutional settings rather than the Community environment. I held positions as a nurse clinician, nurse therapist, nurse manager, nurse researcher and university lecturer. I count myself very fortunate to have been around at a time in the history of Nursing when nurses were beginning to commit to print their ideas about rôles, dilemmas, and clinical development. Towards these ends I made some modest educational contribution about the traditional mental nurse and, through a number of published papers and book chapters, aspects of the emerging rôle of mental health nurses, especially those of a forensic orientation.

***

In order to protect the identities of all patients and members of staff described in this book, I have neither used their names, nor have I named the hospital in which the events took place.

CHAPTER ONE
THE COMMUNE

WHEN, AS A YOUNG MAN, I ARRIVED at the mental hospital in the early 1970s I could not have conceived how the minute niche of humanity that was contained there would manage to rein the varied traces of perversity, beneficence and plain utilitarianism into the relative equilibrium that it did. The manifest ideals of the hospital as an official enterprise were intertwined with the latent agendas of its staff and patients. The wrongdoing, such as there was, was not limited to the wilful or witless malice of individual staff, or patients, or their relatives. There was also a certain injustice in the psychiatric exiling of swathes of the population, and the profligacy of institutional economics, some of which often compensated the low incomes of the staff. These and changing expectations stoked the cries of reforming indignation, leaving the many other good intentions and reasons for celebration, that the institution should have also earned, reduced to dying embers. And, while these multiple contradictions seemed to defy and undermine its integrity, it was, in many respects, more or less analogous to any organisation striving in an accelerating world where the customary past is forced to invite in the earnestly intruding present. The original vision remained in part, decayed in part, and much else survived only in people's memories. And what else lay in those memories other than conscious images, scenes, motivations and reflections? For those individuals that wished to discover, there would be an exhumation of what had informed each personal conscience, what had lain active beneath their consciousness; all as relevant a part of the institutional environment as any of the foundation stones.

* * *

1

The hospital thrived in a high clearing, away from the main highway, rimmed about by a bank of ancient foliage, as if swaddled far from the public gaze. Its buildings were accessed via a three quarter mile, metalled drive that inclined steadily upward from an unprepossessing entrance of two separated brick pillars and an abutting gate lodge. This insubstantial, rather squalid memento belied a more notable past when the brace of pillars would have been a sentinel portal supporting the linked arms of double iron gates and an uninterrupted, walled perimeter that clasped the entire estate. What had then represented a formidable cordon of defiant separation had since been ushered into history and the entrance now gaped into the drive, which continued to accommodate the contemporary private traffic, and the hospital coach timetable. Aesthetically, it was far from being an anonymous thoroughfare. A reasonable climb took it along one side of a valley with sloping paddocks of idly browsing ponies and horses that reached down to the main road and railway. It dipped under the overhanging, heavy shrouds of horse chestnuts and rustling beeches, brushed the skirts of rampant rhododendrons, and came to level out beneath a dark loft of yew trees that nestled round the far, hairpin bend and turned into the facade that fronted the institution. Over decades it had supplied and fed that fraternity like an umbilicus reaching in from the maternal, conventional community and the original, Surrey County Administration that had conceived it. That original Administration, like devoted, but equally helpless, guilty and shamed parents, had ensured that there be no stinting of the public purse for the deranged and defective offspring, and a fair fortune was scattered over a site of hundreds of acres. When bloated to its maximum girth it came to spawn 40 wards and more than 2,000 inmates at a sitting, all on a hill overlooking a verdant valley in rural Surrey.

Originally christened as one of the County pauper lunatic asylums this very branding should have been a sufficient deterrence to any person who ventured a casual visit into the psychiatric compound. Yet, a first visit which stemmed from absolute necessity was no less disconcerting. The off-road, concealing isolation of the institution, compounded the public ignorance, the sceptical folk-lore, the defamatory language, and what was considered a justifiable prejudice toward its inhabitants and very existence. At its most discriminatory, the provision was needed to separate the marauding packs of the mentally afflicted from the composed lines of social pedigree. The understanding that its inhabitants had been "committed" to its confines helped perpetuate the generally accepted notion that "public citizen" and "psychiatric inmate" were mutually exclusive ideals of entitlement versus non-entitlement. So, when the ephemeral beam of public attention swept across the concepts of the "insane" and "asylums" it caught only the dark silhouette of a deserving and anonymous exclusion. With this legacy, the current authorities tried their best to bury the historical reputation of the lunatics that were once involuntarily committed and certified, and of associations with the Parish workhouse, loony bin, straightjacket, padded cell, white coats, derangement and dangerousness.

* * *

The morning had seen that early light of summer, glistening on the water-sprayed grasses, drying the rising steam of horse droppings and dissipating the damp haze that clung to the lower depths of the valley paddock. I had never known such anticipation as I felt, that day, that inaugural day, cycling up the drive, searching ahead and through the regularly spaced trees for the inexorable presence of the hospital's water and incineration towers. For these were more than monuments of old technology. Those towers symbolised and advertised the presence of a dwelling for lunacy to the surrounding populace and stimulated the individual imagination. As further buildings came into view, it seemed that the very institution had been woken, had reared up like a colossal menace, and approached like a scornful company prepared to challenge the latest trespasser to breach the asylum. As if the institution was somehow intuitively alerted to an uncertain presence, to a frail ego, to a pretence of equanimity and normality, to an intruding subterfuge, and now glowered with indignation. And, at its shoulders, the leafy land that had been transformed into a psychiatric terrain, gathered and leered down to fuel and stoke the visitor's susceptibilities and run the gauntlet of the macabre mythologies and prejudices of history that were all scrambling for my attention.

The scale and physically imposing architecture of the first building – the hybrid resemblance to the public school, private mansion or country retreat – all hinted at an imperious authority. Yet, the very creditable façade merely amounted to the entrance to the administration block. I traced those deliberate skills of builders who had elaborated the grey, cream and black brickwork that edged the vaulted windows and which were set into a contrasting background of redbrick elevations. To left and right other buildings within sight, though not as aesthetically crafted, still lacked for nothing in plain impressiveness. A view from overhead would have described a methodical estate structure that had been lain out across the land like a vast beetle, the projecting limbs of the residential wards articulating with the central body of administrative organs. But, the builders could never have conceived the mystical aura that their creation evoked, or the competing impressions that this was either an elaborate complex of State oppression or an eccentric, benevolent guardianship.

Despite these conjectures, I allowed myself the irresistible diversion, and not a little resolve, of being dared away from these comfortably public reception grounds and into the mouth of an adjoining pathway. That root-buckled path lay claustrophobically confined by the imposing yew trees above and the privet hedge, laurel bushes and iron railings on either side. It ran adjacent to a grassed, rose-bedded garden that banked up to the conservatory of a ward, and finally spilled onto the airy expanse of the recreation field. The field spread out toward a far boundary of hedges and adjoined block after block of the inelegant residential limbs of the estate which housed the patients themselves. Each of the two and three-storied blocks was regularly punctuated with large rectangular windows that resembled the gun ports of heavily fortified galleons. But gun ports are conduits for action, for men fused with purpose, where power is unleashed from firing portals against a threatening force. It brought to mind how much could be taken for granted at a window – gaping, sealed, sun-flashed, framing a mother waving with a child, spilling music or wind-buffeted curtains, colour-splashed, burgled, leapt out of, and dropped from. But these ungenerous sash windows, divided into several smaller panes, had never fully opened, much less entertained activity. Stilletoed into the external stone of the windows were the metal bars that said more about the whole enterprise than any other single feature. They let in air and light, and let out the occasional cry, but prevented any substantial appearance other than the still silhouette of a vacant face and upper torso. No one would wave, nobody would escape from this route, or fall to their death, or climb upon the slated roofs. I stood in awe of these shuttered holes and what might lie within them.

The path dissected the fine cut of the sports field from what little had survived of the trimmed lawns and flowerbeds which, in their heyday, had lain like a gay frill around the buildings. At the margins of the paved courtyards, perched as coyly as dovecots, were the benched, wooden shelters that would lean over the patients who sought their protection from rain or rays. Isolated from the dominating residential blocks was a little dwelling from whose opened, French doors spilled a handful of elderly females in pinafores who bent over their needlework, in the sun. They were cheerily chatted to by their uniformed charge irrespective of her patients' reticence, or inability to engage. Moving on, the path joined a narrow, back lane that wound behind the ward blocks and the domestic staff residence and led into a dismal utility area amongst which the tall, mystical stem of the water tower dominated the estate. For all I knew it housed the most dangerous lunatics in the vigilant conditions of a sort of keep. Edging away, I rejoined the lane that circled the many other blocks of grim back wards, took in the uniformly crème-coloured windows and doors, passed the several grand greenhouses that nestled within the horticultural plots, glanced at the sign over the industrial unit, and was relieved to find myself brought back to the point from which I'd set out.

The external tour had left an impression of a ludicrous abundance of institutional investment and social compensation that contrasted, starkly, with what most patients would ever have encountered in their social roots and life experiences. Then there was the irony that all this concerted, energising facility owed its existence to the debilitated immobility of its residents. Was it all justified?

What a quietness there was! A listening, easy silence that stretched like a silken thread across the courtyards and between the walls of the buildings, waiting on the capture of any sound, waiting to be stirred. A stillness jabbed by the raucousness of pairs of bounding magpies on the ground, and the crowing swirl of rooks that roosted in the high beeches and oaks, drifted in this space, rubbed against these walls, slithered along the ground. The sense of desertion instilled in me an anticipation of distressed cries, of confronting an enraged and rambling lunatic, of observing an escape into the fields and a posse of pursuing attendants. Such fantasies spurred a fretful self-consciousness of being in a place for which I was not emotionally equipped, and of the possibility that I might be prone to a psychiatric susceptibility. I was partly reassured that sharpened thoughts and feelings, such as these, were appropriate, given the circumstances. But it seemed only too plausible that there was a risk in applying for work in this field, which was like volunteering for the psychological front line where the strengths and weaknesses of each person's varied history might be tested beyond their capacities under the daily morbid bombardment. On that first day, when I had cause to acknowledge the hereditary evidence of mental disturbance that had erupted like a varicose rash through my extended family, I could not avoid harbouring such doubts. There was simply no way of knowing whether I was constitutionally equipped for the time and experience ahead. These several protestations accumulated like a bunch of savagely gathered flowers while I continued over to the porters' lodge at the administration entrance. Glancing above to the small stone clock tower wrapped in a leaden cap, I knew there was still time for all these competing speculations to yank me away from the obligation of the imminent interview and so I stopped, and leaned in a long, ambivalent pause, vibrating like a stricken moth on a sprung web. In those moments, I also anticipated the immediate relief there would be from just turning about and retreating but was even more cognisant of the dejection that would follow after a few hours of cowardly withdrawal. And, if it was not inconceivable that I might not survive the day, the fact that I was actually to invest in a subsequent career that would span three decades of my lifetime was utterly implausible in those moments.

I was some yards off from the vaulted, wooden doors and their polished chrome handles when they suddenly gaped wide and closed like a gigantic eye, as someone appeared and disappeared in an esoteric passage. Pushing at one of these on its easy hinges, I also passed through and stepped onto the cracked, black and white tiles of an extravagantly lofty reception area and its trappings of refinement. Wood-panelled benches lined the lower walls to one side and faced the vast mahogany desk that took up the entire opposite wall. Perched behind, a diminutive, late middle-aged gent with a pencil moustache, bow tie and shirt-sleeve grips, spied the comings and goings. He flicked his quizzical brow toward the stranger in the barest of acknowledgements.

'I'm here for an interview with the Head Porter,' I said, responding to the unspoken enquiry.

'There's your man,' he replied, with a minimalist prod of his head toward a silent form at the far end of the desk. The Head Porter, his very self, rose, reluctantly, from his elbows. His erect bearing, that could have been defined by a military past, was slightly compromised by a faltering effort to manage his aches and pains, I should imagine, as well as his ample girth. Whatever else I might have expected as a visitor it was not a reception committee which languished in rôles that approximated to the membership of a private gentlemen's club, let alone its Commissionaires. The Head Porter presented himself in crisp sports jacket, large bow tie, kerchief frilling from the breast pocket, wide braces clutching onto trousers with plumb line creases, suspending the turn-ups above the patent shine of his shoes, and cigar stuffed between his thick ringed fingers. These affectations adorned an otherwise serious, London vernacular. If this unexpectedly polished presentation was an indication of the status of the senior porter staff, what was to be found of more elevated positions in the place? My own presentation sported a T-shirt, casual jeans, Doc Martins and shoulder length, curly hair.

No worries! It was not a long while afterward that the erstwhile university hopeful, turned virtual dropout, was being congratulated for just having had a successful interview for the vacant porter's job. To meet the necessary quorum, the Head Porter and I had been joined by the former's deputy, dressed in a more conventional dark suit and straight tie. Contrasted with the persona on parade, the interview had been an agreeably undemanding formality and remarkable only for its brevity and candid pragmatism. There was a job vacancy that needed filling, a reasonable applicant to fill it and, unless some serious flaw such as a rapacious or murderous past history could dissuade them otherwise, the staff complement should be back up to strength! Following confirmation that the position could commence as soon as the administrative wheels allowed, the three of us rose and ambled down to the reception area. The Head Porter turned to his deputy, who now lounged across the brilliantly worn, daily polished, mahogany counter and remarked in his clipped but affable fashion: 'Likely, some of our staff will want to draw our friend, here, into some bad ways during his time with us, wouldn't you say?'

'I certainly do,' the Deputy replies. 'I'm afraid there are far too many who will set him a bad example.' The Deputy Head Porter's prominent, boyish cheeks churn into an attempt at seriousness before settling into a sceptical grimace.

'For a lad of your education you could do very well here if you apply yourself and keep your nose clean. You might want to think of that!' continues the Head Porter, seeming to want to influence his new employee's career prospects. 'We'll start you off with someone of experience and see 'ow you go. Now, I'm sure you'd like a tour of the hospital to give you your bearings. Would you like to follow my good man, then?' With that, his manner glazes into the vacant drift of a muse customarily drawn to inner distractions, and his half-closed eyes peer pensively through a swirling cigar cloud of his own making.

So, as the latest employee of porters, I gratefully trail behind the reassuring nonchalance of the Deputy Head Porter who ambles with hands in pockets, arms idly flapping his sides, into an exotic warren of bare corridors, strips of fluorescent lighting, and the communal smells and noises of the world of the institution. As the fancy takes him, the Deputy Head Porter exchanges a few words with various staff and patients in what is, clearly, a practised art in negotiating a comfortable passage through the hospital labyrinth. Gregariously engaging here, quietly ignoring there, but not stopping even briefly. Armed with the advantage of familiarity, he shares scraps of local wisdom with the new recruit.

'What was your first name, did you say? Steve, wasn't it? Never worked with mental patients, I presume?' he asks with a resignation reserved for all new staff. I shake my head in confirmation on both counts and say, 'That's right.' Leaning toward me, my guide confides a cheery countenance.

'Well, that's no great disadvantage as you'll soon find out, matey. We all started off that way, didn't we? I hope you enjoy yourself, anyway. It's a totally mad world in here but you get used to it. And don't worry, lunacy's not contagious else we'd all be fucking barmy.' His head and shoulders recoil as he resumes his lumbering progress, only to lean back several yards later with a sardonic smile. 'But that don't mean to say that half the staff aren't as mad as arseholes.' He smiles with comical conviction and prods his head, knowingly, at the staff who happen to pass them. His observations become more personal. 'See that one there? She's a Ward Sister and totally, bloody bonkers! Watch yourself; she likes the men by all accounts. She'll have your trousers down soon as look at you. It's true; believe me, bloody true, I tell you.'

The Deputy Head Porter's tour is performed with the affable ease of an occupational harlequin who juggles the integrity of office alongside the derision of the cynic and the shrewdness of the "wide-boy". This performance is timely, and fortifying, for a recruit whose own progress is still being fired upon with insurgent unease. There is a real pleasure, and relief, at being so casually confided in and it helps dispel the incriminating sense of self doubt and brittle sensibility. That first impression of the internal sanctum of a mental hospital procured its own wonderful reality. Of overlooking a burlesque procession: the resounding din that bounds through the tunnel like corridors; the confusion and immediacy of so many incongruous expressions, gaits, mannerisms and chaos of clothing; and the concentration of strangeness. Fears are assuaged by the incongruous jollity and foolish, mocking calm of the chattering Deputy.

I followed my guide's back until we pushed through a grubby, smudged door into a room of unprepossessing and cramped dinginess allocated to the porters and domestic staff who were congregating for their midmorning break. As a rest room the broken springs and long dispersed sheen of the motley, threadbare furniture disdained both hospitality and respect toward its incumbents. Introductions were ignored. Faces looked up toward what was to them but another stranger and the merest interruption. I had entered a veritable Babel of languages and dialects, Filipino and vociferous Spanish chief among them. Those who were English speaking were a minority presence. The rest room's crowded swamp of labourers was a colourful forum of the comical, assertive, retiring and eccentric and I gladly soaked them up, not least for the contrast with the student body from which I'd emerged. Taken together, there was an accumulating sense of foreignness: the fantastic institutional atmosphere with its geographical and social isolation; the alien strangeness and diversity of the patients; and the multi-cultural differences which now swirled around.

My companion introduced and assigned me to a prematurely middle-aged Irishman with a southern brogue that limped hoarsely across his larynx. His appearance managed to regenerate the fragility that lingered around my premature show of confidence. The Irishman went by the nickname of Skipper – not his own, but the one with which he had been adorned by his workmates on account of the fact that his appearance was a comic caricature of an old seafarer. The baldness of his head was exacerbated by the most delicate film of taut skin drawn across a sparse nest of delicate veins so that all seemed as fragile as an infant's skull. His thin tufts of orange hair hugged the lower back of his head while spreading as a broad moustache and beard across his cheeks, chin and chest which were all of a sickly pale, mortifying complexion. The upper edges of his deeply sunken cheeks were like sandbags defending his bright blue, world weary eyes as they rested in their orbital trenches. You could imagine a film of death passing slowly, fatally, over his eyes as the Reaper's demands descended upon him like a cloud of mustard gas.

Tea break ended, this somewhat spectral soul stood to show his new assistant some of "the ropes", if I was interested, before departing. But as he rose I noted the difficulty with which he winched himself into a stiff stoop, the neck locked, arms straight down, so that he rocked from side to side as he proceeded in short, dragging steps and clipped along like a mechanical toy. Together, we left the porters' rest room and the new employee struggled to catch the subdued, almost rasping, dips in the Irishman's voice. The seafaring image was further enhanced by his pipe smoking rituals. The pipe took an age to light owing to the elaborate mannerisms and his practice of chatting throughout. When he took it out, it heralded a period of seated musing and pontificating while seeming to hold at bay a world impatient of his shuffling presence. It was captivating, watching the slow preparation of the bowl, the fingering and tapping out of old debris, the tamping down of the damp flakes, the releasing of the wet aroma, the hunched concentration around the filmy eyes at the point of lighting, the noisy pull of air and spittle, the magical, blue smoke that swirled from the bowl, and the fumes that shunted out of the pursed line of his lips. There was birth and death in the business. Like a scorpion fulfilling its destiny the match arched over the pipe bowl, struck out and inflamed the moist tobacco and, with a lethal flick of the hand, was immolated into a smoking stillness. It was not exactly confidence inspiring to be teamed up with the curious character of Skipper who was perfectly capable of dropping dead, in company, at any time.

After a few days of the work, it was quite saying something that the greater part of my initial trepidation had all but disappeared. The comfortable working routine was not difficult to conform to and encouraged me to give the asylum a fair chance as a possible workplace. By so doing, I hoped that it would also provide me with a grounding in work routine which was drastically wanting after the casual timetable of college. Quite unexpectedly, then, I complied with the early starts of the morning shifts which meant cycling five miles over two hills and clocking on for seven o'clock in the morning in every weather condition on offer! It meant accepting the transient status of being in "casual" employment, the relaxed personal dress code overlaid with the undistinguishing, grey, porter's overall, and the variable work ethic of workmates. Sprinkled about the hospital were the relatively few professional personnel who, owing to the greater status conferred upon them, exuded a greater gravitas. It occurred to me that if my earlier youth had worked out differently this was where my educational background would have better prepared me but, in the absence of any such determination, I was content to bide my time in a relative obscurity for the present. Proof of this was the growing resignation I had acquired toward the inglorious tasks to which I was assigned, as a "Foul Linen Porter". These commenced with the daily collection of the hospital's red and white bagged, fouled and dirty linen which the wards either evacuated into the feet of stairwells, or which tumbled and thudded like suicides down the long, clanking, metal, disposal shoots on the ground floor. It was into these offensive niches that the "Foul Linen Porters" delved and exhumed the contaminated contents, then stacked them – ever precariously as the piles grew – onto a long handled push-cart. Initially, it was almost a personal affront to have to stoop and handle the putrid, rancorous, urine soaked and faeces soiled linen and clothes that had marinated overnight in the pits set aside for their collection. But I reminded myself that, comparatively, it was never as bad as the putrefying wild deer I had once come across at the roadside, the chest burnished by a heaving lung of maggots, nor the stagnating effluent from a whisky distillery I had once encountered on the moors outside Inverness. And, when I came to inhale the odour of the hospital's elderly bodies, it would never approach the retching offence of gangrenous ulceration. As I was to learn so often in my working life, the unimaginable became the familiar.

Between us – the most unlikely pair – the foul linen cart was then pushed and pulled along the corridors before the Irishman's durability sapped from the bone yard of his crumbling frame. In truth, every occasion of heavy lifting demanded such a surge of effort that the struggle quickly left him sagging with fatigue. Surely, this wasn't the right task for such a weakened body? Likely, the hand of necessity had left him no choice but to accept whatever employment rewarded his slim credentials. And now a protected employee of the State he would, at least, be treated with some merciful sickness benefit or pension in his retirement to support the paltry remuneration of a sick worker who could not function to any great capacity. Before we parted, there was time for this decrepit eccentric to display one of those remarkable traits which you believed could only have existed in the deferential past. For Skipper combined an unquestioning veneration of his superiors and an obsequious readiness to do anything directly asked of him by them which he matched with an equally generous scorn for the ignominious colleagues from whom he disdainfully distanced himself. But, for the short time that we were allotted together he was an agreeable companion who, in treating his charge to his curious view of life, revealed what must have been a most singular isolation. The little threads of homespun philosophy, which seemed the only real food that sustained him, would not have served him too well, either. How he might have survived in another occupation, or whether he had even tried, could not be properly entertained. It was likely that this place had been an asylum for him at any rate.

Having been collected, the "dirty" and "foul" linen bundles were conveyed to the hospital laundry where they were unloaded onto the amassed detritus of the day's other collections. The laundry's physical proportions indicated just how much work was expected to pass through it. It was still managing to evoke a scene from a manufacturing past of neatly defined functions, labour intensity, outsized machinery, hissing technology, and fluorescent dinginess. Since its inception the laundry had always been an employment outlet for female patients but a few of the current crew were male patients. Like any manufacturing process, the laundry required that every person be appointed to narrow, specialist tasks and they performed each stage shrouded in a damp heat with the pervading odour of cheap detergent swirling about them. The fouled and soiled articles were first tipped and separated into mangled piles of torsos as if heaped from a massacre, before being dragged and heaved into the chambers of industrial washing machines by the staff, clad in rubber gloves, aprons and Wellington boots. The area perpetuated its own vile, decomposing aromas. And when the chambers had cleansed and spun away all the signs

12

of atrocity the drums came to a heavy halt, and the doors were rolled away. Then, the slumped garments were hauled out hot, heavy, steaming and damp, and tipped into vast laundry hampers ready for their reintegration into the world. Then, the industrial driers blew their reviving air into them before they were laid out on the flat tables to receive the resuscitating irons that would massage them back from the dead. So, too, was the bed linen revived at an end stage where the starched sheets were fed through the vast rollers onto the wide platforms into a rigid potency. And the pinafored laundresses lunged around, folding and packing the warm piles into white delivery bags. It was, indeed, a small piece of the manufacturing past, fast receding.

* * *

'Watch yourselves, come on, get out of it, move yourselves.' The main corridor was disturbed as the gliding prow of a food trolley was bullied out of the exit of the main kitchen, startling the obstructing knots of patients who shuffled aside as best they could. Like momentarily ruffled birds they quickly reassembled into the middle of the corridor for they were used to such disdainful intrusion. The irascible grunts of a porter were more or less anticipated. As if jostling for attention in the stream of crowded movement the many competing voices leaped up and down the long stretch of corridor like salmon slapping their way along the linoleum floor and bare ceiling and walls, seeking higher reaches of water. The floor which was, for the time being, filthy with spills and skids and ciggie butts, waited for a porter to fulfil part of his job description.

Arthur approached, having managed to shave between clumps of bristles, flat-footing his short, raised steps which had been choreographed by years of uninterrupted medication. He was compelled to deliver one-fisted, snap punches repeatedly to his chest to accompany his flat-footed gait while his preoccupied mumbling seeped below tired eyes. He was receptive to the newcomer's interested glance which encouraged him to reciprocate with a very full and boyish grin. But as Arthur punched his way past me, the face tumbled back into a customary, motionless, stare.

An elderly, pale lady – in point of fact, every patient was conspicuously pale – made her protracted progress along the main corridor, heaving her frame into one of many temporary halts. Her long, grey, grease streaked hair straddled both shoulders like bunched willow branches. A stained pinafore tied at the front was part of the old-fashioned world within these walls where she vainly tried to cling onto the remnants of a busy life. Her gaze sloped down to feet which were grasped tight, and bloated, in the carpet slippers, and bunions crooked as fractures that characterised the many patients who lived an indoor, hospital existence. Her inner isolation beckoned for no punctuating greetings or encouragement from others and she acknowledged no one, in turn. Passing by, a slightly built, female nurse from the Far East, all of five foot, gave an excellent impression of leaning into a blasting wind as she stretched a long armed grip to the female patient whom she was hauling to some venue. The nurse was almost immaculate, but for the well scuffed shoes that were ignored a cleaning, and she shared a vociferous giggle with a passing colleague from her home country. Partly encouraging, partly chiding her ward, her eyes suggested but a routine, efficient interest in her work but this was more than offset by being able to send off a monthly cheque to her needy family "back home". A male member of staff exited the little oasis of stark cleanliness which was the staff toilet, which he took good care to lock behind him. The male patients' toilet, on the very same corridor, was a stinking wall of stale, old piss that had been drained of all etiquette and snubbed of a regular cleaning by the porters.

Among the corridor traffic one sound arched way above the others, heralding the menacing approach of Hyacinth and her current, pugnacious distraction.

'I'll scratch her fucking eyes out if she comes anywhere near me, the fucking cow. I fucking will. I'm warning her! She thinks she can get any fella here. She's nuffing but a fucking whore and I'll tell her to her face. If she thinks she's better than me she's got another fink coming. Bitch! She's not going to talk to me like that. I'll get the police in; tell them what a whore she is. She's poisoning my food, stealing my make-up, tries on my clothes. She's jealous of my looks. She's an ugly bitch, that's why. Who does she think she is?' It was surprising to note the impact this made on the immediate company. Most patients did their best to remain disengaged and anonymous and the staff strode, carefree, among them. For with Hyacinth, everyone was visibly wary, wanted to avoid contact with the situation, and studiously pretended not to notice her presence. She was a thick-set, powerful African-Caribbean with an equally powerful reputation. No one thought it a good idea to tackle Hyacinth when she was so volatile, especially when it was likely to end in a public scene. There was no knowing what it might deteriorate into. In her current disturbance, she hurled two defiant, assaulting, brown eyes toward anyone not averting their attention as they passed her while they, for their part, were hard pressed not to conceal their relief.

* * *

Such cameos became integral to the daily working schedule and imagination of anyone employed in a mental hospital. In such a secluded world, performing a porter's role certainly did no harm to personal confidence or local status. Even so, it could not entirely dissipate a discomforting awareness of holding a lowly place in the hospital's social order. Necessarily, you were being ascribed to that social caste in the hierarchy who managed the least savoury jobs, that no one else would have to dirty their hands with, and to a fraternity with few career expectations and a low wage. The lowest order, that is, except for the patients themselves. It was they who were firmly prodded into the foundations of the institutional pile. However you looked at it, you could console yourself that, whatever employment a staff member performed, it was accompanied by some small degree of authority which could be lauded over the patients. Furthermore, each had some element of responsibility, an earned income, was able to return home after work, and had possession of a staff key! After two to three weeks, I gratefully attracted the favour of Messrs. Head Porter and Deputy Head Porter and found myself nudged ever so slightly up the social order, much to the understandable chagrin of the resident porters-in-waiting.

'There's a service porter's position going which we'd like you to have a try at lad,' I was informed by the Head Porter while ignominiously spread-eagled alongside the foul linen cart on an unofficial break of my own choosing. I didn't know what had surprised me most, the gift of an unsolicited opportunity or being caught idling about. Meanwhile, the summer vacation came and went and, since the future lacked any academic commitment, or urgent interest to change anything for the present, I scrubbed away the

15

piss, shit and vomit from my current job description, accepted the sideways move, and began to settle with even greater satisfaction into the routine of the institution.

Now ascribed as a Service Porter, I was lifted from the incontinent recesses of long, dingy corridors and piloted into the brighter vistas of ward life. The daily coming and going to an allotted half a dozen wards servicing their daily requirements – mainly delivering meals, provisions, linen, clothes, newspapers, correspondence, furniture and pharmacy medication, and providing a conduit between all the wards and other departments – presented social opportunities, too. Nursing staff, the predominant professional ward presence in terms of numbers – male grey suits, white coats, traditional female dresses and caps, name badges with wondrous titles, bunches of keys and office space – were notably, and surprisingly, informal. Conversely, assigned the grey coated inconsequence of a mere porter, I supposed I offered no threat to their routines and comfort. With a licence to roam more freely it was now possible to have ready access to almost any part of the hospital; to ascend the exclusive, scrupulously polished and wood panelled staircase to the freshly painted offices and hidden meeting places which were assigned to the medical, administrative and senior nursing staff; at a more prosaic level, to enter the main hospital kitchen.

This was an industrial kitchen functionally equipped and proportioned for mass production. The striking presence of rows of metal meal trolleys lined against the walls and plugged into the electrical mains, suggested a herd of cows whose daily toil was to be linked up to the milking apparatus of an oversized milking shed. The idea was to maintain the meal temperature for there could be a significant delay before meals were finally laid before the intended consumers. Off this main area were some sizeable recesses where various tasks were carried out, such as peeling vegetables, washing utensils, or preparing the individual diets. An affable looking young male member of the staff approached to take the late meal order slip that I was delivering from one of my wards. For me, this was the prelude to a new acquaintance and another educational slant into hospital life.

'If they can't deliver on time, serves them right if they get all the wrong bloody meals! They don't seem to realise that we have to prepare some of these things, today, for tomorrow, if you see what I mean!' he says in greeting after a perfunctory glance at the slip. 'About time they got their bloody act together on that ward, no offence to you, like, mate,' he continues with benign mischief. However, he seems in no hurry to act on the new information and stays with the newcomer. 'Haven't seen you about, you new here, then?'

'Well, been here a couple of weeks on the general porters' staff and I've just been given this service porter's job out of the blue!' I reply.

'Lucky old you. Be seeing a lot more of you in here, then. That's not bad going considering you've just got here. Normally, you have to wait quite a while for those jobs. You must have blue eyes. Oh, so you have! You've been given a bit of a leg up, I'd say.'

'Do you think so?'

'Well, think about it. You've not been here five minutes and you're landed with one of the cushiest porter's jobs when they've got loads of other blokes queuing up for their chance to get it! As I say, you must have very blue eyes, my man!'

'It didn't occur to me. I just thought I'd been noticed because I put my head down and worked hard.'

'I doubt it, mate. Probably because you can speak English and are English, I'd say!'

'Some people aren't going to be too pleased with me, then!'

'Oh, I wouldn't worry about it. They'd do the same if they were in your shoes, look at it that way.' Nevertheless, now that the scenario has been presented, I start to anticipate some workmates harbouring some resentment about what, after all, seems to be barefaced favouritism. Do I really care, though?

'What wards you got?'

'Er, I've got the nearest male corridor to this end of the kitchen,' pointing behind me. The kitchen, centrally positioned, has two entrances, one leading to what had, originally, been the female side of the hospital, the other disgorging straight onto the male side.

'Oh, you're going to be highly popular with the other service porters, too, then, 'cos you've only been given the easiest service porter's round out of the whole ruddy lot! Push the trolleys to that door, put them on the slope, and they'll find their own way to the wards. It's all downhill when you're loaded up, lucky sod,' he smiles with an easy mischief. A picture is conjured

17

of the little herd taking themselves off through the gate to pasture with only the encouragement of an occasional guiding prod down the incline of the corridor. Though I realised I had been given the easiest group of wards, relative to the position of the kitchen, it could easily have been allocated to any of the other service porters. There was no escaping the injustice that most of the other porters had to heave their meal trolleys through several thousand yards of corridor and up some demanding inclines. One way or another I had been granted some paternalistic favour, it seemed.

'Christ, it must get hot in here, it's almost unbearable as it is,' I say. 'It's like the tropics.' The entire ceiling is completely covered in glass and it must be one of the biggest single units in the hospital. It is humid and physically uncomfortable in the overwhelming closeness and the chef's long, lank hair gave further credence to the intemperate heat. 'How is it that the kitchen gets so much space?'

'Oy, don't start complaining! It's just how we like it. At least, we've got room to move. Not like some of those pokey little holes in the hospital. You probably haven't seen some of those places, yet! The tailor ferreting away in that dark little den! Have you been there? Go and have a look-see. Like stepping into the East End, rag trade, it is – front parlour, got no light, and only tichy windows. He's got suits hanging on rails all round him, no space to move in, and he has to duck and dive, all the time. Other than that, one little, old patient sits sewing in the corner. I kid you not, my son! He's got no regular company all day and has to rely on people popping in for some conversation. So, you'll need to make sure you're not in a bloody hurry. Would drive me bloody potty! No, we're lucky in here, mate. There's always something happening, people in and out, you can't get bored.' I try to capture a past scene that would have required all this kitchen space and capacity. The chef starts up, again.

'Yep. Used to be a lot different in the kitchen. Way before my time the chefs and cooks used to make all the meals from scratch – pies, pastries, stews, roasts, bread, puddings, the lot. Yep, had its own bakery, an' all. Now most of the stuff's bought in from outside firms, ready made. All we do, most of the time, is unwrap it and serve up with veg. That's why the food's such shit,' he continues, with not a great deal of conviction, I think. 'No, there used to be dozens of staff working in the kitchen. There needed to be. But they worked bloody hard by all accounts. Same applies to the gardeners when you think of it. There's, what, three of them now! Used to be at least a dozen but their work's all been knocked on the head. Same all over. They're trying to cut back and save on the dosh.' He is a young, congenial lad who speaks with a fair speed that is accompanied by a marked slur. But he seems happy to spend time with a new face.

For my part, I then run through what is becoming a small ritual of having to explain why I am working here, how I've messed up at school, and that I'm hoping that this is only a temporary measure because my sights are set on going to university. In truth, it's not that there is any great certainty about the university bit but I can't allow anyone to think that I would have selected a job of this nature, by choice.

'Clever bugger, eh?' grins the chef. Clever bugger can't help feeling the glow of the sharp slap of flattery even for so fleeting and casual a remark and I hang onto the sensation of inflated recognition while the chef/cook continues. 'One of me brothers is a clever bugger. A chess champion, and that. Anyway, sounds like you're a local lad. English as well.'

'Sure. Why d'you ask?'

'Makes a bit of a change, that's why!' a furtive glance behind him before carrying on. 'It's like the United Nations here, pal. We've got every colour under the sun on the staff.'

'I've noticed. Never imagined to see the city in the countryside, so to speak.'

'Yeah, you'd expect it in the Smoke, wouldn't you? They've been flooding into all the local bins, from all accounts.'

'Bins?'

'Looney bins. What else would I mean? It's no good anyone complaining that they've taken all our jobs, neither! Our people just don't want to bleeding work, that's their trouble, see!' I am surprised and delighted at such contentious stuff being openly admitted before a complete stranger on the assumption that I will, presumably, affirm the comments. 'And that means they gets to take over all the spare hostel rooms, too, which is all very well, but...' He leaves a protracted pause, for effect. 'Now, take yourself. Just imagine, if you weren't swanning off to university, you might be in need of a cheap room in the hospital, see?'

19

'Hang on a minute, are you saying that people who work here actually live in the hospital, too? You are joking, aren't you!'

'What you talking about? Doctors, nurses, porters, domestics, kitchen staff, anybody mate. Some people don't have a choice. Can't afford to buy houses around this area; far too bloody expensive, so they're more than happy to end up living in.'

'But, actually living in a mental hospital – it's unimaginable!'

'I kid you not, my son! Even the top buggers get a whole house and garden because it's a perk of the job, see! No one minds nurses getting to live in the Nurses Home, like, it's traditional! But that's a perk that foreign nurses get now and there's been loads of them recruited since I've been here. Only good thing is that some of them women are bloody gorgeous. Now we've got all that lovely crumpet on tap,' he smiles, lustfully. 'Mind you, they don't always play the game, know what I mean!'

'So, you're not really complaining about the Nurses Home being filled by foreigners so long as they're female and a cracking good bit of stuff?'

'Now you put it that way I suppose not, really. Mind you, as I was saying, they're not easy – most of them are as tight as a duck's arse. Very old-fashioned in their ways, see! When they get up at the Club – that's pretty rare for most of them – they all sit in a little group and don't mix with us British lads, only with their own people. The women, I mean. The blokes are a bit more relaxed. Blokes are blokes, ain't they? No, a randy white boy's got to work very hard at it. Got to be a long siege, I reckon. Can't be doing with it, myself. Still, some people do alright for themselves. There's a gorgeous couple of Filipinos who've been snapped up by two of our boys, so there is hope for us all.'

'Do you know, the thought of going out with a foreigner sounds brilliant to me!' There were precious few at my grammar school and the only Pakistani I had known was destined, so she said, not to be allowed to go on to either 'A' levels or university and to become a housebound wife.

'It would help if they wanted to get out of the Nurses Home more,' continued the chef. 'It's not a lot of fun going to a girl's room which is smaller than a prison cell where you can't swing your willy, let alone a bleeding cat! It's a bit of a liberty and no mistake. On top of that they have to be careful of Aggie, the Warden; she's a right bleeding dragon. No night-time visitors allowed, like.'

20

'Surely not, in this day and age?'

'I kid you not, my son! You have to be pretty careful. If you happen to stay the night, you can be right up Shit Street if she knocks on your girl's door, or she spots you first thing in the morning leaving a girl's room or sees you wandering out the hostel, or the fire alarm goes off. There's many a bloke's reputation been made over a bleeding fire alarm in the middle of the night, I can tell you. You've got a number of choices when that happens: hide in the wardrobe or under the bed until it's over; risk getting toasted; get caught by Aggie coming out of the main entrance; or bugger off out the window – and still get caught. Bleeding hilarious! But, when you think of the rewards, it's got to be worth it. It's very good of the government to think of our needs and put all that lovely talent together like that. Bloody marvellous!' His features crumple into an ironic wink. 'You got a girl at the moment?'

'Nope. Can't say I have.'

'Well, here's your chance. Word has it, by the way, that Aggie turns a blind eye if she likes you.'

'But would I be happy to be seeing someone who actually lives inside a mental hospital, I *mean!*' And I certainly do mean it.

'Listen! This is how the other half live, right! You're assuming that some people have known any different,' interrupted the chef. 'There's loads of people who live in, who've never known much more than staying in a single room that's attached to their jobs. *And*, they'll live out most of their working lives that way. You'd be surprised, my man!'

'Incredible!'

'Well, there you are. Any case, people get used to it. How do you think they get people to work here?'

'So, let me get this straight. Are these rooms, or houses, or nurses homes, *actually* in the grounds of the hospital?' I am incredulous, bearing in mind the possible emotional and social implications of living within a sanatorium for mental disease. It is not the slightest bit controversial for the chef.

'For some, yeah. Not everyone has to live on site, no. Me and my family live in a tied cottage down in the village. Belongs to the hospital, like. There's a long row of them, all look the same, can't miss them. They're bloody pokey but who's complaining on the rent we pay. Dead cheap living at home. Anything goes wrong, the hospital fixes it. Lived there all my life. So have all my brothers and sisters. Only problem is, I suppose, is when me Mum and Dad retire. Then we'll have to get out. That'll be a shock; I've never known any difference.'

'So, who owns these houses, then, not the council, surely?'

'No, nothing to do with the council. The hospital. You just have to work here to get one.'

'Someone must decide.'

'That's down to the powers-that-be,' the chef says, wryly. 'If your face fits, know what I mean?' It transpires that his family was allocated a hospital house because both his parents were nurses, but they had to wait their turn for somebody to die off, retire, or move out. His Dad is now a nursing officer, his mother a ward nurse, his sister is in nurse training, one brother is a porter, another is an electrician, and there may have been others but I lose track! All work in the hospital! He also tells me of his own boss, the hospital's Head Chef, who has a son who is one of the gardeners and his wife is also employed in the hospital. It turns out that this is a common thing. The hospital has a tradition of whole families working here over a number of generations. Years later, I am to discover, among a surviving group of headstones in the grounds of a former Dorset asylum, one that describes one of the hospital cooks who had worked for 29 years in that one county asylum. When she died, the staff and patients had erected the burial stone to her, on her behalf, presumably because she had no other benefactors. It appears reasonable to challenge one of the obvious flaws in all this. 'Do you feel far enough away from work, down in the village, or does it feel as if you're never away from the place? It can't be good to live so near to here!'

'Well, obviously, it's got its advantages. Being just down the road the house is within walking distance of work and the clubhouse, don't forget. On top of that, it's all the other things that actually keep you in the hospital. All the entertainment you need on your doorstep – subsidised booze, free discos, bands and dancing, snooker, darts, cribbage – not forgetting a bit of talent, of course! Are you a sportsman? You look pretty fit?'

'Yeah, play a reasonable game of football and cricket, as it happens.'

'Yep, teams for both of those. You want to make yourself known. And that's what I'm telling you, see, there's so much on tap you don't have much incentive to go looking on the out!'

22

'Go on.'

'Okay, swimming, cricket, tennis, athletics, and bowls in summer; and football and cross-country during the winter – everything completely free! I believe the foreign students are starting up a badminton club, more their sort of thing like – not my cup of tea.'

'You'd need someone to organise all that. Have you got a special department in the place?'

'No, it's not the hospital that runs that off their own back! All the sports are organised by the LMHSA – you haven't heard of that, no? The London Mental Hospital Sports Association. It's been a lifeline to staff in the past! They set up competitions in every sport, across the whole of the London mental hospitals.'

'How many London mental hospitals are there, then?'

'Do you know, I've lived around the hospital all me ruddy life and I've never worked that one out, but you'd be surprised. Bloody dozens of them, I know that much.'

'Dozens! You're joking. But, come to think of it, there were five in the place I was born – Epsom, not too far away. But that was Surrey.'

'Yeah, but they're all included because all their patients more than likely come from London, see! But they built the hospitals right away from London, right out in the sticks. So, with these places being completely cut off the staff had no transport, no money, had to live in, and had to organise their own pastimes. I know because me Dad told me. He always swore that if sports and entertainment hadn't been organised, the staff would never have stayed, so the hospitals encouraged them. He used to tell us kids how me Mum and him played in the mixed hockey team and performed every year in the Christmas pantomime. It helped keep them sane, he said. If you can believe that like.'

'Are the sides any good, then? I mean, are they a decent standard?'

'Interesting you should ask that because we once had one of the best senior sides in the whole county, by all accounts. And that must tell you just how many staff worked here once. Another thing you find is that no outside team wants players who can't turn out each week, however good they are, and all our lads have to work shifts. That's one of the main issues for the sportsmen, see. They don't work nine to five, with weekends off, so they can't really commit to outside clubs. So the hospital side changes from game to game because of it. But there's been some big changes even in my time because so many staff can afford to live far away from the hospital and don't have to depend on the hospital activities for their entertainment. Result, less people available. So, now we're starting to let outsiders come into the teams. Which is a pity really.'

'Play anything, yourself?'

'Nah, not fit enough. Fit to fucking drop, more like. Snooker's my game. Then I can get me eight to ten pints in while I'm doing it. What you looking like that for?' since my expression has obviously registered some surprise, to say the least. 'A man's got to have his fluids, ain't he?'

'How can you afford that, let alone sup it?'

'That's why you drink at the Club, ain't it? That's not all, by the way. Someone's always having a party in the hospital and you either get invited or you gatecrash the do. No one really minds so long as you're known. It's better than many parties outside because these foreigners know how to feed their guests. No, I'm not bloody joking! They make bloody smashing food, and set it out all lovely like! How do you get on with curries?'

'That's my poison, actually.'

'Well, this is the place for you then, mate.'

'God, is there anything that's not on tap, here? You only need to go out for a bit of shopping, don't you?'

'No. You've got to find a place to lay a bet, like. But you're right really. Especially if, like me, most of your friends work at the hospital, you can see the problem. If you're not careful, you're never away from the place, know what I mean?'

'Drugs, sex and rock and roll,' I quip.

'You better believe it, my friend.'

'You kidding me? What, drugs an' all?'

'Course. Nothing heavy, like – very hush-hush. Have to know your contacts. You can lose your job if you're caught.'

'I'll stick with the crumpet.' As chance would have it we are distracted by the appearance, from one of the kitchen recesses, of a slim, short female in a white coat, blonde hair twirled under her cap, who makes a sensual progress across the kitchen floor, and which we both follow, lustfully.

'God help us, I can see what you're bleeding interested in!' exclaims the chef. Our bodies sway in that little ritual of tentative uncertainty between two people who have just met. 'You can still get that but you have to fit it around everything else,' he continues, in good humour. Then the amiable chef, with his noticeably bloodshot, glassy eyes, is called away by another member of the kitchen staff. 'What's yer name, then?'

'Er, Steve. And yours?'

'Josh. See you some time, then.'

'Mine's a pint!'

'Mine's several!'

'On your bike!'

'Up yours! See yer.'

The kitchen cooks beneath the heat and light generated by the high, glass canopy. Two of the staff, splashing in Wellingtons, hose the floor and sweep into the frothing, filthy channels the effluent of two working shifts that is regularly sluiced away into a central grill. All the kitchen staff wear white overalls and blue and white, chequered caps and are engrossed in their individual tasks. I am reminded of the occasion as a lad of about 16 when I had wandered into Billingsgate, the old, covered fish market of London's Lower Thames Street. Attention had first honed in on the down-and-outs warming their hands and stamping their feet over vital fires immediately opposite the market entrance. Wandering inside the entrance, I could still see the spouting bursts of water hosing down the smells, discarded ice, and the fish guts; still recall the long handled, upright carts stacked high with wooden crates of fish being wheeled about by the sturdy porters who were wearing porkpie hats and crying out to the down-and-outs – 'Push up the 'ill, then!' – without even looking toward them. Then to see the first among them who could bustle forward, only too pleased to earn himself a tanner. But it is not fish I smell here. It is a pervading, indescribable concoction of aromas that has stained the kitchen space for decades and oozes continually, I imagine.

* * *

Answering my bleep – the only really visible sign of a recent job elevation other than that of actually pushing the food trolleys – I was summoned to perform another of the specialist services to the hospital – to help remove

25

a dead body from the male infirmary. A dead body! I headed for one of the few scrupulously clean wards where the lino floors reflected light around the neatly folded bed packs and intravenous drip-stands which all stood present and correct. A dreadful anticipation was not hugely diminished, on arrival, by the sullen presence of a deeply unshaven Greek porter who leaned over the specialised metal mortuary trolley which was for dead body removals. The Greek acknowledged my presence with the merest hint of a nod and, with minimal effort, dragged away his belly, flipped back the hinged trolley lid, ripped the bed curtain aside, and beckoned his assistant to lift one end of the shrouded form awaiting us. Before there was time to squirm with indecision I, the new assistant, was being beckoned to lift the shrouded form by the feet. The notion of a "dead weight" was surprisingly untrue, as it happened. It didn't droop much in the middle and was surprisingly easy to transfer. Under the scrutiny of the officiating charge nurse, a dapper Chinese Malaysian, we carefully lowered the wrapped pupa into its metal carriage. As if ceremony had been tolerated long enough, once we had left the eyes of the ward, the leading Greek sped the jolting, clanking, mobile sarcophagus through the back corridors and their 90 degree corners, refusing any deviation for oncoming patients, then down the main ramp where the hospital utility buildings were located, and onto the outdoor road surface where the wheels buckled and spun, and the carriage reared and crashed, the noise resonating like the clashing pans on a tinker's wagon and, with the jarring reverberations running through our arms like a manic, first world war machine gun, all conspired to turn what should have been a reverent journey into an unwieldy farce!

Finally, in a remote and inconspicuous corner off the builder's yard, we halted at a diminutive, chapel-like dwelling and pressed through the death doors of the morgue which protested with a desiccated groan. The body wagon halted across the floor of clinical sparseness and the disturbed showers of dust cloud rolled across the streaming pillars of light that leaned through the ample windows, casting a momentary spray of life before the white tiled walls and the enamelled autopsy tables. The new arrival could begin its rotting course like the others that had been carted here over 90 years en route to the afterlife. By now, the more relaxed Greek was fingering a roll-up and asking his companion if he had ever been in such a place before – which response was a disapproving 'not likely' – and he then approached the over-sized cabinet drawers that took up one complete wall. In a mischievous flurry of disrespect he scoured the tiers of drawers, clutching at each brass handle in turn, and briefly yanked out each of the trays in an ostentatious flourish to impress his young associate with the presence of any resident. All to no avail. Laughing loudly, he randomly settled on one of the empty trays to intern their own, latest occupant. Turning back to the carriage, he snapped back the hinged metal lid, allowing it to crash down against its side. Groping into the yielding, metal coffin we both hauled out one end of the spectral form and swung it onto the gaping tongue of the temporary grave. But, since it lay clumsily skewed toward the near end, the Greek moved along and tugged and jerked it further along the drawer in a succession of resounding, thumping clumps of the complaining skull, in this last act of perverse ceremony! Should you laugh? Should you be shamed? You didn't know what to feel.

Months later, I would learn from the male nursing staff that when the crooked, elderly patients had died in the past, the staff would jump on their limbs to better prepare them for the laying out!

* * *

I retraced my way along the main passages to the hospital shop to buy cigarettes. Otherwise known as the patients' canteen, this was grim, smoke filled and grubby walled, with discoloured curtains at the dirt mottled windowpanes. Ostensibly opened as a localised shopping resource, it was an important effort in assisting the hospital's mobile and relatively undisturbed patients not to lose complete contact with the realities of the wider world. Incidentally, it also served as the daily meeting place for hospital society, such as it was. Unescorted access to the shop – patients not requiring to be accompanied by staff, that is – could only be permitted to those who gave no cause for concern. These patients were not expected to harm themselves or others, or to take drugs or alcohol, or indulge in any other criminal activity, or wander off and lose themselves, or intentionally try to escape. Of the latter group, in any case, most had nowhere to run away to. The slightest hint of any such deviance and they'd be spirited off and kept back on the wards. It seemed ludicrous to anyone who wasn't a patient that with all the hospital units and grounds in which to wander these people should choose to collect in this dismal dump. But, perhaps, it was a small cloister of sorts where there was a relatively liberal peace, detached from the demands and squabbles of the wards and staff, where inner worlds could congregate on wall lined benches with sufficient space between each to avoid being too aggravated. Many would never achieve an absolute stillness, though, owing to the medication agitated rhythms that trembled uncontrollably through their limbs. It contained its own impoverished worldliness: a drinks machine which was used as much to appease the smoke-dry, medicated mouths as to offer some variation in drinks from the ward tea. Accidents, infirmity and the sheer frailty of the plastic cups caused the contents to be frequently spilled and dribbled over clothing and the floor. Patients with some little pocket money, who may only have afforded to purchase single fags, tried wheeling and dealing and borrowing and pleading, and sexual favours were cheaply purchased when funds were short. Here, they could even spit without much fear of sanction from each other. There was always a supplementary search for fag butts and tobacco as the acres of floor within and beyond this little cloister, the passages and corridors, the waste bins and the grounds would be scoured and picked over with the thoroughness of sweeping condors.

'Hello Steve, how you doing, me old mate?' says an overweight, beaming, shiny skinned Dave, whose unkempt clothes were stretched across an ample girth and whose truly famous half-brother in the music business has had intermittent contact with him over the years to support his battle with schizophrenia. Dave lets his loud, rattling, unconstrained laugh drift freely above the tight gathering. The laugh has an irksome, attention halting character to it but this is counterbalanced by his way of conveying a warm acknowledgement. The speckled burn holes to the front of his shirt receive another shower of ash as he slowly passes the fag over his stained pot belly and chest for another huge drag – how many during his lifetime? – and exhales, with a bleak look toward the ground while clutching the butt between his thoroughly charcoaled thumb and fingers. His thick tongue, compliant with years of pharmaceutical tuition, lashes uncontrollably, in and out, and around his dry, rasping mouth and his whole frame is a perpetual, methodical fidget. Each drag on the fag swirls about his preoccupations.

'How's that football coming along?' But the question is more rhetorical than inquisitive. 'Used to play it a lot, myself, you know.'

'Really?' I cannot imagine anything more remote, momentarily, than this unlikely frame ever having been a competitive athlete.

'Yes, I was pretty sharp in me time. Played up front, centre forward. Good scoring record, like. Now I couldn't score with an old prostitute. Ha, ha, ha!' His uninhibited, rasping laugh rattles around the close room, oblivious to others' presence or sensibilities. I am impressed by both his candour and his obvious decline.

'Seen that famous brother of yours, lately, Dave?'

'No, haven't heard from him in ages. Probably not easy for him to come here when you think of it. Him being that famous, and that. Can't blame him if he wasn't bothered, I suppose.' It is difficult to detect either regret, or cynicism, for this is said without much emotion. 'He's told me it's influenced his song writing, though.'

A frail, middle-aged female, draped in a dress and cardigan of the thinnest possible quality, holds up a diminutive dog-end to Dave's cigarette in an unspoken appeal for a light. She's scraped this together from off the floor. Dave complies with the unspoken intrusion without irritation. There is a generally shared code among the patients to help each other with tobacco, even with those who are skint, in the fairly sure knowledge that most of them will return the favour sometime. There is a messy smudge of brown powder around her nose that looks like lightly congealed blood but is a fashionable feature of life among the longer term patients – the use of snuff. Patients buy it in tiny tins from the hospital canteen and use it regularly to clear the nose after first noisily snorting a pinch from their forefinger and thumb. Then, the residue stained fingers and smears on shirts or pinafores emphasise their already shabby appearance.

'What's your woman situation at the moment? Lots of lovely foreign girls in the place, eh?' Dave asks through a tooth-catastrophe of a grin, more out of politeness than relish.

'Oh, you know, I'll try to do my bit when I get my chance. There's *some crumpet* in this place, though, eh!' complicit with the sexual innuendo which he believes to lie beneath Dave's enquiry.

'How are you doing with the ladies, anyway?' This is, also, more in the way of a polite reciprocation than any lewd curiosity. I've come to learn that sexual relations between patients are actively discouraged by the staff, who are grateful that they don't seem to figure highly among the priorities of hospitalised schizophrenics. In fact, sexuality among patients is riddled with legal and social difficulties and it is hoped that, in order to avoid all the nasty complications, everyone is just too sick to bother. Like most areas of social rehabilitation in the hospital, I am to learn that this is one area that is more or less ignored except when there is an absolute necessity to do otherwise. Sexual avoidance is so strongly expected by the staff that it is not even really promoted and, for the few females with a known sexual propensity, the contraceptive pill can be prescribed. Sexuality is a definite taboo in relation to any aspect of the psychiatric hospital. Even as a porter, I have been informed of my own legal liability under the 1959 Mental Health Act which can prosecute any male staff member for having sexual intercourse with a female patient! It could culminate in a two year prison sentence. The same sanction does not explicitly apply to the female staff!

'Oh, got more important worries than women,' he mooches, dully without a hint of interest. His mood has shifted to a distant, preoccupied reverie. Another long, distracted draw on his fag and a casual glance around the shop follow before he continues with a subject that has cropped up between them, before. 'Read any good books lately, then?' The mood lifts temporarily.

'Just finished *Death of a Salesman* actually,' I answer, having, in truth, recently studied it for exams and incidentally reminding me of how little I've read of my own volition, since.

'Good play,' he reminisces. 'Old Logan, the salesman, and Biff and Happy, his boys,' he says, with immediate recall, as he rattles off the main characters and outlines the plot, laughing his raucous laugh, as if his belief in life has been revived. He is a companionable presence but, as with most patients I've encountered, it feels as if Dave is stranded in a sticky bog of time while the rest of the world hurls itself around him. It is not hard to be shocked by his ready and accurate retelling and this prompts me to think about what else is stored within this surprisingly erudite soul. This revelation is all the more surprising since, though Dave has a charismatic appeal, his general reputation around the hospital includes a propensity for aggression and awkwardness from time to time. From the evidence of his decline it is not inconceivable that Dave will have to see out his damned days in this place. I wonder how many of the staff will have read the play?

'Have you read anything, yourself?'

'No, can't seem to concentrate anymore, not even on the papers,' Dave replies. 'Don't know whether it's me illness, or the medication, or whether I'm just bored with life, but I just can't be bothered. Just don't have the energy, these days, you know? I know I'm depressed a lot of the time but what's to be done about it, that's the question?'

'Have you brought it up with the ward staff?'

'Yeah, of course. I've been put on these antidepressants for years but they don't do any good. They can't give you back your life, can they?'

'Is that your problem, like, depression?'

'No, the doctors say I'm schizophrenic. Most of the patients in the hospital are supposed to be schizophrenic!' he adds, exasperatedly. 'Beats me. Just look around, we're all different. How can we all be schizophrenic?'

'But you're depressed, too?' It dawns on me that most of the patients I've come across, so far, appear nothing if not depressed and I wonder how much depression is related to the schizophrenia.

'Been depressed for as long as I can remember. Apart from when I was very young, like. You see, I was always reading when I was younger. I always had a book in my hand. I had a good schooling, not exactly a classical education, but good enough,' Dave says with a wistful stare as if reconnoitering the hinterland of his adolescence and rueing his decimated adulthood. 'You just have to hang onto as much as you can,' he concludes. There was no ready answer and as I take my leave, I can only sense the shambles that is this man's daily curse. For his part, Dave accepts the departure with the air of someone who has given up any prospect of making a difference to his life.

We have been edging toward the shop door and are now being passed by Deidre, whose presentation is generally notorious. The most notable physical feature of this short, stocky Cockney is the deliberate, yet, inelegant, stomping gait that shunts her straight, lank, raven hair about her head. Her face is normally cast downwards while on her travels but, whenever she raises her eyes, it glowers somewhere between a pitiful fearfulness and fury. A thick smudge of snuff below her nose sustains an overall impression of a Hitler look-a-like. Another prominent feature is the thickened muscle of a tongue – care of pharmaceutical intervention and psychiatric prescription

– that involuntarily probes the surrounding atmosphere, forewarning her of potential threats from her environment. Characteristically, she is in possession of a wad of magazines that she clutches before her, and at which she systematically glances on her travels. She accords them the reverence and affection that might be accorded a teddy bear or doll and they would seem to provide her with a relational alternative to the adult world about her. In other ways she presents with a childlike persona. This includes her resistance to the hospital's dressing etiquette by never wearing tights or trousers or covering her legs, however inclement the weather, preferring the skirts and summer dresses of the hospital's supplies. Her temperament seems stuck in an earlier phase of her life, for if she catches sight of anyone looking directly at her there will be an immediate show of volatility, sometimes culminating in quite a commotion. Generally, this sensitivity to others' scrutiny, considered to be highly paranoid, causes her to be intolerant of even the slightest acknowledgement. But, on rare occasions, she can confound all expectations by appearing to be on a charm offensive, passing people with the most personable goodwill, with coy smiles and giggles. Her laughter can then yield itself up in an open, toothless, infectiously coarse track of pleasure that lingers long after she has passed. This is not the case, this day, it would seem. I had watched other staff taunt her on her travels and, gauging that her mood is set to her usual paranoid mode, I deliberately blaze a direct glance toward her.

'Who are you looking at? Don't you look at me,' she remonstrates in a coarse disgruntlement curdled from a lifetime of misanthropic yelling at others, at imaginings, as if it is one of her life's purposes.

'Good morning, Deidre,' I inject into the situation, anticipating her instant backlash. Not disappointed, I am regaled with a glare from her maddened, huge, brown eyes at such effrontery.

'Bollocks.'

'Now then,' I reply, assuming a feigned effort at chastisement, 'that's not very nice now, is it!'

'Bollocks. Who d'yer think you're looking at?' her voice gathering impetus.

'Have a nice day, Deidre.'

'Bollocks. Double bollocks.'

'All I said was…'

'FUCK YOURSELF!' Her explosive response is catapulted back at me, particularly since I've shown no sign of retiring from the scene. She is probably more used to people backing off when she slopes along in their direction but there are some who will wind her up on a whim. Dave, who lounges into the canteen entrance, steadies his narrowing eyes upon the episode while I return a glint of satisfaction in his direction. Deidre's remonstrations can now be heard further along the corridor.

'Look at someone else, BASTARD! Who's he think he is, fucking God? Go away, go away, GO AWAAAAY!' is the searing parting of Deidre's interaction. Our attention still lingers on her fading, stomping frame.

'She'll never change,' Dave sighs resignedly.

'You just can't help having a bit of fun with her,' I say, with some exhilaration.

'No, providing you haven't lived with it for years, I suppose!'

Some months later, the news sung along the hospital wires that Dave had quietly slipped away from his ward one day and, without any indication to anyone, walked down the hospital drive and onto the platform of the local railway station just three quarters of a mile from the home he had known for years. His smashed frame was found on the track after ending up beneath a train on the London to Brighton route. Whether the misadventure was an accident or an irrepressible act dictated by delusion or abandonment, or by hopelessness and depression, was never discovered and probably not greatly pursued. He had had years to contemplate the end of his life cast, as he was, into the bleak, unforgiving routine of hospital existence. But conscience can be a troubling lair and the speculation gnawed at me about the disturbing coincidence – surely it was no more than that? – of Logan's own suicide in *Death of a Salesman* about which we had conversed, together, that day in the hospital canteen not so very long before.

* * *

Taking advantage of the unmonitored schedule under which I worked, I chanced a fleeting visit to the hospital chapel, the entrance to which was an unassuming recess along one of the shorter main corridors. I had acquired a

33

certain stance on churches that, while including all the usual aesthetic, religious, architectural and historical dimensions, held other fascinations for me. It could only be marvelled at that they had survived at all in the face of maintenance costs, decimated membership, surrounding redevelopment, theft and vandalism, and the attenuated ideas of religious thinking. But my real interest was my identification with them as these abandoned places in which there could be found some brief restorative immersion. It was an irony that they were more of a comfortable repository for the reclusive visitor who could be assured of avoiding mass intrusion – any intrusion for that matter – from a modern culture that kept its disreputable, insolent distance from the thought provoking challenges that they represented. This place would have had its history, its stories, not just the Christian story – the builders, their crafts and gargoyles; those patients and staff who'd done the Bible readings and stood at the lecterns; the many vicars leaning from the pulpit; the carved pews, the damp reek and woodworm; the permanent congregations, the dead, the dying; the literate, pontificating; the upholding of the Crown, the Sovereign, the Sovereign's armed forces, and the British Nation. All these survived in a dwelling that helped to ensure a continuing, closeting sanctuary – a space for meditation and rest, for solace, for the consideration of life and death, for a separating silence, for the slowing of time in the constant struggle for the present.

Over nearly a century the thick oak doors, blackened by sinners' hands, yielded to the smoothly worn, iron latch being lifted and then dropped to ring out like a muffled, blacksmith's blow through the echoing vaults of the chapel. Set among such a busy community, the insulated quiet was all the more confounding. Positioned very prominently at the heart of the institution it was built on a grander scale than most village churches, which indicated the size of the hospital population relative to the average, local parish community. In their time, these asylum chapels had attracted a weekly congregation of around a quarter of their total patient numbers! The imagination tried to visualise the long dead congregations who would have had no choice but to crowd into the pews to attend the services in earlier years. But, as befitting the spiritual malaise of the times, it did not draw in the crowds these days, all the more surprising in the context of the magical and supportive potential that it might hold. And, in the sanctified plots of graveyard headstones within the hospital precincts were harboured other signs, other than administrative records, of a hundred years of pauper lunatics' lives, deaths and burials until even these were desecrated by indiscriminate housing developers, who ground the lot into foundation meal. For the present, the Church of England chapel may have been relegated to only symbolic significance whereas, as the Established Church, it had previously occupied an omnipresent position in every asylum in the land.

The question was how had the Anglican Ministry managed to be included in the inauguration of the public asylums when, in principle, any denomination could have patronised an asylum community during the latter half of the nineteenth century. After all, the asylums were not only foreign territory to the traditional rural parish. They had never been integrated into the emerging towns, either, but were geographically and symbolically marginal to both. Was the Anglican Church adapting to the times and asserting itself amid its ailing fortunes and the creeping dissolution of its authority in the countryside, as well as the competition in the towns?

In terms of a ready-made parish community on the rural fringes of large towns, the asylums had a lot going for them in conforming to a traditional, Anglican model of service. They mirrored the self-contained physical perimeters of the rural village, and contained a resident constituency of socially subordinate, deferential and dependent parishioners, on which it could hang its paternalistic vestments. Most asylums were also set in a semi-pastoral setting, where the pastor could still be a shepherd to his flock, albeit a new breed.

What did the Church of England have to gain from such an undistinguished association when its foundations, and allegiances, were already secured through populated settlements, the Crown, private patrons and landed squires, the very core of parliamentary power? Did the Church hold out the most favourable tender in relation to the rest of the religious competition? Did the State need its power, its credibility and the sheer abundance of its resources? Or was it that the existing political symbiosis between the State and the Established Church continued in perpetuity as they jointly weaved an authoritative coil of control, guidance, and benevolence through the institutionalism of asylums, prisons, hospitals, and schooling of the nineteenth century? Like skeletal joints, the Church of England articulated with the State's management of society's mental diseases mainly because it was an intimate part of the established political and administrative structure and could not have been excluded. Nourished by its governmental host, irrespective of whether it believed it could comfort its ailing, insane family, the Church of England bound itself around the mental hospitals like resolute, persistent ivy.

Nevertheless, what really mattered was whether the chapel's presence was pertinent for the patients. Who would deny them any such solace if, considering their abandonment by the outside world, and by family, the Church would always offer them some consolation, some validation? The Church was a resource alongside science, medical skills and nursing care. And, in the event that all the science should fail, there would remain the alternative prospect of spiritual hope, miraculous cure, and pre-ordained destiny. An abiding endeavour, a laudable resolve, to try to reconcile religious consolation with the mysteries of the psychologically unsound; to promulgate the illusion of spiritual wellbeing while painfully conscious of its inability to understand these lost minds.

* * *

Without the preparedness of the British labour market to relocate far from its geographical and social origins to fill the available vacancies, the hospital authorities would have had quite a job in attracting recruits to the isolated world of the lunatic asylum. To assist in maintaining the requisite levels of recruitment the authorities ensured that staff interests pervaded the asylum estate and a plethora of economic and social comforts were afforded them. Every practicable sporting and entertainment facility was provided on site to encourage the sense of a localised community. As significant as any, in time, was the staff social club which would have been accessible to any staff member, professional and non-professional, alike. In practice, it had plenty to recommend it to its predominantly working class membership.

It was a purveyor of inexpensive intoxication, gossip, conspiracy, character assassination, and entertainment. Saturday nights and special events on the calendar spawned discos, bands, or dancing, and when the New Year celebrations arrived the congregation was pressed to the very walls and herniating into the car park. Totally egalitarian, in principle, it attracted staff up to the level of the Director of Nursing, himself, who was an avid player of the slot machines. Here, he could display the common touch, drinking, gaming and chatting like everybody else and it did nothing to diminish the staff protocol. With the added security of being on private land, the Social Club was virtually exempt from the scrutiny of the law so that, though like any public house it had normal opening hours, closing time became a glazed and moveable line.

The resources amounted to a working man's country club or facility enhanced Working Men's or Royal Legion Club. It was a haven from the unpredictable, social traffic of the neighbouring towns, and the hostilities and lack of safety of public houses and their immediate vicinity. But, if you were wanting a haven of anonymous drinking this was well nigh impossible, here. No one entered the place and remained a stranger for long. Solitary tranquillity and quiet obscurity could only attract a sceptical attention set among heckling music, the chattering hum, the thump of darts, the click of snooker and pool balls, and the exhibitionist clatter of the gaming machines. For the especially sociable, the clusters of tables and chairs and their cling-ing revellers would press around the central dance area like heavily fruited trees about a tiny wood-clearing. Such was the exceptional expectation of the clubhouse.

That this was the epitome of the working men's club was no accident. As with all mental hospitals, this one was populated by the full gamut of health professionals, paramedics, and ancillary staff, from both sexes. Unlike the female dominated nursing in general hospitals, psychiatric hospitals contained an extraordinarily high level of males, the majority of whom would comfortably have been designated as the traditional working class. In terms of the social club it was, undoubtedly, this working class atmosphere which drew in the nursing, ancillary and artisan groups but dissuaded the involvement of most of the other professional categories such as doctors, social workers, pharmacists, etc. If the professionals were ever present it would have required an occasional event such as a colleague's leaving do which was conveniently managed during the lunchtime hours.

The Club was a necessary heart transplant from that which sat at the core of the institution. Through it the staff could bypass their on-duty personas and perfuse the alternative gossip of hospital life. It also generated such a considerable flow of funds that it was more or less self-financing and self-administered. Because of the potential sexual benefits of attending a Saturday night at the Club, it was worth giving the old testosterone a good scrub up, so that it leered and lunged from every pore as you gawped at the off-duty colleagues and their friends that caught the eye. For the Club had the advantage of building on the already established working acquaintances between people and these often facilitated casual sexual relations. The festivity of uninhibited drinking and burgeoning lust was further accommodated by the proximity of the Nurses Home, and the domestics' living quarters, where the prospects of a libidinous finale would sweat and spill all the way to a woman's moist and satiating hospitality. In truth, the Club often facilitated our sometimes outrageous liaisons.

As with so many others, then, I was more than grateful for the confluence of benefits that the Club venue facilitated – the affordability, the recreation, the social availability, the superficial bonhomie, as well as the occasional soul-searching companionship, and the identification with a recognisable community in which each held a number of rôles.

There was a malignant irony to all this, of course. In other respects, it had to be said that the Club epitomised the wider social segregation within the hospital. Most symbolically, the Club was a quite divisive construction that facilitated the distinctly separate interests of the staff as opposed to the body of patients for whom the psychiatric enterprise was meant. In itself, it was an architectural blemish; a modern, single storied, dumbed down prefabrication, with not a traditional wall in place, and contrasting with the authentic stone and brickwork magnificence of the hospital history. It was set alongside the long established bowling green and the heated, outdoor swimming pool. However, the patients never accessed the bowling green and, with the exception of limited daytime sessions, the swimming pool was the exclusive preserve of hospital staff and associate members. This entire complex was the preserve of the staff only, free from all patients other than the one or two who worked at the Club. More than this, the social demarcation was even more physically marked by the road that ran between the complex, confining it to one side, and the main hospital situated on the opposite side. Furthermore, no one made any effort to alter this social apartheid.

Alcohol had a colossal influence. Notoriety was spilled from its copious consumption. There was the rotund, but still mobile, older charge nurse who sat apparently untouched after supping 20 pints of beer a day! Or, there was one of my own contemporaries who downed four pints, just for lunch, then to partake of a feet up, beer marinated siesta in the dayroom of his infrequently visited back ward. For many staff, the inter-hospital football games were played through the ethanol fumed gasps of the pre match drinking session. At a later date, during my second year of nurse training, I celebrated my birthday lunchtime in the clubhouse with several colleagues who plied me with Southern Comfort – a drink I've been repulsed by ever since. I was to discover on wakening during the early evening that I had spent the entire afternoon crashed out on a patient's bed and my disappearance was covered up on my behalf! Christmas festivities were not spared. Every ward, every nook and cranny in the organisation, were open all hours. Each ward and department clubbed together to procure its own bar and the staff imbibed in unlicensed, and sometimes licentious, celebration. The booze was demarcated from the patients, stashed in a separate room and not shared with them. We could get as smashed as we liked provided we stayed on our feet and were capable of fulfilling our duties. The funniest alcohol fuelled memory was during my night duty training in my third year that coincided with the Christmas period. The Night Senior Nursing Officer, Mr. Green, had come to visit my ward colleague, a female staff member with whom he had had a long, Platonic acquaintance. They disappeared into the "bar" for several hours and re-emerged giggling and holding onto one another. I hadn't much taken to the fellow but when I saw them struggling to make progress out of the ward entrance and along the corridor I had no option but to muck in. Necessarily leaving the ward unattended, I came alongside them as they lurched about, laughing uncontrollably, and uttering the proverbial "Shuuuush, we'll wake everybody!" Bridget is surprisingly together considering her predicament, plus my estimation of her as a highly conscientious individual.

'Oh, Steve, thank God. Come on, we need that strength of yours. We've to get his lordship back to the night nursing office before he's found out. At least he can answer the phone,' my colleague, exasperated, says in her Irish lilt and between shrills of joyous incapacity.

'No problem,' I say, but truly unimpressed that things have reached this dire level. I coax a languid arm around my neck, pull hard on it, and haul him up while Bridget makes a vain effort with the opposite side. We stumble along the corridor. What the hell he's managed to down I don't know, but he's sufficiently legless to be incapable of standing unsupported. She is not hugely better and I find myself dragging the pair of them. Green draws me back.

'Now, I don't know you very well but don't you get breathing a bloody word of this to a soul, do you understand, Mr. Burrow?' his voice drawls, his intoxicated eyes searching for mine in an uncoordinated dance.

'Oh, he won't. Don't be daft,' interjects Bridget. 'For Christ's sake, will you try and get a move on, now!'

'I shan't breathe a word, sir.'

'I hope your word is good, Mr. Burrow.'

'Oh, Jesus, his slipper's coming off,' says Bridget, hopelessly collapsing in laughter. 'I can't get it back…' she cannot finish the words. And, sure enough, one of his slippers – yes, slippers! – has managed to peel itself from one foot. I push him against the corridor wall and hold him upright with one hand, while reaching down to his errant footwear. It is pure slapstick and I cannot contain myself from erupting into the infectious clowning of the others. I am so overtaken with laughter that my strength and resolve to hold up the said Mr. Green disintegrate and the three of us find ourselves slowly sliding down the smooth, smooth wall onto the shiny linoleum floor until we are a heap of witless, breathless incapables.

'Jesus, if I haven't wet myself that'll be a miracle, so it will!' suggests Bridget. 'What'll I do if I have?'

'I'll have to change you,' blurts out Green. More rasping laughter and we just cannot pull ourselves together if our reputations depended on it.

'Now, come on,' I insist, rising to my feet earnestly now. 'I've to get back to the ward so you have to reach the nursing office, Mr. Green.' Eventually, and I mean, quite some time later, we reach the flight of steps leading to the first floor offices. The three of us now have to negotiate this limited space between us by, necessarily, spacing ourselves over several steps over several levels. Well, we hauled, and stumbled, and tripped, and slumped, and leaned, and pushed, a laboured ascent of two flights while our coarse cackles echoed around the resounding chasm of the stairwell until we dislodged the inebriate into his office and I made my exit.

There was also a pathetic element to the Christmas fanfare in that there was a wide variation in indulgence. Seasonal revelry was guaranteed if the host wards contained popular charge nurses and sisters and you either kept their society or were allocated to that ward, at that time. These sociable characters were a natural draw and ensured that the bar was substantially stocked. But, toward the more straight laced or less sociable hosts, you felt more inhibited about either being invited or inviting yourself. If in doubt, the potential festivity could be gauged by quietly sneaking into the ward dayroom, prospecting the atmosphere, and spiriting yourself out pretty sharpish if it appeared to be dead!

* * *

'You're wanted down at the tailor's to be measured for your uniform,' I'm instructed by the Charge Nurse while on my first ward as a mental nurse. 'You may as well go, now, we're not too busy, are we?'

'Got you. Back as soon as I can.'

'No rush, son.'

A hospital is one of those corporate environments that make substantial efforts to distinguish differences within the employee hierarchy. The identification of nursing staff is no exception, so that my acquisition of the hospital uniform is a vital thread – nay, a million threads – in the rite de passage from civilian to psychiatric nurse and of displaying my place in the local fraternity.

In the fabric lined dinginess of the tailor's shop, the hospital's resident tailor gleams through cut-glass specs and winds a bespoke trail around his customer's body, straps a tape measure across the chest, then across the shoulders, then along the shoulder to the wrist, gathers his thumbs at the waist, flirts with the inside leg, and stoops to negotiate the turn-up with a 'how's that feel?' at every step. And, as each measurement rises into the firmament, the flash of pencil, drawn like a dart from behind the tailor's ear, pierces it through and impales it onto the notepad beside him. As the scribble of dimensions is reckoned into a woollen, three piece suit, with spare trousers and waistcoat, no expense spared, the tailor also stitches into the lining of his imagination as much news of the hospital as is possible from his latest courier!

41

'Don't suppose you know much about the place seeing as you haven't been here too long?' he asks in a pitch that was so high that, perhaps, he'd sewn his vocal cords into a tight mesh on one laboriously uneventful day. In this backroom atmosphere, you could not help but be sympathetic to the tailor's quest for gossip and wondered about the mental diaries each member of staff must have had of all the other staff. This attracted the curious idea that in any quarter of the institution, at any time of the day, and who knows how frequently, anybody could be the subject of someone else's gossiped missives and that, alongside whatever you were enacting within your own narrow orbit, there were parallel universes all around in which your existence might be drawn upon, mimicked and deplored. You wondered how often the tailor, ensconced far from the hospital action, would figure in the thoughts of the hospital community and how much this reflected both his relevance, and relative obscurity.

'Do you manage to keep tabs on most things even though you're stuck down here, out of harm's way, then?'

'*Course*. Don't think I want to be ignorant of what's going on, do you? As for being out of harm's way, well, if you want to know what's going on in the place you just have to know the right people to ask. Simple as that.' Away from the supply of the main social network the isolated tailor was a separate generator that powered his personal institutional connections. Even though he's talking, incessantly, the tailor is in permanent motion, as if physical actions have to keep pace with his verbal commentary.

'If anybody wanted to know anything, then, you'd be a sound source, would you?'

'Yeah, but I might not tell you what you wanted to know!' and he screeches a laugh through his sewn cords.

*   *   *

For all its occupational variation – psychiatrists, visiting GPs, nurses, occupational and industrial therapists, psychologists, pharmacists, administrators, porters, domestics, dentist, clergy, electricians, plumbers, cobblers, tinsmiths, upholsterers, seamstresses, tailors, engineers, drivers, gardeners, chefs and cooks, financial staff, recreation officers, tutors, barmen, and others – you were able to say you moved in a fairly intimate working circle that conferred a certain stability that you would not have anticipated in other fields. As much as any working environment it was a place of rhythm and connection. But, doubtless due to its reservation like allocation, there was a shared identity and intimacy which snatched you from the nebulous disconnection of the ordinary daily cycle.

You just couldn't help but be enthralled by the voyeuristic draw of madness, and of the very asylum, and all its mystical connotations. There was the intellectual draw of the radical psychiatric climate of the era – the psychiatrists, Laing, Esterson, Szazs, and Cooper – which was informing wider social and professional studies and ideological debate, and fuelling the popular imagination and the informed public.

The institution vitalised a personal sense of belonging, beyond merely conferring an occupational identity, at a juncture in my life when I was on the verge of "dropping out" for want of belief in anything. Of course, I had some awareness of comfortably sliding into the surrogate security and inclusive-ness of the institution. But what did I care when the self-affirming belief in an inner seed of selfhood had been resuscitated; that seed of uniqueness, that cried out against the point in time and place that had appointed me to a grotesque family and its malign dynamics that were none of my choosing. In turn, I often thought how many patients had viewed the fixed points of their births, families, education and cultures as having blighted their entire life opportunities.

I had stumbled into the sanctuary of the asylum, into a place set apart, that was made all the more beguiling by the speculation that most of the general population would not have remotely tolerated the alien departure from normality that it represented. This fact was frequently confirmed by the oft quoted enquiry from outsiders – 'How on earth do you manage to stick it?' I was always surprised that anyone should seriously entertain the idea that working in the psychiatric field, particularly in asylums, must be considered vocational. It was understood that nursing was embedded in the religious communities and that Florence Nightingale, herself, had not only had a voca-tion to care for the sick but had attempted to enter a religious order to gain a nursing training and the majority of her earliest recruits were either professed nuns or Anglican sisters. Well, yes, there was something about entering the relatively closed asylum world, the very low level of financial remuneration, and its remote approximation to the religious postulant's confinement that drove the demands of the world beyond its perimeter into relative inconsequence. But, surely, there the similarities ended!

I had begun to understand exactly how I could "stick it" as the doubts that had beset those first few days quickly dissipated. Within but a handful of miles from home it was possible to access the tranquillity of the asylum estate while avoiding the drudgery of urban commuting and the frenetic irritation of the urban road race. To my mind, the estate and surroundings had been purchased from private ownership and transformed into a parkland, like any other municipal park, for the benefit of its invited residents and employees. This aside, there was a compelling attraction to the organisational order, the deliberately defining authority, the demarcating hierarchy and status, the complex interplay of professional purposes, and the feeling of control that these all gave to the psychiatric enterprise, despite elements of unpredictability which characterised both mental illness and the patients. It set out definitive descriptions, purposes, goals and procedures for its workforce that became a way of life, in itself.

There was the added fillip of embarking on something that went beyond mere gainful employment and salary. A lot of personal fulfilment emanated from working in the nationalised sector and it could not but inculcate some measure of public spiritedness within me. There was also much satisfaction to be gained from such variable work rather than an over-determined job. More than the nationalised sector, it was a Public Service, and that began to mean something to me. So, it did not feel that you merely arrived at a place of work as a functional employee. Rather, you were engaged in a responsible, and definitive, public service that promoted staff loyalties and common recreational and social purposes, and combined patients' dependency along with some residual striving for independence, all occupying an amenity stacked settlement. The economic role into which I had, fortuitously, drifted was not one which demanded the feverish competitiveness from which I had felt so alienated when weighing up a career path. This was a relaxed, unpretentious passage that would obviate concerns with undue ambition and social status and that afforded a passing flirtation with altruism. The derisive remuneration that it accorded was a small price to pay. The job and its component opportunities proffered a new social independence in another proxy home. What it also facilitated, for someone like myself who was content with economic sobriety, was that I could avoid the voracious economic mainstream. It was possible to step back from the more habitual trend that enjoined people into surrendering their uniqueness, time, consciousness and free movement, for an employment market which would have all these stapled down for life. It felt that you could remain on the fringe of an economic system that was a feat of structured inequality, that gorged upon the exploitation and disproportion of unequal careers, differential incomes, and their associated life opportunities; a system that survived on enticing most people into perpetual competition, and consumption, and the illusionary rationale of materialism. You could see that this went way beyond the seductive allure and self-interested advantage, and power, of acquiring private property. Material aspiration, and material gain, represented the definitive measure of what it was to be successfully human, and what was most likely to satiate human nature. The accumulating rewards of the materially successful seemed, self-evidently, to protect against life's unbounded uncertainties, even insanity.

All in all, it took on the contextual nuance of a psychiatric Kibbutz by dint of being cut off from the mainstream, of its insularity and self-containment, of its attraction as an alternative way of life, where everyone entered into a new, extended family in which they would be acknowledged and respected, and away from the bustling conurbation. It was an affinity with the isolation, and the almost healing peacefulness of self-imposed exile, that inexorably drew me into the institutional orbit and with which I identified as a self-acclaimed outsider.

Not that this high-mindedness precluded another emphatic motivation which was a mischievous, morbid attraction at having the chance to peer into the tantalising mists of the psychiatric world, the compelling histories of individual patients and their mystifying pathologies. Psychiatric presentation could be routinely monotonous, sometimes magnificently variable. There would be those occasional, mystical encounters when preoccupied patients might stop before you, fix you with grimaces and mumbling exhortations, meaningful only to themselves, holding your gaze as if it helped them hone their concentration. Your service was to provide the current screen on which the patient might then launch the delusional missiles from their explosive minds.

For me, the transition from outsider to insider would become a renewal, and somewhat of the order of an atonement, a reconciliation, a rebirth of sorts. It was all of this that informed my life changing deflection into psychiatric nursing and the subsequent years of working in hospital environments. As to whether this merited being called a vocational transition, when my own bleak prospects had been transformed by a fatalistic surrender to fortune, was hard to determine. It was even possible to entertain the comforting fantasy that there might be an external force outside of my conscious control which, in some act of companionable guidance, had fatefully intervened on my behalf. This enabler, cognisant of past struggles, and my disinclination for more conventional fields of employment and lifestyle, may have been instrumental in directing me to work in this curious arena of psychiatry.

And, then, there was the salacious reputation that such an establishment engendered. As to whether I had yet witnessed, or had had any first hand experience of, any of the reported stigma and shame associated with asylum care, was not at all clear; because for me, at that time, the establishment was far from being an oppressive, social anachronism. The very building had become reified as a paternalistic image of tradition, reliability and continuity and, whenever its image came to mind, it bestowed a feeling of assurance.

Anyone can be made ill at ease by their initial exposure to such an institution as an asylum. Most will harbour some of the common misgivings, the traditional mythologies, and derogatory prejudices about anything associated with the psychiatric scenario.

Not forgetting the dynamic roots that, conceivably, reached deep into the Surrey town into which I was born, which contained a tight complex of five psychiatric hospitals, one of which lay adjacent to my paternal grandparents' home – the house in which my father had been reared. Visits to their place rarely precluded at least some mention of, or our personal contact with, the local patients owing to their high visibility among the local population, the alleyways of my grandparents' daily walks, and their considerable sympathy toward them. What connection would all this bring to bear? It didn't take a career of introspection to fathom that securing work in the mental hospital had served more than a mere pragmatic purpose in that I might also gain some purchase, some awareness and insight, into the haunting unhappiness that accompanied me on my journey.

46

Therefore, the prospect of being employed in the hospital was as much an emotional accommodation and attachment, a trial integration into an institutional climate, and an embracing of its curiosity value, that more than compensated for the minor equivocation that you were putting your independence at risk. And, as things panned out, most of what the hospital portrayed rather resonated with me. Even if I was an exile into institutional cover this might well be where it was possible to discover some peace and healing, and a new persona, and to suppress the preoccupation with failure, alienation, and oblivion. In total, it offered part occupation, part counterculture, part alternative village life, part transitional home, and a potential journey of self discovery. Intuitively, it felt that there was some guidance into an unworldly sanctuary that would facilitate some temporary nurturing and self acceptance until a degree of recovery from the fraught dramas of the past was reached. Maybe the journey to the asylum doors was about putting myself away? If so, to what degree did the same apply to others!

* * *

The wild buddleia always provoked an indelible personal image of the hospital for me. These sparse stalks worked fast to raise the several pairs of silver haired and green leaves, around which there sprang an abandonment of heavy plumes, each fluting to a narrow apex. Every plume appeared but a single, hanging bulb, until an interested party homed in on the flecked orange and yellow stamens that reached from the centre of a tight gathering of lilac and purple flowers. And the abundant blooms swayed and bounded to the rhythm of the winds like swinging incense burners, ritually spraying the air with their aroma. They hosted the life about them, danced with the peacock butterflies, tortoiseshells, and red admirals, in an embarrassment of energy, colour and dizzy fragrance. With a reputation for being a rambling, imposing nuisance it was not overly welcomed into the ordered and manicured grounds so that what little of this managed to establish itself on the hospital estate was necessarily unplanned, frugally dispersed, and opportunistic.

By choice, the hospital's gardeners would not have granted them space among the domesticated shrubs, bushes and trees of the formal plots but their qualities surprised and, where they set themselves down, they were sometimes permitted to stay and were saved from a hacking end. All the while, observations continued on their lack of refinement, their gaunt imposing sprawl but, equally, it could not be denied that they had a certain drawing power. For its part, the buddleia appreciated any space in which it could flourish and display its very modest kind of splendour, earnestly seeking the recognition and rightful place that it deserved amongst the more venerated flora.

CHAPTER TWO
INVIOLABLE PROTECTION

I COMMENCED A PSYCHIATRIC NURSE TRAINING IN 1973. After having so swiftly shed the dull grey skin of a porter, I was reincarnated in the more illuminative white coat of a nurse. Other regalia symbolised the transition in the form of a made-to-measure, three piece woollen suit which was the modern nursing uniform, and a name badge. After a convivial, if undemanding, six week introductory theory block in the Hospital Training School my particular student group found itself dispersed among the various wards for the next three months. Having anticipated encountering a wild sea of psychiatric morbidity on an acute or long stay ward I was, actually, to enter the dispiriting environment of a "psycho-geriatric" ward. Different individuals will have quite opposing perspectives on such an experience. Some, undoubtedly, relish the chance to care for the elderly infirm. For me, the sharp whiff of urine that assailed the olfactory senses as you entered through the locked entrance was but an early warning of an experience for which the preceding six weeks' training had done nothing to prepare me. The "geriatric" side of the psycho-geriatric equation meant that these patients were elderly enough to require a separate, more protective environment in view of their physical and mental infirmities. In addition to impaired general mobility, there was frequently either single or double incontinence, that is, they were liable to urinary and/or faecal soiling of their clothes or bed space, often on a regular basis. Mobility was often so difficult that support was required to walk, sit, lie down, dress, undress, bath and eat. Some could perform absolutely nothing for themselves. Their advanced years required physical care and attention for a burgeoning range of medical conditions so that the medicine round was a painstaking affair, dishing out a plethora of non-psychiatric medications, ointments and creams along with the psychiatric ones. Then there might be medical dressings to be applied, some done under stringent aseptic procedure. There was a routine to the care of these 28 patients, or so, which went something like this. Enter ward dormitory as soon as night nurse has handed over any relevant information, which would normally take but a handful of minutes during which the staff would have their first cup of tea. Two or three female staff allocated to the female dormitory and the Charge Nurse and me to the male one. The dormitory lights would be switched on, blazing the area like Berlin Wall floodlighting, and we would rouse the patients with encouraging cries.

'Get up Chalmers, you lazy bugger, and stop wiping your shit on the bedstead. When will you learn to use the toilet to do that?' The Charge Nurse is an experienced soul and, despite the surprising admonishment, is pretty sympathetic and tolerant toward his charges. Chalmers has, indeed, picked his own faeces from his backside and methodically smeared it all along the top of his metal framed bed head. But he makes no effort to rise and remains put, straight as a pole, with his exceptional, hawk shaped nose sniffing over the top of his bedding. He is muttering continually to himself and fixes his malevolent, dark brown eyes on me, the newcomer. 'Don't worry about him, just pull the sheets back and he'll get up.' Which is what I do. Instantly, Chalmers bends his long, skinny limbs and rolls from the bed in a sprightly fashion and stands quite still. 'Go on, get dressed, you cantankerous bugger.' He bends, disgruntled, whips open his bedside table, and snatches his clothes from the shelves. Methodically, he climbs into these vestments, all the while casting glaring eyes about him before kicking his feet into his shoes and slapping his hands together with the calculated chagrin of a seasoned malcontent. If he hadn't been so old his appearance would have been quite forbidding. 'He knows how to stand up for himself but I've never heard of him hitting a staff member. If you upset him he'll rear up and put his Dukes up to you. I'll give you a demonstration later.' It seems to me as if Chalmers' stare could burn a hole in your face.

We proceed around the other patients, the Charge Nurse taking on the more difficult ones while I struggle through the rudiments of plain dressing not made easier by the confused patients who, unintentionally, resist my input. This elicits another major deficit of the psycho-geriatric – the prevailing senile and pre-senile dementias, often given a diagnosis of Alzheimer's Disease or Creuzfeldt-Jacob Disease. Obviously, the extent of intellectual deficit varies from person to person but the general presentation is that of a widespread confusion to the extent that sufferers can no longer pursue any activity or daily routine, forget how to accomplish the simplest of tasks (including how to physically eat), become frustrated at the slightest obstacle, and are apparently incapable of adding any new experience to their repertoire of memory. Therefore, they have no alternative but to live in the past and their daily lives may be peppered with misidentifications as they associate the staff or visitors with the family or close associates they knew in the past. Seemingly, by living in the past they are drawing on the only remaining mental capacity they have left while the present merely piles on unwanted, tiresome layers of demands which they have not the facility to incorporate.

The male patients only wear pyjama tops, without the trousers, in bed, unless they are consistently continent. This is to reduce the inconvenience of having to change an unnecessary article of wet clothing as well as the bed sheets. But it wouldn't do to send patients to bed totally naked. One incontinent patient is led, therefore, semi-naked, into the adjoining bathroom where the Charge quickly washes his genitalia and bottom with a soapy sponge, then dries and dresses him. Then the patients are shaved. Easier said than done, that one! Charge does the job efficiently enough, while griping incessantly about the useless contribution of the hospital's nursing officers. It occurs to me that he must have been turned down for a post in the past and now relishes projecting his animosity toward the current post holders. He teaches me the rudiments of shaving someone else along with securing their tie. It is surprising how inept you feel when you attempt such simple tasks for the first time – to stand before someone and complete tasks on their behalf. In themselves, they are highly symbolic of the whole philosophy of care – a state of empathic reversal. In adopting another person's self management you are having to hold in focus that individual's incapacity and work on their behalf, not your own. If you sacrifice this in pursuit of an efficient and speedy completion, largely for your own benefit, you can only become increasingly frustrated and antagonised by the imperfect, decrepit world of the patients. Then it is you who will have the problems.

51

The male side of the ward is a good deal easier than the female side so we manage to disgorge our patients into the male lounge or set them in their seats, ready for breakfast. The Ward Domestic has been setting the tables and pouring the tea from a large metal teapot in the middle of each. The tea is tepid, limp and uninviting because every precaution must be made to avoid accidents and scalding. Charge Nurse instructs all available patients to come to the table while he hands me each individual's meals. When the more capable patients have been allocated all their meals the staff settle to feeding the more confused ones who are incapable of feeding themselves. This is a complete revelation. Some patients do not even realise that it's a meal time and are consistently surprised by the sensation of spooned food being pressed to their lips, as if they've been woken from some reverie. I take my time trying to coax a path through the gummy lips of a female and I am told by a female Nursing Assistant to push my spoon in harder, and then prepare the next mouthful. 'Otherwise, we'll be here all blinking day, my dear!' All the staff are now spoon feeding the more confused of the assembly and chatting together about whatever subject comes to mind. In between mouthfuls we lean this way and that to assist the more able eaters; to extricate a cup of tea that has been placed in the middle of a bowl of porridge; to prevent the tea being poured over the porridge; to guide an inept hand that fails to connect a spoon's contents with the mouth; to prevent one wandering hand from indulging in someone else's meal, and to restrain anyone who prematurely leaves the table.

While the patients are still at the breakfast tables the Enrolled Nurse wheels out the medication trolley, unlocks it, and starts dispensing the tablets with my help – not that I can assist in any really useful way. I know neither the drugs nor their purposes and cannot even properly read their names in some instances, but I am able to be a conduit between her and the patients. I do not hand the meds. to the patients. In most cases I must push items of varying consistency and size between hesitant or protesting lips, and follow up with a shot of water to wash the offending items into the throat. I pick up devious tips from my colleagues. I claim that the meds. are the patient's favourite sweets, or an unfinished part of the meal; hide them in a spoonful of porridge; pounce when the patient takes their next mouthful of breakfast; or hold their nose until the mouth opens for breath. If I fail, guilty tongues and lips will reveal slithers of broken, but unswallowed, medicinal remnants and further shots of water follow. When a patient has consumed their meds., he or she has permission to leave their table in the dining area at the centre of the ward and to make their way to the day areas at either end. However, the incontinent females are "toileted" as a matter of routine – toilet training it's called – in the hope of encouraging peeing and avoiding having to change incontinence pads later. As many as can be managed at once are placed either on mobile commodes or fixed toilets in the corridor leading toward the female dormitory. For the one or two who may try to get off, they have to be tied around the waist to the commodes. The judicious use of incontinence pads is the next great strategy to be dealt with in the fight against a person's failure to marshal urinary or faecal continence. To minimise the arduousness of changing urine soaked or faeces filled clothes, the business is accomplished with the very minimum of inconvenience and ceremony. Smell often diagnoses the incontinent/soiled patient, who is guided or wheeled to a bathroom or toilet area. Without the incontinence pad all the dirtied items of clothing would need removing, each disposed of into the appropriate hamper or polythene receptacle, and every article of clothing replaced. Intervening in this inconvenient process is the plastic lined, absorbent incontinence pad which is laid between the patient's legs and around the genitalia and buttocks. Left to its own devices this would corkscrew a path down one or other leg but it is held in situ by a pair of pants made from netting. The idea is that a soiled pad can be extracted, and another placed in its stead, without the need to replace the pants or the clothing. The absorbency can further short-circuit the need for a soap sponged wash if the nurses wish merely to wipe up the soiling with the pad alone.

We divide by gender and retreat to the dormitories again, and proceed to make the beds together. Making beds has been one of those procedures which were made a great deal of in the Introductory Block and an ideal procedure is presented to us. I am pretty enthusiastic to be getting on with this, believe it or not. But we don't have pull out bed ends on which to conveniently place the unmade bed linen, blankets and counterpane, and as we sweep them back they have nowhere else to go but onto the floor. This is disconcerting for it's messed up the methodical procedure that I have ready prepared. We change the soiled sheets – nothing too desperate, just a few faecal smears in most cases, but one bed that is soaked in urine; hence, the plastic covered mattresses which are light as a feather and easily turned. We use the sheets to mop the urine pool. Of course, I'm already familiar with the division of the soils into red and white linen hampers. When we've finished tidying all the male beds I ask about the faecal debris on Chalmers' bed and who is responsible for cleaning it up. I am told that that's the Domestic's job! The dormitory is now shipshape, cleared of spare clothing and soiled linen, patients and untidiness. We leave the area and make our way to the ward office to pick through the daily papers and mail that have been delivered by the Service Porter. Between ten to ten-thirty, all the staff are prepared for their own breakfast. We've worked solidly since about seven-thirty. We have to wait a while for the female nurses, but they eventually extricate themselves, having sprayed their patients about the female dayroom, in order to concentrate on our breakfasts of toast, tea, and anything left over from the meals delivered for the patients. Often there are spare boiled eggs which go down very well indeed. Breakfast is taken together in a small side room next to the office, from which patients are excluded, but the door is left open to detect suspicious and untoward sounds. At this point, observation of our confused wanderers becomes problematic. We are also vigilant of the approaching footfall of authority. Whenever the Nursing Officer did arrive on the ward during my three months posting he was apathy personified and exhibited not the slightest interest in my presence or progress. But he and the Charge seem to chew over a good deal of the hospital gossip together. So, I'm not missing much!

It's not difficult to elaborate on the daily activities, confined as they are to a limited core schedule. These activities are sparsely spread over set stages of the day, but heavily focused around meal times and bedtimes, with very little else besides. Breaking into the monotony is the need to prevent a patient from being divested of their clothing. This might entail an ill fitting pair of trousers slipping to the floor but there are more concerted efforts. A symbol comes to mind of rolling and unravelling a ball of wool in relation to just keeping psycho-geriatrics properly dressed. The nursing staff draw together the loose strands of a patient's clothing into a tight and tidy presentation while the patients carefully unravel the ball to leave a trail of discarded vestments in their wake. It's not altogether surprising that the confused elderly should exercise the vestiges of their consciousness on the closest things at hand. Shirt and trouser buttons are loosened so that the latter take a short trip to the knees. Shoes and socks are diligently peeled off and are tidied into the ward recesses. Cardigans are turned inside out and replaced, back to front. It is so very easy to become irritated by this careless contrariness, especially when you discover there is incontinence to boot. Then you pick up snippets of awareness that correlate a patient's increasing agitation with a need to urinate or empty their bowels, or increased confusion and lack of interest in food with possible constipation. To help manage the apparent chaos and hopelessness of these daily events it's crucial to keep hold of this level of awareness so that ignorance does not usher in the blinding mists of frustration, petulance and demoralisation. But, ignorance is an enticing ally.

Most of what we do, and the way we do it, is for the convenience of us, the staff. I quickly learn the most efficient way of dressing someone, for example. This entails sitting the patient on a bed or chair and putting every article of clothing on without the interruption of having to stand and sit them until the very end of the process. So, dress the top half of the body first, then drop down to dress the bottom by slipping on underpants, then trousers, then socks, then shoes, and finally standing the patient and hauling up the pants and trousers. At no stage do we help the patients dress themselves. We don't have the time. That is, *our* schedule doesn't permit it! Our schedule means that the care is split into a series of tasks and each task is applied to every patient, consecutively, as soon as we can manage it. So, everyone is woken and dressed at the same time, then shaved, fed, bathed, administered medication, etc. This task orientated model of care is an efficient staff model but not an effective patient model. The patients are not learning anything. Crucially, they are not being helped to adapt to their debilities. In effect, we are progressively unlearning and deskilling them but feel it's not worth the candle to change the approach to a more holistic, individualised model of care that focuses on our patients' requirements. It is the schedule that dictates the care and patients either conform to its prescriptions or destabilise it! When we're not doing patient tasks, we're completing non patient tasks. There's the linen cupboard to be organised and freshly arrived hampers of sheets, blankets and patients' clothes to be sorted. There are daily menus and weekly medicine and general stores to be ordered or stacked. The clinic room has to be tidied and cleaned.

From a purist point of view the psycho-geriatric patient group and learning environment appeared to offer little by way of productive psychiatric stimulation. All was as far removed from acute and chronic mental disorder as it was possible to be. Rather than learning of any purposeful preventative measures, positive treatment or favourable prognoses, it was the overwhelming hopelessness of dealing with organic conditions exhibiting progressive deterioration and irreversibility which impressed themselves. Such functional mental disorders as depression, schizophrenia, anxiety, mania, personality disorders and psychopathy were as youthful, energised conditions that coalesced into a mainstream, psychiatric current as opposed to the frail debris of dementias that were washed onto the tidal margins. Psycho-geriatric patients were ascribed a multifaceted, deficit status – physical old age, dementia, and the pre-disposing psychiatric disorder that had been the core of their debilities. But another deficit status was linked onto the debility chain – the loss of adulthood. They were no longer treated as adults since we took all decisions and responsibility away from them. We treated them as infants and, by so doing, potentiated the accumulating decay to which they had already been subjected. The low priority, psychiatric management of dementia, at the time, was symbolised by the wards being located at the more remote reaches of the hospital, at the terminal points of long, quieter corridors, furthest from the hospital entrance, and among the closest to the morgue – at the periphery of the hospital, of educational invigoration, of professional expertise and pride, and patient respect. Utterly unprepared for such experience in my early training as a Student Nurse, I believed I had been taught little of use, learned little, and waited for the end of the three month stint and the smell of the geriatric ward. It was an ungracious stance and an ungratified beginning.

* * *

My second ward allocation was to what was termed a "long stay ward" for about 30 male patients. What did a long stay ward mean, exactly? As with all the unaccustomed phrases with which you had to familiarise yourself, you accepted the institutional terminology as conveying a self-explanatory description. In this instance, the ward was designated for particularly damaged patients, often having had multiple previous admissions over the years, largely exhibiting psychotic disorders, not likely to recover a satisfactory level of functioning, and who were expected to remain hospitalised and under treatment for the indefinite future. Many had already been permanently resident for decades.

It was a Sunday, a chilly 7 a.m., on that first shift and I had to admit to harbouring an inner feeling of worthiness. Purposefulness, indeed. Fresh out of psycho-geriatrics and an intervening couple of weeks in the Training School, I positively thrilled to the prospect of a most unconventional drama, in so unique a theatre, with such an improbable cast, when compared with the working experience of most people. Three short flights of stairs in an unprepossessing stairwell led me up to the ward entrance which was barred by a locked door. As with every locked door in the place, it had been impregnated by so much usage over the generations of attendants and ancillary staff as each key, thrust into the shiny lock at the level of the groin, turned with an effortless, coital ease. The immediate reception area into which it opened was a small dining room of functional metal and laminated tables and chairs which led off to a store room, kitchen, bathroom and toilets, along one side, and onto the elongated ward gallery along the other. The area had a pervading smell of rancid dishcloths and previous meals and the legs of the tables and chairs, like stiffened fly papers, had captured and congealed the accumulating years of food debris. Around the skirting, the embedded filth of years now resisted the cursory cleaning schedule of the ward Domestic. The adjoining gallery, some 25 metres in length, was furnished with a single table and four chairs halfway along it to serve as a lookout post for staff observation and it culminated in a tiny TV lounge of ancient armchairs pushed squarely against the walls around the low stump of a television which most patients never watched. Along gallery or lounge, there was not a single other artefact to offer any distraction – pictures, flower pots, ornaments, tables – so that the polished linoleum floor lay like an illuminated strip of runway allowing patients the chance to take off, and land, at regular intervals along its length, according to their rambling schedules. The environment was decorated in a limitless bleakness such that the little wallpaper that survived was hardly noticeable in the colourless uniformity. The walls, ceilings, windows, doorframes and furniture were of such a continuous blandness that the chipped holes, scuffing, stains and other accidental damage might have amounted to an acceptable graffiti if the patients had intended it. Into the top and bottom of each sash window the vertical runners were impeded by bolted wooden blocks which only permitted the windows to be raised or dropped four inches to prevent escape and injury. In this frugal space, the ragged, frail, stained curtains erupted and fitted in the cooling window draughts but, otherwise, hung limply, thirsty, dried out, scourged by the careless, manhandling years of the sun.

With some anxiety for those first few minutes ahead, I approached the office door from where voices tripped and tumbled into the fierce glare of the ward gallery that, even at this early hour, was fiercely illuminated by the complement of suspended neon lighting. Knocking and presenting myself at the open door, almost apologetically, I went through those first protracted moments of unavoidable uncertainty to which any stranger is exposed in the midst of an established and curious company. A gloom of early risen faces lifted to get a purchase on me as the newcomer while I burned, awkwardly, under their light scrutiny.

'How do?' offered the Night Nurse with a face tiered in miserable folds, and pathetic eyes, in an otherwise perfectly congenial personality. 'You must be pretty new, your white coat's clean and ironed! Must be trying to make a good impression! We'll see how long that lasts!' He is well meaning and affable and turns back to the little assembly.

'Hello, lad,' says the one who appears to be the senior. 'We're expecting you. Find yourself a place and pin your ears back, for now. We'll make our introductions in a few minutes.' He has the casual air of someone who's dealt with this a hundred times.

'Ok,' I say. These tentative introductions slightly tame the unwanted attention to which I'm being subjected before the rest of the white coated assembly duly lean back toward the solitary night nurse who has managed the ward all night on his own and is now giving his report. He is a man of about 50, wearing carpet slippers, whose chronically forlorn eyes clearly appeal for human company before he retires to the single daytime bedsit that will follow hard on his solitary night.

'Well, Jamie was a right bloody pest all night, again,' the energised Night Nurse relays. 'He shit everywhere, I'm telling you. I give him a bath but I haven't cleaned the room walls, the dirty bastard. I've tried giving his nails a good scrub but you can never clean him up properly 'cos he won't keep his hands still, as you know. They're still full of shit so watch yourselves! He was hallucinating all over the bloody place and he hasn't slept a bloody wink. So I give him more largactil but it didn't touch him. I don't know what you want to do about medication, whether he should see the Doc. or not, but this is the third night on the trot. Whatever you do, try and keep him awake so's he sleeps tonight, will you?'

'Doctor? Doctor, what's that when it's at home?' poses the Charge Nurse, who is the oldest one amongst us, who takes up a familiar refrain.

'Funny how Jamie seems to go like this every now and again. Thought it must be a full moon, but I checked, it weren't. Ha, ha, ha!' continues the Night Nurse. 'Apart from him there's no one else worth mentioning,' and the report on the 26 or so patients appears to be over. 'Here, what do you think about the latest bright idea from management, then?' He waits for the expectant pause and the shake of heads before pronouncing his nocturnal news. 'Every patient has got to have their own personalised wash bag with their own washing gear,' he sneers. 'How bloody ridiculous is that? Don't they live in the real world, these people? They won't use the bloody things, anyway. How many times have you seen one of this lot use a flannel, or brush their teeth. More likely to shove 'em down their throats, or chuck 'em out the windows, or stick 'em up their arse.' There is a little ripple of appreciative laughter at this delivery and the Charge Nurse comments on 'another management masterstroke'. But, avoiding an unnecessary and prolonged chat on the subject, his authoritative 'Right, cup of tea boys', shunts us all into motion and we file out to imbibe at the first of the morning's tea stops.

While pondering about the washing business, and just how the patients do wash themselves if they don't have their personal washing gear – after all, these are not geriatrics – I follow the others decanting to the gallery table. By now, it is about 7.20 and all four of us are drinking tea and smoking while the night nurse changes from his slippers into an immaculately polished pair of black Oxfords. Every piece of him is completely immaculate, actually. The shirt is crisp, his tie drawn into a taut, natty knot, the trousers hang like blades, and his hair is impeccably oiled and groomed. Because it is a Sunday there is no urgency to commence the daily routine and it provides an opportunity for a more relaxed welcome to the newcomer in their midst. The Charge Nurse, who cannot be too far off retirement, has a gravel grating, north eastern accent set into a heavy jowl and consolidates the personal introductions.

'So, your name's Steve, is it? That's what we'll call you then, all right? You wouldn't want a nickname like hippy, or hairy bastard, or something?' he asks, intimating that my long hair seems to buck his expectations of an appropriate working appearance.

'Don't take any notice of him,' chimes the Night Nurse, who has still not vacated the ward.

'Er, Steve will do just fine.' Charge Nurse seizes the chance of yet another newcomer to treat us all to a memoir.

'Well, Steve, you hippy, hairy bastard, and the rest of you lot for that matter, when I first came here the newest staff member on each ward was called the "tin boy". His first priority of a morning was to go to the hospital kitchen with his tin and fill it up with the ward tea ration. And woe betide if he was late for work, or dropped it, or came back short! Those were the days. Everyone knew their place. Not like now where everyone's got too much cheek and no respect. *And* you wouldn't be allowed into the Charge's office unless you'd been invited. *And* you'd only speak when spoken to. And there was no Christian names, neither. It was Charge Nurse so and so!' Though we all enjoy the joke we must all decipher that these days must now be sorely missed and, also, how well we could have managed in such a set up.

Then, the first tea of the day over, we three students head off for the dormitory on the third floor where most of the patients sleep. The Charge Nurse has a self-appointed group of patients whom he'll manage along the side rooms – a line of single rooms adjacent to the ward office along the inner wall of the gallery. The top dormitory where we've arrived also contains a number of side rooms along one wall while a row of closely spaced beds lines the opposite wall. In between each of these beds are low, single cupboards, where the clothes from the previous day have been placed. There is no other object or possession of any description to be found on, in, or around these wardrobes. The other two nurses are rapping out coarse commands. 'Come on, out of those beds... NOW!' One patient, nicknamed Captain, dressed in only his pyjama top, which leaves the rest of his lower body naked, has wandered into a side room which is neither his own, nor his prerogative. 'Captain, come out of that side room,' raps one of the staff. Captain does not appear. 'NOW!' Captain appears and returns to his bedside where he reaches into his cupboard and yanks out a bundle of clothes in which he haphazardly drapes himself. His shirt drips over his anorexic shoulders but is left unbuttoned. He has no vest or underpants. His trouser flies are wide open, revealing his genitals, and he clutches his trouser tops in one hand because they are outsized and beltless. Cramming both feet irritably into his shoes, he is too impatient to fit them properly so that his heels ride on the backs of his shoes. Wrapping his trouser top in one hand, he shuffles away to the dormitory exit.

'Wait, Captain,' shouts one of the lads, 'come here.' Turning to me, as an extra pair of hands, the nurse indicates that I can make myself most useful by sorting Captain out, nodding toward the restless, errant maverick. By now, Captain has done an immediate about-turn, so quickly that he stumbles heavily and tips himself into an undignified and petulant heap.

'All right, grab him and take him downstairs to the store room which you'll find next to the kitchen and pick out clothes from his cubby hole that actually fit him. Obviously, one of yesterday's evening shift has just taken out any old pair of strides for him. We'll manage this lot. Then come back as soon as you're done, ok, mate? And *watch* him because he'll scoot off if he sees daylight. That means holding onto him, if necessary. Don't take any of his mucking about. Be as firm as you need to be, okay?' I wonder at my intrusiveness as I take hold of Captain's arm and am completely surprised that he doesn't remonstrate with me. There is no flesh, no muscle. All I can feel through the jacket is solid bone mass. Captain seems willing to be escorted down the stairs until he suddenly lurches down to retrieve a discarded dogend and raps a fist around it. Only a member of staff could have been so profligate as to cast away a butt that still held tobacco. He continues on, seemingly oblivious to the close attention being paid to him, even as he is physically steered into the store room where the Charge Nurse greets him and points up to his named cubby hole.

'You've dressed patients by now, I'm assuming?' he queries. I reply that I've only had the elderly to dress, so far, and this causes the Charge Nurse to chortle, 'Oh, well, that's all you need, then. You'll have to help him, though, because he'll not be arsed, if he's left to himself,' nodding toward Captain. For his part, Captain is standing quite still and I become aware he's fixed his eyes on mine with an unblinking, inscrutable intensity which is quite unnerving. Is it merely an idle stare, or a wilful resistance, or does he want to gouge out my eyes? Though I can't tell, of course, I'll bear all these in mind. I'd have to say that, though this may be the most intransigent face I've ever encountered, it is not devoid of expression. Whatever it reflects, the expression seems to permeate Captain's whole person. His hooded gaze settles like a hovering kestrel, intensely exploring the features of a stranger before it will eventually bank away to cross the store room walls, then flap to a halt and lean upon a window ledge as if perching on a crag where he can slip back into the recess of an unreachable isolation. The face is crossed with old, pale scars around the eyebrows, forehead and chin and the nose is a fractured, pulpy mess that noisily shunts breath when his mouth is closed. Had he been a street fighter or an obstructive patient, someone in more or less constant trouble, but now made docile by medication and years of institutionalisation? The questions recede for, long before Captain has been reassembled, he is wanting to be off, impatient of any social etiquette. I take the risk of holding him back and instruct him to put on some socks, which Captain manages despite an alarming unsteadiness before stooping to lever on the pair of disgustingly encrusted shoes, which appear never to have been cleaned, before he wheels about and escapes into the gallery. He has not uttered a word throughout.

I return to climb the easily spaced, slightly concave stone stairs (worn like a cathedral entrance) to the third floor, again. The stairwell seems even barer than at the lower levels for some reason as if you're climbing the remoter reaches of an uninhabited tower. This is partly true as the dormitories are locked off during daytime with no upstairs access to patients whatever.

'Have a look-see if anyone's hanging about in the toilet, would you, mate? It's up at the end, on your left.' I move along and push open what I assume to be the toilet door, to find myself in one of those dark, noxious piss holes such as are often passed off as public lavatories where each individual holds his mouth tight and nearly retches while the stale ammonia clings to the inside of his nasal passages. As bad as any such public lavatories, it has no decoration, no soap, no towel, no curtains, and little light, and bears the architectural and atmospheric ambiance of an anus. One completely nude patient stands over the urinal and the heavy spatter of piss noisily drops against the galvanised floor and runs in a frothy, full stream along to one end, where it plunges through a drain cover. There is urine spattered over the raised step of the urinal and it is disquieting to think of the number of bare feet that have trodden this back into their beds and are now having socks drawn over them. It is none too comfortable to speculate on just how much piss and excrement traces smear the patients' fingers, the trouser buttons and zips, the shirt buttons, the shoe laces.

Patients in varying degrees of dress and tidiness are milling about the far dormitory door. When most seem about ready one of the nurses calls out 'Okay, downstairs' and everyone files out and their footfalls echo about the descending stairwell. Issuing out into the dining area, they move on into the gallery where they disperse to every corner of the floor area. The locking of the door that separates the gallery from the dining room keeps them herded away and prevents them interfering with preparations for breakfast. For his part, Ernie, the kitchen helper, a patient from this very ward, is setting out the tables and has made the pots of tea. He does not have the same air of debility as all the others and seems perfectly capable of salutations, reasonable conversation, and humour. He is Scottish. It appears that everyone has their allotted place in the dining room. The Charge Nurse suggests that I just stand back to observe how the team manages things, and I'm more than happy to oblige. The gallery door is opened like the side of a mouth by the Charge Nurse and an alarming clap of vocal energy is released through the gaping space.

'BREAKFAST!' he yells, dislodging each patient from their ruminations so that they turn toward the dining room in a ravenous anticipation of their first food of the day. There is little time to consider such niceties as your attention is smothered by the ensuing desperate throng of humanity at breakfast time on a long stay ward. The rush of bodies that have variously loitered before the thunderous call, surge like buoyant waters through the dining room entrance, then fan out across the room like a flash flood bursting its banks into a small meadow. The scene settles down to a conglomeration of lightly turbulent ripples – like a small shoal of fish beneath the water surface – as each settles with feverish eagerness to tackle the first food they've had since about 5.30 the previous evening. What follows at a particular table is

63

an unbelievable spectacle of neediness, or greediness, or insufficient sociali-sation, or pathological disorder. These voracious few take but a handful of seconds, literally seconds, to devour their porridge, bacon, slice of bread and tea. The hot tea is swallowed in loud, burning draughts as their furtive glances locate a neighbour's food on the adjoining tables. However, without further ado, they are ushered from their seats and physically shepherded away from the area like man-handled crabs which, once captured, are only able to desperately flail their claws about, prevented from pinching and snapping at the interfering world about them.

The meals have not been of their choosing but are selected according to the kitchen's own timetable. The plated meals have been kept heated in the trolley for some considerable time and manage to combine the presenta-tional flaws of being dry and rubbery, and overheating, to reduce the already diminutive helpings to paltry portions. After all, this is not a hotel! The tea is fresh, though. It has been made by dropping the teabags, milk and sugar into three or four commercial, galvanised teapots and pouring the feeble brew into each patient's cup for them. It is little wonder that some patients are voraciously hungry and even more surprising that the rest are not! For the majority of the seated ensemble, you could as well have been seated in a restaurant, as the table etiquette, if not faultless, is pretty appropriate, though it lacks the vitality of avid conversation and the joy of fellowship.

At this point in the schedule the staff focus turns to feeding themselves and it is the patients' excess food which supplies us, made all the more palat-able (since a culinary delight, it is not) by the fact that it's a freebee! I've already learned that these surplus portions are engineered by inflating the ward's daily meal order on the justification of a possible hospital admission or internal transfer from another ward, uncertainty about what some patients will accept to eat since a surprising number are virtually mute, or made from plain error. But a more scrupulous economy would have attenuated a practice that has fed many of the staff over decades. On the contrary, the prevailing official approach to the practice lies, confusingly, across an implicit accept-ance, downright condemnation, and a thoroughgoing ambivalence! For instance, while there is no serious effort to institute sanctions to curtail this customary perk, a measured caution is practised to avoid the inconvenience of being officially caught in the act of eating. To avoid any professional embarrassment a little accommodation has to be employed by all parties. The kitchen department must not be rigorous about its economy and try to limit supplies. The nursing hierarchy, who must eventually peel themselves away from the industry of their offices to visit their ward-bound subordinates, must not be too rigorous. To help effect this arrangement, the ward staff and Nursing Officers must each have knowledge of the other's routines so that each may run parallel with the other, thus avoiding any unfortunate awkwardness.

Not having been able to eat at the ungodly hour prior to the early shift, I'm only too ready to assuage my appetite and to wrap liberally buttered slices of bread around a couple of sausages and scoff them quickly, and satisfyingly, along with the other staff. I hastily run the bread through some dried and congealed baked beans. This means that there is little ceremony permitted with what is, in essence, a hasty cramming of food consumed in the standing position while remaining alert to intrusion. There is no delay in the equally swift despatch of the eating utensils, after cursorily washing them, and the swift removal of all personnel from the kitchen as if fleeing the scene of a crime and all its attendant evidence.

As it happened, I could not possibly have anticipated the good fortune in having joined the psychiatric nursing service at the peak of a particular recruitment influx in the early 1970s. In that era of London staffing shortages, the London mental hospitals engaged a substantial quota of immigrant nurses while hospitals in other cosmopolitan areas around the country barely saw a non white foreign recruit and certainly not as students in training. The immigrant recruitment at this time procured a host of young, educated people from Malaysia, Hong Kong, the Caribbean, Mauritius and West Africa who filled the advertised nursing vacancies. Having all had an English education, and sat exams set by British Exam Boards, this foreign increment to the student nursing body were more academically qualified than the vast majority of their British counterparts. But their arrival into the hospitals was not a vocational move for many of them since it provided but an initial entry point from which they intended to launch a career into law or accountancy, business studies and similar areas. For my part, I discovered these foreign students, in very large part, to be culturally sophisticated, hard working and conscientious, who made very sound friends, and who were strong upholders of traditional family ties, monogamous relationships, social hospitality and generosity.

Tea break over, the next stage is the equivalent of the Roman lavatorium and all the patients are called for their communal washroom ablutions, only almost none of them volunteer themselves to wash, or shave.

'Have you had the chance to shave anybody, yet?' asks the Charge Nurse. 'You have,' he says in response to my nod. 'Well, since there are plenty of us we'll let you observe for today while you just tidy them up, all right?' The washroom contains five sinks with three or four portable metal chairs, a couple of face flannels, one or two combs, and a pile of towels. But only about two patients seem to be managing themselves. All of the rest assume the acquired listlessness of a disconsolate string of unemployed labourers queuing in the vicinity of a factory gate, waiting for work, shuffling their progress in the queue, listening for a foreman to call out their name, perfectly silent other than the irritated grunt from being brushed against by another. It is the Spanish Ward Domestic who will observe the gallery while they each take a towel and a wet razor and set about shaving virtually all the patients, consecutively. Charge Nurse gives a master class. 'After a good lathering with the brush and soap stick it's best to draw the skin tight with one hand so that you can do a nice clean scrape over a firm surface. Otherwise you're surfing through a load of folds and wrinkles.' Having seated one patient and thrown a towel around his chest and shoulders, he literally slaps the foaming bristles across the patient's lower face, lodging foam barnacles well up into the nostrils, and over the mouth and ear lobes. With a few crafted carves of the razor the whiskers are stripped off at arm's length and whisked into a full basin of hot water. The soapy remnants around the ears and nostrils are wiped with a flannel and the towel is crumpled about the face before being whipped away in a grand, flourishing finale. Within an instant an indicative finger is tapped on the patient's shoulder and pointed to the exit. 'NEXT!' he bellows.

'Captain,' he yells. 'Get away from that bin, you dirty little bastard.' Captain is presumably rummaging for fag ends and spins his pale, slight frame about, barging aside a couple of his fellows. 'And don't bugger off. Stay here where I can see you. Stand just there. THERE,' he yells, and indicates an exact spot. Captain's face is a stony slab that must hide some simmering chagrin. 'The secret of psychiatric nursing, Steve, is being able to talk to your patients,' is the ironic assurance of the Charge Nurse. 'You don't have to love 'em, and you don't need to want to take 'em home with you, but you do have to bloody well talk to 'em. Hello, Whitey! How are you, you old buzzard?' A heavy boned, broadly proportioned soul with the face of a benign rogue and the barest traces of his remaining silver hair, wearing a sagging jacket and trousers which indicate that he was once a hefty build, ambles over to take his place in the chair with a show of self-possession and a gummy smile that he is happy to share with everyone. It is the first time I've noticed anything like a quiet self-assurance amongst any of the patients on this ward, with the exception of the kitchen helper. Whitey appears to have no fear. He has the rough edged scowl and carefree swagger of a former petty criminal, a wide boy, perhaps? As he waits upon the stroke of the razor, over-lathered like a cartoon character, there is a protracted pause on the Charge Nurse's part, accompanied by his steady gaze down at Whitey so that a deliberate tension gathers like a threatening wave that is lingering off the shore. Whitey registers that something's afoot, raises his ailing sight upward, and intently searches the eyes of the Charge Nurse while muttering barely audible phrases to himself through his virtually toothless mandible.

'Come on, Whitey, what the hell are you doing just sitting there?' teases the Charge Nurse. More mandibular mumblings before Whitey expresses himself in more of an enquiry than an admonishment.

'What the hell are you playing at?' is registered by the nursing company. The tension mounts while the nurses await a more explosive reaction and they are not disappointed for long. Staring more lividly, flashing his eyes directly at the Charge Nurse, then away again, his mettle rises and he shouts 'Come on you, what's the matter with you!' No one stirs and there is prolonged silence. 'Come on, you bastard!' Whitey is clearly not afraid. Still no action from his antagonist. Whitey cannot contain himself and is suddenly on his feet, his right arm drawn back and his fist ready to strike, flashing his eyes to left and right, and continuing to air his verbal abuse. 'What you fucking doing, I'll fucking kill you, you bastard. Yerrrrr!'

'It's all right, Whitey, that's enough now, you know I'm only kidding,' interjects the Charge Nurse, quite unperturbed. In an unbelievable instant, Whitey breaks out in a raucous good natured laugh that breaks the tension like a snapped twig, and there is laughter all round. 'This one's a real character,'

I'm informed. Whitey's broad grin seems grotesquely compromised by the two remaining teeth on his lower gum that stand like two deformed, yellowing fence posts and his otherwise toothless jaw bends like a deflated ball. The image draws my attention to the absence of any toothpaste or tooth brushes at the scene. 'In my early days, when we had all those patients to handle, we were each given one razor blade, each morning, for all the patients you shaved. You just had to make do and hard luck for those who were at the back of the queue! Whitey's a real treat to shave because he's got a great, chunky, bloody face, great to get hold of. See that?' The razor grinds the stout hairs across Whitey's tight and ample flesh in an uninterrupted swathe of waste lather. 'Now you have a go on someone,' gesturing toward me. It takes me a lot longer to finish my poor agitated souls and, despite being keen not to cut anyone, I still manage the occasional nick at the point of the chin and under the nose. I've learned to amend such mishaps with a good wipe from a cold flannel but I've seen many a patient in the hospital who's sported a good sliver of toilet paper in an effort to stem a nasty cut, or two, or three! It takes me a little time before I manage a clean shave without sustaining casualties and the tell-tale signs of the barber's nick. The patients' limited, but relevant, contribution is to follow the progress of the blade with their tongue so that the skin is pushed out to provide the firm surface that will maximise their comfort!

At some time after breakfast, the next procedure of the day is to dole out a cigarette round. Each patient that smokes is handed a cigarette from a stash held in the staff office. The system is such that each smoker has a weekly quota of cigarettes kept aside in his name from which the staff will draw a daily ration to enable it to last the week. But it is far easier to open up one packet at each fag round and hand out all its contents instead of delving into each individual's separate packet. This is the task orientated method again – that is, one size fits all and at the same time. None of the smokers are allowed to retain their own supply, nor are they permitted a lighter or matches, so that they are also dependent on the staff to light the cigarettes. It seems a petty infringement of liberty but past experience is the only real education for a large institution and the lesson learned is that a liberal regime would be irresponsibly inviting accidental and intentional fires, as well as stealing, and immediate consumption with an arid period to follow. None but the most trusted of patients will be permitted ownership of matches and only the kitchen man fits these scruples on this ward. So, the patients smoke the first, single cigarette of the day which, like their breakfast, they have been awaiting for a very long time. Now, they must wait until the schedule has time to dispense another. Moving with a gait that is so stiff that it might suggest he has callipers strapped to both legs, Larry approaches the table. Larry is a tall, slim, singularly tidy individual with unexpectedly clean hands who, occasionally, lapses into garrulous bursts of disordered chatter.

'Shall I have one, then?' speaking of the fag packet that is teasingly being held out for him. 'They cost money, they do. Oooh! Lots of lovely money. You can't get much for your money these days. Lovely grub.' Throughout this loud and strident monologue Larry rubs his hands with remarkable vigour, wipes a finger over his lips compulsively, and smiles with a contorted grimace. His eyes stare into my own but, nevertheless, have a far off focus. He so closely invades the space between the two of us that I can smell his slightly offensive breath. 'No thanks, I don't smoke,' he continues. For a moment, he has quietened, and his features settle like a flattened sheet while pensively scouring my face as he caresses his forefinger along his ample lips. Then, as if an emerging wind slowly wakens him from a silent contemplation, his face billows and gathers itself, and blasts his inner world into the vocal shapes that are his deranged and uninhibited monologue. 'Do you know him, then? He loves money, he does. Oooh! He's a lovely bum boy. He's got a big cock. He shows it to the Queen. Mustn't tell anyone! Lovely day, today. Don't forget to tell your mother. Does she like a big one? It costs loads. Loads of money. Whey... hey!' These dissociated comments crescendo steadily louder so that this last sound is delivered as a raucous, exclamatory cry, while vigorously clapping and rubbing his hands as he walks away in a wide-stepping, jaunty stride of mad energy. In the diminutive day room he is seen to briefly shove aside another old boy then, like a minor squall, the excitement passes and he is becalmed. He stands with arms crossing his chest, with one hand brushing his smooth chin with the attention of one contemplating the outer universe, while not oblivious of the humanity in his vicinity. I muse on what if anything has stimulated Larry's stereotypical behaviour, for he rehearses the same behaviour repeatedly, as if it constitutes the only means he knows of introducing himself. These tentatively related sentences are professionally diagnosed as the "thought disordered" ideation of schizophrenic patients.

And, as time will tell, Larry's interaction is only ever limited to these small windows of stereotyped preoccupation and he is incapable of attending to a recipient's response, let alone a conversation.

The next ward task is the bed making. Not just because it is easier for the students to focus on this, but because it limits the potential problems; the door adjoining the dining room is locked and every single patient is herded into the gallery where they can choose to linger or retire to the dark and dismal TV lounge. In my continuing novitiate role, I accompany the Malaysians to the third floor dormitory where every bed is still unmade and where we'll spend an age making them. It's a domestic task which doesn't sit too comfortably with me bearing in mind that these patients are more able bodies than the psycho-geriatrics. I voice my astonishment that patients are not encouraged to make their own beds.

'Wouldn't that make things a lot more normal and save us from having to clear up after them, and we could be doing something more relevant with them?' I query.

'Oh, yer! You are joking, aren't you?' is the sharp, mildly rebuking reply. 'First, most of them couldn't even do a simple thing like that. Second, even if they could, we'd probably have to go round after them, anyway. Thirdly, they'd all do it in their own time and some would refuse so it's quicker to do it ourselves. Same goes for the shaving, changing clothes, most things, everything in fact. It saves time in the long run. And let's face it, none of these are going anywhere, are they?' The two of them are now mocking me in a polite fashion. 'You'd be great in charge of a ward! If you leave things to the patients no one's ever going to get the work done! We'd only have to run around afterwards undoing what they've attempted. Anyway, they're too institutionalised to even begin to do things for themselves, most of them.'

Bed making. Standing at the dormitory door at the row of beds there is an image of desecrated burial plots, writhing like opened graves having yielded up their occupants whose bindings, now discarded, drape offensively over the disturbed, freshly heaped mounds and wrought iron surrounds. We all speed through the dormitory, chucking the bedding onto the floor at the foot of each bed, gathering and checking the sheets for excessive dirtiness – they'll stay put if not too soiled for they'll be a communal change within the week – stuffing each sheet, cellular blanket and counterpane into hasty corners around the mattresses, all of a light, insubstantial consistency, and slinging on the pillows before moving to the next. Surveying the finished row of beds along the gallery I appreciate a seductive, inner voice praising this transformation of careless chaos into orderliness.

Following the bed making routine, when I am seriously doubting whether there is ever going to be time for any real contact with patients, let alone any psychological interventions, I am called upon to accompany one of the other lads to assess Jamie's potential for coming out onto the ward day gallery. Jamie, the patient alluded to by the Night Nurse, is the indelible portrayal of madness, in anyone's books. His schizophrenic symptoms have manifested themselves since his adolescence in what, at that time, was called hebephrenic schizophrenia and characterised by disordered and abnormal thinking and conversation, highly incongruous emotions, delusions and hallucinations, the most bizarre mannerisms imaginable, and a general unpredictability of behaviour. He manifests all of this on a daily basis, far from improvement or recovery, and with a probable prognosis of having to spend the remainder of his youth and years in hospitalised dependency. At meal times he has to be brought directly to a table where he is managed on his own – his side room is the first in the gallery adjacent to the dining room so as to reduce patient contact and disturbance – and is returned immediately afterwards. His locked side room, where he spends almost the whole of his time, is opened and we enter a room twice as high as it is either long or wide. Because of its position, and time of day, the room lies on the side of the ward furthest from the sun, as remote as a closed cupboard. The side room light is switched on – from the outside! It is a design feature that they cannot be switched on from the interior by the patient.

'Hello, Jamie, how are you feeling? Do you want to come out of your room?' Jamie is looking to the floor. 'How would you like to come onto the ward?' says the Malaysian. The pungent smell of old faeces and urine is offensive, on first contact, and I am quite revolted. The room's proportions are very disconcerting, as if deliberately frustrating the occupant who is crammed into a limited floor space but has a vast, unfilled canopy above which can't be accessed. The room needs to be tipped onto its side. The high window seems purposely constructed so as to allow in light without allowing the patient to have direct vantage of the outside world. Consequently, neither can they

71

absent themselves from it. Jamie is completely naked and lists against the far wall like an unprepossessing sculpture. There is one sole furniture item, the bed, which has been freshly made with newly laundered linen and blankets to replace the previously soiled ones. With so little to stimulate him, Jamie has taken off his clothes. He has an impenetrable expression around a pair of large, blue eyes that seem totally disconnected from any person, object, or idea outside of himself. He appears to respond, but vaguely, to anything that is said to him and his speech is but an incomprehensible moan, interspersed with staccato howls, issuing from a thick-lipped mouth which opens in wide grimaces as if suggesting pain. Jamie then slides along the walls with his hands raised in front, clicking his fingers continuously, as if engaged in his own ritual dance. He does not linger on our faces for more than a few seconds at a time, being more drawn to the wall with which he is in contact.

'He's probably hallucinating,' suggests the other student. 'See him looking around and talking? He's responding to his voices. They're the only ones that would understand him, anyway,' he giggles. Jamie's attention does, indeed, seem harassed by a distracting presence that moves about the floor, walls, bed and the attendant company and is insistent on his full cooperation despite our efforts to engage with him. It is an unforgettable experience of a human being somehow controlled by disturbing external or internal influences that, in former times, would have been described as a spiritual possession, no doubt. 'You see how thin he is? That's because he's always on the move, responding to these hallucinations. It burns up his body's stores. And that's why he eats like a pig because he's so ravenous. Pitiful really.' Jamie disgorges a startled howl and other incomprehensible sounds from deep inside his throat and soul. His long lashed, wide eyes are stunningly attractive, but suspicious portals to his inner turmoil, appealing in perplexity one moment, then becalmed for a while. For the time being, he is driven in a psychotic dance; his neck and facial grimaces twist and bend in concert with his emotions, and the bony, faeces stained, clicking fingers rise and fall to the rhythm of his unseen partners.

'He's a skeleton, shouldn't he eat more?' I dare to propose, both intrigued and perplexed.

'Yeah, sure, if you want to clear up the shit afterwards!' To be truthful, I am more than a little relieved when the Malaysian concludes, 'No, I think he's a bit too disturbed to come out,' and looking directly at Jamie and in a voice intended to momentarily scatter his preoccupations and hallucinations, 'We'll come back and check you again, a bit later, all right Jamie? Maybe, we'll get you out, then, alright? Now, let's dress you and try to keep your clothes on, will you?' These are statements rather than questions. Jamie cooperates fully by raising his legs and arms and ducking his head at the appropriate moments during the process of being dressed. All the while we avoid the hazard of his blemished fingers. 'Now, do you want to have a piss or a shit?' Jamie clearly shakes his head. With that, we both evacuate this dark pit, lock the door for the time being, but leave the light switched on.

Considering the relatively short time I was exposed to Jamie – since he was often confined to his room over the ensuing weeks – he made an indelible impression on me, as he must have done with every single student. Though only in his late thirties, Jamie was deteriorating into the sagging rump of a man in his sixties as his long boned limbs, that protruded like fresh branches from an old, gnarled trunk, struck an image like a healthy skeleton. Through the frail, white skin the knee joints, elbows, rib cage and collar bones were but proud scaffolding that need only bear the weight of the wasting buttocks and strips of muscle stitched into the bones. The terraced ribs protruded like an overhanging rock before dropping away into a slightly distended stomach. How much was the accelerated ageing directly related to his mental state or was it caused by some, as yet, undiagnosed physical illness? Could Jamie appreciate his own premature decay or did the schizophrenia which had squatted in his person deprive him of the capacity even to realise that? Was the mind so withdrawn that the body was merely a store of energy that constantly fed his preoccupations, only to be cast adrift, pilot-less and without course, until needing to be pirated and plundered again? But Jamie's frame was worn and battered, not just ageing. His shoeless feet were shod with the calluses that had hardened over the barefoot years. Old, brown bruising coloured most joints and fresh bruising to the feet; periodically, red scratches and pickings scourged his torso and legs; torn fingernails and knuckles scraped and bloody and ingrained with dirt suggested someone who was desperately clawing his way out of the place. Jamie's whole body was at war, enacting the daily skirmishes of his thoughts and feelings. On not one occasion did it become possible to really converse with Jamie. Neither was there much of an understanding of what he tried to

73

communicate. It was also a moot point as to whether he ever really fathomed what was even said to him or whether he was capable of doing anything with it, if he did. If there was any consolation it was that Jamie was not typical of most of the patients but, probably, epitomised the crazed picture that fuelled the morbid fires of the public imagination. During the period of my allocation Jamie never left the ward on one occasion, participated in no group activity, gained no exercise. It was assumed that he couldn't really do anything or be taken anywhere. To have done so, would have required one staff member to be specifically allocated to him. It was also assumed that he would present too much of a spectacle to anybody who had not had contact with him. He was a little disconcerting even for those that had acquaintance of him! Was it really worth the bother! In the end, wasn't it easier to keep him back on the ward! And, yet, he responded like an acquiescent little boy when treated gently and his charming eyes would look up to you with a puzzled, grateful penetration.

Encouraged by the two young students, both foreign nurses from Malaysia (one a Chinese Malaysian, the other an Indian Malaysian), I accompany them into the ward kitchen. It is a narrow, gallery kitchen of stainless steel boiler, china sink, wooden draining boards, tiled floor and cockroaches. They take up the staff cups from a separate tray kept on a shelf and methodically scald each one in the boiling stream from the hot water geyser. None of the kitchen tea towels is used and paper towels are taken from a wall dispenser to dry them. Mindful that their new colleague is English and may not have similar standards to themselves, they acquaint me with a few priority despatches, just in case.

'Lesson number one, don't forget to scald the cups each time you make a drink,' they inform me. 'You're not at home, here, you know, and you can't rely on the kitchen orderly to wash them properly; he's a patient.' They've assembled a tray of necessaries in preparation for taking the tea to the gallery table again. All finished, I follow them, leaving the kitchen door wide open. 'Lesson number two,' continues the same character, turning assertively in a light-hearted rebuke. 'Always lock every door after you unless you definitely know it's supposed to be open. If in doubt, lock it, then you can't go wrong.' We are now lounging around the gallery table on our main morning break now that we've completed the major hurdles of the morning schedule. I'm offered a cigarette from one of the others and have to acknowledge that I've run out of my own.

'What, you run out of fags?' queries the Charge Nurse and generously suggests a solution. 'Here, have one of these.' He passes me a green and white packet containing the "No.10" fag, which are the smallest and cheapest on the market which I nonetheless gratefully accept. 'Come out of there,' barks the Charge Nurse at a patient who has idly wandered across the threshold of the open office door which is an unspoken demarcation line between common land and a no-go area to the patient population.

'Give us a fag,' quietly asks Archie, who has spotted the cigarette display. An ageing, timelessly preoccupied patient with a prominent limp, Archie has obediently turned and sauntered over to our table, arms linked behind him. One of the few teeth remaining in his mouth flourishes at the centre of a very likeable grin that creases his mellow eyes. He has a habit of tacking onto staff conversations and humour, echoing their words and laughter, yet oblivious that he has not been included.

'No you can't, you had one a short while ago.'

'Go on, be a sport.'

'No, you heard what I said, fuck off Archie,' the Charge Nurse casually replies to the approving grins of the other staff. Archie also tries the tack of laughing it off and remains expectant.

'Go on.'

'Fuck off Archie,' Charge Nurse repeats.

'Go on, give us a fag,' Archie urges, unflustered.

'You're always asking for fucking fags. You'll get one later when we dish them out before lunch, along with everyone else.'

'*You've* got my fags. Me sister brought some when she visited me at the weekend.' None of us know if this is true but it matters not. 'Give us one, will you?' repeats Archie with surprising equanimity, quietly pressing the point. There is no answer this time since he is now being ignored.

'Go on, give us a fag. I want a fag.'

'No, fuck you,' replies one of the other students, completely casually, in response to Archie's persistence.

'And fuck you, too,' shouts Archie as his composure is suddenly riffled and he rears his jaw in frustration.

'Fuck you, too. Go and fuck yourself.'

'Go and fuck YOURSELF,' yells Archie with more vehemence than malice, but his chagrin subsides as he slowly turns and drifts away with his preoccupation and his limp. Archie stoops away, shaking his head from side to side, quietly disgusted. There is a general ripple of appreciation while the Charge Nurse chucks me the No.10 pack.

'Better hand those out after your break,' he says to one of the Malaysians as he thrusts an unopened pack into his lap. I ask whose cigs. they are and it turns out that they are bought for the patients from their allotted hospital pocket money. Although the staff purchase a lot of goodies on the patients' behalf, there's no direct involvement of the patient. When the weekly patient shopping order is due it is the ward supplies which are supplemented rather than the patients' individual necessaries. So, if the ward is short of hair shampoo this order can be assigned to any single patient and shared among all of them.

'So, those are patients' fags?' I conclude.

'Don't worry about it, they get more than enough and everything's free for them,' says one of the others. It does not worry me, though. On the contrary, I am getting the hang of things pretty quickly, like everybody else. And, as I was to learn, the current system represented a revision of a previous effort to remunerate patients but which actually profited the nurses, financially. Patients used to sign for receipt of a small amount of weekly pocket money which was delivered to the wards and distributed to each patient by the Charge Nurses. Only, they never quite received the full amount, not by a long chalk, and the Charge Nurses benefited hugely by all accounts. Which of the systems was the more perfidious was hard to decide!

* * *

I could not have had a more relaxed and agreeable introduction to this unequalled experience than was facilitated by these guys and for which I was grateful. Nevertheless, it didn't allay the nagging misgiving that the Charge Nurse, whose name was Reg, like so many of the male nurses that I'd so far encountered to date, had to be an unlikely candidate for "nurturer of the year award". I tactfully insinuated my curiosity as to the reasons that he had taken up this job.

'Do you mind me asking how you came to be working in this field? I mean, you're obviously from the North-East, was it the job that brought you down here?' The current Radio One hit, blaring away in the background, is the staff selection for, as far as I'm aware, the patients have not been asked for their preference. Would that even be possible? Would there be any awareness of different stations or would they have the slightest interest? Again, it's a lot easier not to have to test the idea. For good measure, the TV is also quietly pounding in the confined lounge area. Anyway, we are oblivious to the patients' likes and dislikes from the looks of things.

'Well, when we come out of the army, after the war, we got home to the North-East to find there was no work for us. They were recruiting people for the lunatic asylums all over the country but there were more jobs down south. Then there was the accommodation that came with it, so that's how many of us got into the job. It was a necessity, really, not because we had any ambition to do it. It's the last thing I'd ever have thought of doing.'

'Are you glad you did it?' I enquire with a scepticism which I can only trust is not too obvious.

'Well, I can't really complain. I could have ended up in the mines! It's put a roof over me head, it's earned me money and a living, I found me Irish wife here – and some bastard's going to answer for that one day – it's got me a good social life, and I've learned all about lunatics,' he elaborates, with what appear to be genuinely mixed feelings as if he's still not sure whether he would rather have been somewhere else. 'But things were a lot different, here, then. Thing is, we were used to discipline in those early days. Most of us had been in the forces and knew what discipline meant. So did the patients, you mark my words. Everything in the hospital was more regimented, more definite, if you know what I mean. You probably won't believe this but, in them days, you could have up to 60 patients to a ward and before the new drugs of the 50s they couldn't be managed like they are now.' Smiling incredulously, one of the Malaysians speaks up.

'Are you seriously saying, Reg, that there used to be 60 patients here, double the numbers? How did you squeeze everyone in, in the first place?'

'Well, you didn't have lockers for starters. Every square inch of the dormitories was stacked full of beds. Patients had to climb over each others' beds. There were more staff, of course, but with those numbers you had

77

to have them. *And* discipline, otherwise there'd have been chaos. People were expected to do as they were told. It was bloody tough but we enjoyed ourselves, nevertheless.'

'What, exactly, do you mean *enjoyed yourselves*?' says one, firing off a quizzical smile.

'Well, you had to see the funny side of things, not take anything too seriously. So, we mainly survived on our sense of humour and helping each other out, come what may. If you hadn't got a sense of humour you were fucked, really. I mean, you wouldn't really be able to fit in, in the first place. And, in those days, you felt management was on your side, not like today. It was a bit like being in the army but without many officers. And the few that there were sort of looked after you provided you hadn't done anything too extreme and, even then, it wasn't impossible. But, now, they wouldn't help you out these days. You got to watch your back, the shower of bastards, they've forgotten where they come from. It was the ward Charge Nurses who were the real bosses, like sergeant majors, and you respected that. You didn't mind taking orders from them.' I suspect that Reg's reminiscences now have the lash of vitriol about them and ponder whether this is as much about his sense of envy for those who have achieved more advancement than himself. We three students exchange looks of a curiously knowing mixture of amusement, fascination and scepticism.

'So, was the ex-military background your entry qualification for becoming a mental nurse?' I ask.

'For some of us, yes. That, or being a musician or sportsman! They were the three entry criteria. Yes, seriously,' in response to our wry expressions. 'Me, I played football so that helped, too. When I played in the hospital team it was a bloody cracking side in those days. We were one of the best amateur teams in the whole county *and* we got all our players from inside the hospital. Had so many staff, see? You can't even imagine that, today, can you? Now, you can't even get a decent side together using outsiders. It's difficult getting any sport up and running'. We three look on, sharing a silent but cordial disbelief for a set of entry stipulations entirely bereft of any academic knowledge or qualification, unlike their own situation. But it seems to make sense that, in the absence of school certification, to have been in the military or a sportsman or musician must have credited them with a measure of discipline and self-motivation, and a necessary experience in teamwork, as well as skills to either entertain, teach or encourage patients in a range of recreational activities.

'Before the patients were given a lovely drop of largactil or paraldehyde and suchlike, in the 50s, we didn't have a hell of a lot to play with, you know. Before that, we had to manage on the personal authority and physical strength we had as individuals and what we learned on the job. We certainly didn't need no fancy fucking qualifications,' he smirks with detectably disdainful conviction. Times were changing and you wondered what it must feel like for someone in his situation to see new recruits come into the job with paper qualifications that had no particular relevance to the job, that were infinitely transferable and, adding insult to injury, were supported with better training methods and different techniques than those enjoyed by Reg and his contemporaries. Today's recruits were arriving with a virtually revised, professional language that must have left him and his ilk feeling overshadowed and underrated. 'I'll tell you what else we had to experience in the old days,' Reg continues, excavating his memoirs. 'You never seen a one hundred percent, catatonic patient, I bet?' One of the Malaysians, with remarkably soft, adolescent skin and noticeably large spectacles on a delicately chiselled nose and cheekbones, who has already confided to me that he has a stomach ulcer for which he takes medication, casually answers without a hint of one-upmanship.

'Isn't that a form of schizophrenia where the patient can go into a stupor for days?'

'Correct,' confirms Reg. 'Actually, it can also be the opposite when they can be on the go all the time. But, you're right, you do see the stupors, mostly. If you want a fancy word to learn for the day they call it being "negativistic". There, stuff that up your pipe! Basically, they can't do, and won't respond to, what you ask them to even though it's for their good, and there's not a bloody thing you can do about it. I bet you can't believe that, can you? The patient just stands there on the same spot, or lies on his bed, doesn't speak, eat, or move a hair. When you try to feed them they'll clench their teeth. And you can move their arms to any position you like and they'll just stay there in that same position for hours. What they call "waxy flexibility". There, stuff that one up, as well! Gives you the bloody willies when you first see

79

that, I can tell you. When they need a piss or shit it's just done on the spot and there's no good giving them a good hiding because they can't help their selves. Funny thing is that, though they seem completely out of it, they can tell you all about what happened, and who said what, later. Since largactil, though, it seems to have put paid to a lot of the catatonics. You see Billy over there? He's diagnosed as catatonic but you wouldn't know it, now.' Billy has been displaying his extraordinary repertoire of characteristics and bodily postures. A diminutive, grey haired man, his face is wizened with what seems the mute, insular self-possession of one who always stands alone not seeming to be interested in anything, holding his jacket collars together at the neck, and never quite looking anyone in the eye unless directly spoken to. Even then, his eyes seem nothing more than stony, oblique glands that penetrate the disturbing space between his own and the speaker's face, un-registering save for the intense irritation in the glaring frown cast about them. Beyond these direct encounters, it seems these eyes have almost given up the purpose for which they were made and merely stalk the orbital bones that shelve them. His mobility, when it happens, has a temporary urgency of purpose which launches his bony limbs into several lengths of the gallery until he draws himself to a sharp halt, stills himself, cocks his head as if listening to a long distant cry deep within him, and then bustles off to his private obscurity as if aggravated by the disturbance. Reg draws our attention to Billy as he stands at the far end of the gallery. 'Here, lads, listen to this. Billy, come here lad!' Billy flicks up his head in undisguised irritation, and stabs his face in the direction of his tormentor before compliantly striding toward the staff group still clutching his jacket collars. Reg, tutoring an introduction, begins in a raised voice, 'There was a young girl…'. As if a switch has been thrown to release some verbal engagement, Billy takes up the refrain with a grave rendition, and extends the last syllable of the rhyming lines:

> 'THERE WAS A YOUNG GIRL FROM WEST HAAA… M,
> WHO WENT FOR A RIDE IN A TR… AAAM,
> THE DIRTY CONDUCTOR GOT UP AND FUCKED HER,
> AND NOW SHE'S PUSHING A PR… AAAM.'

Billy is punctuating the verse with his own peculiar accompaniment of rhythmically nodding his head, as if shaking out his irritated compliance with the whole business. There is raucous appreciation from all while Billy registers no such pleasure and turns away, knowing, from experience, that he is no more needed. It is the last small step of a ritual that has become so recurrent that, once prompted, it seems, his rendition is as unhesitating and automatic as a mechanical device. Much to our surprise, Billy not only recounts the rhyme but exposes a voice which is profoundly deep and dramatic. Perhaps the voice of an actor used to projecting himself to the farther reaches of an auditorium, though much must owe itself to his advancing years. It is an example of the nursing staff's sense of humour that they purloin the particular qualities of their patients in order to entertain each other. I cannot help but be thoroughly amused by the rendition, either, and it does not take long before each of us, during our allotted time there, has mastered the little art of conducting Billy's recitation – several times, as is our fancy!. But this pastime never quite dissipates the unnerving thought that, from close behind Billy's stabbing glare, he harbours some seriously harmful fantasies toward his agitators.

'Just going back to the patients for a minute, if you believe drugs have made that big a difference, what good have they done Billy or *any* of this lot, for that matter?' chips in one of the Malaysians.

'Well, in Billy's case, he doesn't have any more catatonic episodes, does he? And he can still recite a good poem,' he adds, orchestrating the laughter between us. 'Those 1950s' drugs have made all the difference in the world, there's absolutely no doubt about that. The chemical cosh, wallop!' he says, smacking his hand on the table with exaggerated emphasis and to the amusement of the group. 'Before largactil and the other drugs it really was bedlam, believe you me. You imagine having to deal with catatonics like that, as well as all the other disturbed patients, before that came along! Christ only knows how the older attendants coped for all those years when they quartered even more patients than we did. But you can see why they needed straight jackets and padded cells. And, as sure as eggs are eggs, there would have been a good few hidings dished out in those days, believe me. I'm telling you, they were different times all right.' The three of us are very suitably impressed but one of our number cannot help expressing the mixed anxiety and amusement which each would admit to.

'How could you actually strap someone into a straight jacket?'

'Well, *you* can restrain a stroppy sod when it's necessary, can't you?'

'Yes, but holding someone down is one thing. I just can't imagine wrapping someone up so they're unable to move at all!' he winces. 'That would seriously worry me!'

'They could move as much as they liked once they'd quietened down,' sniggers Reg, stimulating more laughter. 'It's like everything else, lad, you soon learn. You can get used to anything when you have to.' I lean back on my chair to scan our charges along the gallery and TV room, trying to take in the stifled animation, the sagging shoulders, the emotional stillness, the barest hint of facial activity, the absence of any friendships, or banter, or motivation, or interests, or expectation of anything, nothing, as if all their vitality has been institutionally syringed from their being. I think to myself of the human wasteland here.

' Do you think it's the schizophrenia or the largactil, because if this is what's left over after medication's done its job, it's as if they're still in a sort of straight jacket, in any case?'

'It could be both, but it might be neither. It's definitely got something to do with being in these places for years. They get institutionalised, you see?'

'Do you mean that they get *institutionalised* or these places *institution-alise* them, do you mind my asking?' I ask.

'Ah, well now, that's the million dollar question, ain't it? Don't much matter, does it? Once they're institutionalised they ain't going nowhere. Truth is, you can't really win now 'cos the system's working against you in some ways. This lot would never have been allowed to stand around like this, totally idle, when I first came here, you know. Not bloody likely. All the dodgy bastards were kept back, of course, but every able-bodied one would either be on a working party on the farm, in the laundry, the kitchens, the gardens, or on general duties in the wards or anywhere in the hospital. We didn't have any ward domestics, at all, do you know that? Patients cleaned up and we helped them. I suppose you could say, after a fashion, that they worked for their keep. And, I guarantee, they were a damned sight happier. And staff were a lot happier, too, because we were busier. Now, we've encouraged them to be idle. So, they've had to sell off the farm, for instance. And, it's more expensive to run the place now that it's no longer self-sufficient and we have to pay people full wages to do the same jobs. So, that's why a load of employment has been lost in some areas and loads gained in others. It's all arse about face to what it should be, that's for certain! I'll tell you who to talk to about that. Kev, the hospital driver, you ask him. He's the expert. I tell you, it just don't make sense.'

'What if they didn't want to work?'

'Oh, you could tell who were capable of working from those who weren't. Some might need a little bit of encouragement, if you know what I mean? Then, they go and bring in all these silly bloody changes because we were accused of exploiting the patients as cheap labour. Well, I ask you!' and he's worked himself up into a little bit of a lather, 'if you can explain to me,' and a grand gesture sweeps over the scene, 'how these gentlemen of leisure are better off these days, then I'm a bleeding, Dutchman!' Reg still maintains his pace. 'You see these spastic, bloody lino floors? If you rip up that crap you'll find decent, wooden block floors underneath. They used to get polished every day – buffed up, we called it – with proper beeswax and ruddy great iron buffers that weighed a ruddy ton and someone would be pushing them up and down for hours. Staff would do the buffing an' all until they shone like a skating rink. We were proud of the wards in those days!'

'Assuming this was the sort of ward where most patients couldn't work even if they tried, how the heck did you manage to buff up all this floor space with 60 patients crammed into here? You pile them up in the corners on top of each other?' asks a sceptical Malaysian.

'Didn't matter one way or the other. Used to bang 'em all out into the airing courts. All the grounds area alongside the wards used to be enclosed with a wall and each had its own shelter. Any wards adjoining the airing courts could use it for their patients. It was like having an enclosed garden, really. When we let them out, they could mill around to their hearts' content for hours. Got a damned sight more exercise and fresh air than they do these days, I can tell you. Then, some bright spark decided to knock down every inch of wall all over the hospital so, now, we can't let the buggers out because we can't control their movements so well, and we'd lose them!'

'They've still got something like that in prisons, haven't they? Oh, what do you call them?'

'Exercise yards.'

'*That's* what I meant!' The times were changing. The present seemed to relegate the past, and what had been valued, and what had been considered indispensable, and what most of them had had to survive on. From Reg's understandable point of view, the previous conversation had coursed like an archaeological dig through time and progress. He had raised up the neglected artefacts and curiosities, unwrapped them from their concealment, given them a brushing down, and burnished them in a vain attempt to bring back to life the creditable condition of his former experience. I anticipated there were equally splendid finds yet to be exhumed – a thrilling prospect.

* * *

The following day, a Monday, the weekend schedule is replaced with a general urgency not apparent yesterday. Weekdays contain a particular departure from the weekend's routine. It is now a few minutes before nine o'clock and there is another thunderous bellow from Reg.

'Hall party!' With that, the ward occupants move as if a small herd of animals is being corralled into an adjacent field by an irascible farmer. They compliantly congregate at the ward entrance, inadvertently nudging one another, peering into the walls to avoid each other's proximity, now keen to move on and out of the ward altogether. But Captain, despite already taking his place, peels off to pound the gallery floor, again as if compelled to keep on the move. 'CAPTAIN!' yells Reg, none too delicately, 'COME HERE!' The momentary pause is for the benefit of making last-minute adjustments to presentation – brushing clothing that has sustained the morning breakfast, brushing dishevelled hair. But not brushing shoes. None of these look as if they have been cleaned since the day they were first worn. The group of patients waits, motionless, silent and preoccupied, as if chewing the cud, and exacerbates my awareness that the patients never talk to each other. They are, in terms of social relationship, merely an assembly. Their clothing adds to the impression of an anonymous mass. The uniformity is all staged around a dress code which comprises either a suit, or trousers and jacket. Why is such an outdated expectation foisted on patients when more casual clothes would be so much easier to wear and manage, as well as being so much more economical? It is evident that much is ill fitting and well worn, that some trousers are truncated above the ankle and others turned up into rolls, and jackets have shrivelled to little more than a corset or are draped off the shoulder. The unkindest cut is the unmitigated drabness of style and dark colours.

The Hall Party is counted. It is counted so that we escorting students know just how many people we have to keep track of, and return. Then, it files its inglorious way down the stairwell onto the adjoining corridor which leads like a tributary to one of the main hospital corridors. The single file is broken only by the inability of some to keep pace with the more mobile but familiarity trains them to home in on their venue even if some are delayed by the human traffic of the main corridor. One of the Malaysians stops at a large pair of double doors and throws open one of them while the group straggles in. Once in, it is the nurses' job to ensure that nobody wanders off out of the hall, so that all exits are monitored. The hall is one of the central spaces in the entire hospital and serves a number of communal purposes. It is a massive area that could hold a very large school assembly and is replete with a sizeable stage at one end. The stage is a focus for patient entertainment such as Christmas concerts and there has been a dramatic society and pantomimes held in the past. Today, the Hall entertainment includes films on Wednesday afternoons and a Friday evening dance. The Hall is one of the spaces, along with the kitchens and indoor chapel, which marks the mid-point of the hospital which, traditionally, was divided along gender based principles. The female patients and female staff were housed on the *female side*, and their male counterparts inhabited the *male side*. Male staff did not work on the female side, and vice versa. It represented one of the numerous organisational schisms which divided the community into factions and undermined social integration. The weekly dance, therefore, was one of the occasions when patients would be encouraged to mix with the opposite sex but was strictly monitored. This social splitting was so marked that, even today, male patients allot themselves to seats along one wall and the females along the opposite, until they are ushered to come together for the dances, just as the system had dictated in the past. The whole affair is more relaxed now, and only cursorily monitored by a handful of nursing and recreational staff.

The Hall doubles as a gym for staff badminton in the evenings, is the annual venue for the staff prize giving ceremonies and, during the weekday mornings, is converted for a very low-key range of occupational activities for the less able and older hospital patients, such as is happening today. These morning occupational sessions are run by a couple of State Enrolled Nurses – nurses who train for a shorter period and focus on more practical skills than their registered colleagues. In comparison with the male staff whom I have seen so far, they display a very feminine and caring interest in the patients, of whom they appear to have a sound knowledge. Both are from Southern Ireland, and both very attractive. The atmosphere in the Hall is notably relaxed and patients are free to wander aimlessly if they wish which is what many of them do. Others settle down at the erected trestle tables where undemanding and repetitive tasks are set up to occupy, if not stimulate, them. Since both sexes are permitted into the Hall it represents a rare social opportunity for the men on the locked, "long stay" ward to mix with women. Astonishingly, about half of the men seem not to register the remotest interest in either the men from other wards or the women, so disconnected are they from social intercourse. It is not possible to say whether their social skills and initiative have been lost, or that they refrain from utilising them, but the body language is reclusive, and they volunteer so little spontaneous interaction that they seem to ask only to be left alone. There are exceptions. Whitey is an example of one with the most residual of social skills. He occasionally shows a social initiative, of sorts, as he stands before an individual, concentrating hard on the other's face, muttering inaudibly as if in reflective musing, until his whole face bursts into self-stimulated amusement and laughter. In most other respects, Whitey's social contact is passive until stimulated by staff. Always looking for dog-ends or other trinkets, he casually idles around the Hall walls, peering under the chairs which he shifts about, powerfully, saunters across the intervening parquet flooring and ruffles the long draped curtains with his own style of methodical progress. His sight is poor and whenever he thinks he's spotted something of interest he has to crouch his thick, bow legs to pick it up and fix it myopically before his one good eye to satisfy himself as to its worth, before casually pocketing both his find and his hands into his deep trouser pockets and resuming the customary slouching of his broad shoulders.

'So, how are you today, Frank?' enquires Maud, one of the Enrolled

Nurses, with a familiar and congenial enquiry of one of my ward patients who manages some small amounts of work in between many preoccupied laps of the Hall. It is the same rote questioning put on a daily basis to many of the patients who have virtually no verbal or interpersonal initiative but will tolerate a short engagement and provide a limited response. Frank has already noiselessly come to a halt before the nurse and there is, clearly, a familiar fondness between them. He is a tall man of somewhat anorexic proportions whose well worn jacket merely drapes from his shoulders and outlines the shoulder blades across his back. His gait is a studied mincing of small steps where each genteel placement of his feet suggests that he is cushioning his fragile frame from breakages. I cannot recall whether Frank has yet spoken with anyone that morning but have caught him laughing to himself. His ready smile creaks around a bony jaw that is set like a vice with no flesh, only a taut covering of skin. Both hands twitch in his trouser pockets and he has a slow, rolling movement that courses like a wave through him and keeps him constantly fidgeting even whilst standing still. This may be a self-conscious mannerism, but more likely yet another involuntary consequence of the side effects of drug treatment, called in the trade tardive dyskinesia. It is obvious he welcomes the distraction.

'I said, how are you today, Frank?' repeats Maud. Mouthing a response at a barely audible level requires both she and me to lean toward him. 'You'll have to speak up, Frank. Say that again.' She is looking directly at him with warm, delighted eyes for she enjoys opening up this genteel man who is rocking like a coy adolescent before her charms. It is in this harmless mode that she is flirting with Frank and, presumably, Frank is reciprocating in his own way. The emotional tenor is highly amusing, appropriate and intriguing. For my part, the sensual attraction of this generous, middle aged woman with her exceptional good looks, proportional, buxom figure, and the brightest blue eyes, and made all the more desirable by an unworldly innocence and unintentionally seductive deportment, wafts across like pheromones. Perhaps most notable is the cushion comfortable tone of her speech and the soft manner around which the listener is charmed into their ease. In turn, there is almost a gentility about Frank's persona as the words are carefully pressed between the frothy spittle at the corner of his lips and his small, dark brown eyes project a coy reserve beneath his heavy bushed, humorously frowning eyebrows. Frank's conversation can only manage the immovable preoccupations of his delusions.

'You're Delilah, aren't you?' is the smiling, stereotypical greeting which is reserved for any female, it is assumed. 'You're the Queen of Mesopotamia. You are, aren't you? No, no, no you're not, you're the Queen of Bathsheba. You love women, don't you? No, no, don't laugh. Don't mess about. Go on, get away,' says Frank with jovial mischief. 'You're going to be a very famous woman. How much does it cost to get to Egypt? Have you got any money? It's all rubbish. Give us a fag, will you?' Frank is tripping through his own verbal assembly of thought disordered ideas. But the nurse accepts it all at face value, choosing not to be distracted by the mêlée of ideas and attempting to maintain Frank's concentration. How is it that she is the first person, today, to show this level of interest in a patient, to actually speak *with* him?

Maud is exclaiming with amiable astonishment, 'No, I don't love women, Frank. I mean to say! Whatever gives you that idea, you naughty man?' He moves away to stride his mincing path up and down the length of the Hall before returning to the same spot to look at the nurse, rock gently, and recommence smiling. Maud continues. 'Well, when are you going to take me out, Frank? We could have a really great time somewhere. You'd look after me wouldn't you?' Frank's anvil of a face maintains its sharp angles until it unlocks a protracted, toothless grin that briefly exhales high-pitched squeaks and suppressed giggles. His eyes have taken on an amused, receptive warmth as he delights at this contact. Looking toward me, but still sharing Frank's presence, Maud declares, 'You want to see Frank at break time, the way he sits at the table and drinks his tea and eats his biscuits, a proper gentleman he is.'

So, in this one wholesome cameo of the morning, this small seed of social intercourse, it seemed to me that the characteristics of benign femininity had laid a plank across what I was fast perceiving as the sizeable gulf between the patients and staff. How else had Frank been so captivated by her, the Enrolled Nurse? Had Frank remarkably different qualities from other patients? He had a cuteness, almost effeminacy, that was true. He had a rather delicate way of holding the cigarette he was smoking by the meanest little pinch, permitting it to burn down to a negligible remnant, while he drew on every millimetre of tobacco, permanently burning his forefinger and thumb. Frank had stood out in other respects from his fellows. He had some ability to communicate, even if it was not generally possible to make entire sense of his language. He was noticeably clean and appropriately dressed, in so far as it was possible in institutional clothing, and well-mannered and personable in a distant way. And, although he still appeared to have experienced the same gross deterioration of personality and presentation so prevalent among the long-term schizophrenic community, it seemed you could reach down into him and drag out some vestige of sociability. It was this breaking through to emotional accessibility, the responsiveness, the warmth, the sense of humour that had provided a point of contact between the parties; things which made me realise how much we took this for granted with one another. Or had it more to do with the fact of Maud being a woman and a fine woman at that? Qualities which many males would have taken more lascivious advantage of given half a chance, of course, yet she was more maternal than sexual, and could have been a surrogate support to many a young person in her time. Was she merely adopting what were acknowledged to be the traditional ingredients of nurturing, beneficent femininity, particularly as a mature woman with motherhood experience, within this special context? If so, then, presumably, other women with these approximate qualities would be able to produce similar effects. Perhaps such speculation was all too cut and dried, too convenient, but it had brought to mind that, hitherto, most of my own contact with staff and patients had been confined to male interactions. If I had to configure the male assets, thus far, it would amount to shovels full of disciplined, authoritarian testosterone rather than sympathy, patience or encouragement.

So, was it the case that Frank's uniqueness had been intelligently teased out and massaged by Maud – and the other Enrolled Nurse, for that matter – as part of an objective, feminine beneficence, or that she had a particularly well developed professionalism? Or had all this emerged from her essential decency, about being an uncommonly decent, individual human being? After all, she was generous toward everyone. Or did it deserve any more scrutiny than the straightforward explanation that their personal connection arose out of the nurse's identification with Frank's demure manners, etiquette and acceptable presentation? In short, that she felt relatively comfortable with the refinement that separated him from the more disreputable majority who, in truth, might have even disgusted her? 'OK, Hall Party! Time to go back.

Leave everything where it is; don't go taking anything back to the ward.' Everyone is suddenly making for the exits and the long stay crowd gather at the door, are counted and, with the permission of their staff, depart as they do every morning of every week.

'Blimey,' I suggest to the others on our return to the ward, with lusty insinuation, 'those two women are a right pair of crackers, don't you think?'

'Who d'you mean?'

'Those two lovelies who run the Hall Group, Maud and what's her name.'

'Join the queue, mate. I wouldn't mind a piece of them, myself,' adds one of the equally appreciative Malaysians.

'Oh, you can forget those two,' adds Reg, who is a contemporary of their husbands. 'They're still in love with their other halves.' We know that their husbands have very senior positions in the place. 'Who do you think you are, anyway? You're bloody boys and they're old enough to be your mothers, you randy little sods!'

'Nothing wrong with a bit of maturity, ideal, in fact,' says one of the Malaysians.

'That reminds me of something else,' interrupts Reg. 'You all think you invented sex, you youngsters. Really fancy yourselves, don't you? We all see you up at the club! But, what you have to remember is you've got it made for you, these days, got the run of the place, in and out of the Nurses Home just when you like, coming in and out of the hospital at all hours. Let me tell you, when I first came here, that gate lodge was manned 24 hours a day, the gates were locked, and there was a wall all round the hospital and if you weren't back in the grounds on time you were on the carpet, next day, before the Chief Male Nurse. Big disciplinary issue! For a "bit of the other", we had to get it when, and where, we could, I can tell you. Had to take our chances, and no precautions, neither. No bloody wonder the missus got a bleeding bun in the oven. Then we had to get married.' He is clearly relishing his tale.

'A damn sight more comfortable to get pregnant, over here, than back in Catholic Ireland, wouldn't you say?' I butt in, provocatively.

'What, for the missus? Cor, I'll say. Young ladies could get into a hell of a lot of trouble. You didn't just have to be a Catholic, neither. When you think, though, it wasn't so very different for some girls here, either. All these places have got their quota of girls who found themselves in the club, you know!'

'Well, you hear about that, but is it true?' asks one of the Malaysians.

'Oh yes, you'd better believe it. They'd be admitted for lewd, promiscuous or immoral conduct, believe it or not.'

'Bloody hell! But not the blokes, eh?'

'Life's a bummer!' smiles Reg. 'Actually, men can get sectioned for immoral sexual conduct, too.'

* * *

Whether you liked it or not, the long stay facility was, simultaneously, a uniquely colourful population of individualism, and a homogenous concentration of what was, in the main, schizophrenia. Concerning the latter, it was not difficult to believe that they'd been cast into a mould for producing the "burned-out schizophrenic" – a state of chronic, lethargic debility and incongruous mannerisms, but lacking all the floridity of the more acute symptoms of the condition. There was an odds-on chance that if you had come to acquire the status of a long-term hospital resident you would have been parcelled off with a diagnosis of schizophrenia and placed on one of the "back wards" – another example of hospital euphemism. That was not to say that it was the only diagnosis but it was most certainly the most predominant. Schizophrenia was almost another world. Almost, but not quite, alien. For the schizophrenic population, as was true of any of the major psychiatric illnesses, they ran a huge risk in openly sharing their frenetic thoughts, feelings and activity without stimulating the intervention of a range of agencies whose deliberations, while ostensibly acting on their behalf, often negotiated with them their patients' loss of freedom. Alternatively, for a small minority, whose dangerous ideation caused stark alarm, State agency reaction was inevitable, non-negotiable and quickly expedited. Delusional thinking could result in the most extreme danger, for either the patient or the object of the delusion, because the patient was compelled to act upon their ideas to harm, or kill, or protect, and no amount of rational argument would alter that. Within a conventional county hospital such as this, though, the staff were not normally exposed to what used to be called the criminal lunatic – later, the

mentally disordered offender – where delusional thoughts could be homicidal. But, even though this was not the nature of the schizophrenic patients
in the county institutions, such notoriety fuelled the wary conduct of the staff
so that the attitudes of these so-called experts were little differentiated from
that of the general public, did little to detract from overall scepticism about
the condition, and spared no pretence to bolster optimism in terms of the
efficacy of treatment, recovery, or rehabilitation. At the same time, many
staff wrestled with sympathies around patient helplessness and blamelessness
as opposed to being swayed by the potential for dangerousness. But many,
perhaps most, built up protective strategies to insulate them from a sense
of therapeutic and personal impotence in their unconventional work. There
was the easy, derogatory scourge of the phrases "lunatic" and "madman" that
rationalised the huge social distance that was maintained between themselves
and their patients; that helped to explain away the unexplainable, to control
the uncontrollable. Nothing they could do would minimise the schizophrenics' suffering. Nor was there a possibility that there could be a debate about
the relationship between the real and the unreal. So, when the schizophrenics'
ideas entered into acute psychotic phases, revealing the deeply colourful, oiled
canvas of their beliefs and perceptions, the psychiatric professions dismem-
bered, and patronised, them as "delusions" and "hallucinations". That all this
characterised the long-term hospitalised patient enabled most of the staff to
retain some reserve of pity in what was, otherwise, an almost superstitious
defamation of the schizophrenic's status and ideations. Schizophrenia, in one
way or another, was seen to be an enemy within.

If someone sustained a diagnosis of schizophrenia, the main treatments were drugs classified under the generic title of "major tranquilisers"
because they were understood to quell the general excitability, unpredictability, thought disorder, delusions and hallucinations of the acutely disturbed
patient. It was not until years later that this common usage of the term major
tranquiliser was rectified as a descriptive fallacy and that the correct clas-
sification should have been "anti-psychotic" (counteracting the psychosis) or
"neuroleptic" (reducing nervous activity). This misnomer was an informative
metaphor for the perceptions of the psychiatric nurse at that time. It was
the nurses who had to manage the bizarre and irrational schizophrenic deterioration in the acute phases and what mattered to them in the immediate

present was the subduing of any disturbed behaviour. The priority was the taming of unconventional conduct deemed to be beyond rational control, or threatening, and the concomitant symptoms of paranoia or persecution which were equally intolerable. Therefore, since the desirable treatment effects that helped make patients more amenable and manageable could be attributable to the heavy-duty medication, the common wisdom was that the symptoms had been *tranquilised*. Their concerns were not, so much, whether the medication had effected an anti-psychotic or remedial outcome.

* * *

There were diagnostic exceptions on the long stay ward, such as a patient named Timmy, who had a generalised diagnosis of mental handicap. He had no known parents, or family, or friends in the community, and had only ever experienced institutional life to anybody's knowledge. And yet, he displayed such an inimitable character that he was acknowledged throughout every echelon of the hospital community as one of its abiding celebrities. He was one of only a handful of our long stay residents allowed off the ward during the day. Prematurely aged, he looked about 50 but this was a wild estimate. Word had it that his previous violence – a tendency to bite people so ferociously that he eventually removed a patient's ear in a hospital for the mentally handicapped – resulted, not only in his transfer here, but also in the surgical clearance of his upper set of teeth. No one bothered to seek confirmation or evidence of the absolute facts because the patients' case notes were almost never read by the nursing staff – as if there was an unspoken acceptance that there was no point in finding out useless facts about a patient's past when they would have no bearing on his institutional future. Though this may have appeared a curious phenomenon, in the circumstances, it had its own, perverse logic. A reading of the case notes would have revealed the most extraordinary biographies, so why did we staff not avail ourselves of the rich history that was probably the only record that traced the development of their illnesses? Partly because it was just that – history. The very chronicity of the patients' debilities, often over decades, locked them into the past from which there was no hope of them emerging or being restored. Other than any specifically infamous

93

information, which was passed on through oral tradition, in any case, there was complete disinterest in a biographical trawl. This was rooted in the perceived hopelessness of their cases. Then, there was the fact that case notes were not set up for easy reading. Apart from the admission account, there were no abbreviated summaries of patients' progress and to follow the attenuated, hand-written scribbles of a visiting psychiatrist was an arduous, protracted procedure. Another reason was that the nursing staff had no ownership of patient records, at that time, for they were the preserve of the medical staff. These notes were only ever removed from their cabinets in order that visiting doctors could make a legal entry about their visits and treatment. It was they, alone, who committed their observations to the case notes and why would the staff wish to avail themselves of these? The only exceptions were the admission wards for newly admitted patients where case notes were far more likely to be read by non-medical staff. And, finally, nursing staff had their own singular means of recording observations and general comments and it was to these that they turned for relevant detail that would guide current patient management.

Timmy's small stature, small head and short clipped hair, provoke attention to his pair of fleshy ears which have been the recipients of his vigorous hands throughout a lifetime of expressing his pleasure. He walks with a short, springing gait which pitches him forward as if to give him the advantage of a few extra inches to compensate for a significant short-sightedness and squint. All his clothes are uniformly outsized for his small stature so that the sides of his jacket droop like injured wings to within a couple of feet of his lip rolled trouser turn-ups. As the most scrupulous hospital itinerant, he routinely scours the grounds, rummaging in every refuse pile, dumpster and bin, and gathering up the collectables which will then be hoarded within the bulging pockets of every piece of his clothing. These scavenged riches can be anything from biros to sandwiches, to tins, clothing, jewellery, and anything shiny. The principle seems to be that if it's intact then it's valuable. An overflow storage has been prepared in the carrier bags which are threaded over his forearms. He is a moving symphony of rattles, clanks and rustles. He is the nearest the hospital estate has to its very own recycling prototype. When not freely scouring the land he dips back into his night hostel for meals and a bed.

With a high functioning disability, Timmy has that convivial charm of the mentally handicapped whose disinhibitions are oblivious to social niceties; provided, that is, that he knows and trusts you. On his rounds of the hospital corridors and grounds he is well known for stopping any of the hospital personnel whom he particularly likes, and he has a jester's adaptability for cameo performances. He recognises them, not just as individuals, but in the rôles they perform, so that his little cameos fit the context of those rôles. His travels take him onto the recreational field where he will watch, and recognise, the footballers or cricketers, for example. When he spots a staff sportsman on the corridors he will stop the individual, draw himself to a halt, and enact some aspect of the game in which he's seen the individual participate. Before the cricketer, he will take up a batsman's stance, stoop, join his arms into an imaginary cricket bat, and proceed to swing at an oncoming ball, before exclaiming in a lisping speech: 'Ball hits the stumps. How's that!' Quickly, he will put away the bat, stand upright and, assuming the rôle of the umpire lifting his finger, will further exclaim: 'Out. He's out! Ha, ha, ha! Cricketers, I shit 'em.' For a footballer he will also come to a halt, assume the referee's position, lift an imaginary whistle to his lips, and blow on it, whilst shouting out: 'Ssssssss. Half-time. Oranges. All lie down and have a chin-wag.' Then he mimics the footballer sustaining a leg injury by bending down to hold his leg, limping a few steps, and moaning with pain, in a wonderfully exaggerated and uninhibited performance. 'Oh, my bucking leg, Oooh! Oooh! Oooh! Get the ambulance! Footballers! I shit 'em. They're all bucking mad.' Then, leaning toward the footballer's ear in order to confide some mischief, says, 'I know who that referwee was. I know who it was. It was that wanker, Darwent.' Wanker Darwent is a senior member of nursing staff who is also a qualified referee, and who referees many of the hospital's home games. 'Yeah, I seen him in his shorts. He runs like this,' and he performs a ridiculous trot, over a few yards, still holding his bags and jangling all his wares, to mimic Darwent's running. This is followed by Timmy's inimitable, joyous giggle and the furious rubbing of both ears which he has probably exercised all his life. He has a young boy's mentality in an ageing body. In a bemusing trailer to his routines, Timmy always wants to know the name of the opposition. 'Who was that team you played, last Sat'day?'

'Bexley Hospital, Timmy,' I remember saying, for example.

'Bexley Hospital? Were they the Bexley boys?' as if he has some vague recollection of a gang with whom he has some association. His squint eyes, with a ring of blackheads around them, look on with earnest curiosity.

'They're another local hospital, not far away.'

'Bexley Hospital?' and he shambles off as if he's turning over a long lost memory of a place with which he might have once been familiar.

* * *

Having finished his breakfast and waiting to be let out for today's walka-bout, Timmy approaches me and strongly tugs at my arm before saying, mischievously:

'Oy, do you know what that bucking Charge Nurse was doing last night?'

'Which Charge Nurse is that, Timmy?'

'You know the one. That one with the bucking, big gut (alluding to a protruding, overweight stomach).'

'Could be either of them for that matter. Who do you mean?'

'You know. That married one.' They are both married and one is a body builder.

'They're both married, aren't they?'

'The one who eats all the food, greedy bastard. The one that drives that big, shiny car,' he continues with a mixture of boyish enthusiasm and earnestness.

'What greedy bastard with a big, shiny car, Timmy? You've got me there, old son.' I know exactly who he means, of course. Timmy's voice is getting more high-pitched.

'You know, that Charge who gets his bucking knickers in a twist!' Now, I definitely know.

'Oh, now I know who you mean. What of him?' Timmy pulls harder on my sleeve and leans confidingly into my ear, spraying conspiratorial spittle.

'He was bucking his bucking missus, last night. Heeeeeeeee.' He leans away, releasing my arm. He delights in the mischief of it all. 'Yeah, he was. That bucking Night Nurse told me. Heeeeeee.'

'Well, fancy the Night Nurse telling you something like that! How the hell does he know?'

'Don't know. Anyway, he's a lazy bastard, that Night Nurse, don't do no work, just puts his feet up all night.' Timmy is giggling with his mouth wide open and baring a bottom row of teeth that have not been cleaned for years, maybe a lifetime. The whitish filming never leaves them and, with his tendency to spray words from these detestable ramparts, it is the one obnoxious feature about his appearance other than his filthy paws. 'He wears his slippers all night.'

'Well, he likes to feel at home, Timmy.'

'Snot his bucking home. Got one of his own to go to!'

'Shall we report him, then?'

'Yeah, get the lazy bastard sacked. Serves him bucking well right.'

'You don't mean that. He likes you.'

'I shit him!'

'Oh, that's charming. He's very fond of you.'

'I still shit him!' This defamation masks a certain sophistication because they both get along very well indeed.

'While you're at it, Timmy, give us a blast on your mouth organ, will you?' Thrilled at the chance to show off, he instantly drops his bags with a giddy skip of joy and reaches into an inside jacket pocket, retrieves a harmonica, holds it to his frothy lips with his filthy nail bitten hands, blows a short, tuneless cacophony, takes it from his mouth and rubs his ears vigorously. Lifting his head for praise, and with his grinning, wide-eyed squint, he turns away, giggling loudly while his hands reach to his beloved ears with sheer joy. 'Oh, what a bloody racket. I think I'll have to put that thing in safe keeping before it harms anybody's ear'oles.' Fortunately, Timmy has the wit to realise that his leg is being pulled and feigns personal injury in a high-pitched, but joking complaint.

'N – Ooo! You're not taking it. That's *my* mouth organ. Who do you think you are? You're not the bucking Charge Nurse. You're only a Staff Nurse. Bet you can't play it anyhow.' This is all done with a mock moaning and concealed delight.

'I'm not actually. I'm a student.'

'Yeah, a wanker.' Bloody cheek! Timmy retrieves his parcels and wanders

97

off with the characteristic, trailing chorus which signifies his pleasure which is recognised by all who know him. 'Heeeeeeeeeeee, he's my mate, he's my mate, he is,' while still rubbing his ears with his one free hand which is filthy, personified by nails-bitten-to-stubs, en route to the dining room and the ward exit. Bearing in mind that his top teeth have been surgically withdrawn on account of his past history he, nevertheless, accomplishes the business of nail paring by scraping the lower tier repeatedly across the nail stumps. At that very moment, Skipper shuffles into the dining area and Timmy illustrates how instantly volatile a patient with mental handicap can be.

'*CHARGE*!' The note is a loud, earnest appeal. 'Skipper's in the dining room. Bucking get out of here, Skipper, go on, get out. You're not supposed to be in here.' Even though he has seen him off it is as if Skipper has personally insulted Timmy and he descends into a brooding, dark menace, vigorously shaking his head and prowling the dining room now. 'I don't like that bucking bastard. I hate that bucking bastard. He don't do no work. I'll bucking hit him, I will,' and he bites on his fist with irrepressible fury. Though not expecting any real trouble, I hastily skip to the dining room since Timmy is capable of physically releasing his frustration.

'It's all right, Timmy, thank you for doing our job for us.'

'I'll give that Skipper a bucking kick up the backside,' and literally, and meaningfully, despite his swinging carrier bags, rehearses the deed on the spot before asking to be let out for his walkabout.

* * *

As the long stay allocation unfolded I slipped between the crumpled folds of the routine that determined the nature of the day and the night as if it had a life of its own. The routine which not only specified where you were, what you did, how you did it, what you thought about the work, and how you related to patients, but who you were. These were not matters which could be entirely determined by rational reflection and intent. You were part of a body, from the entire hospital establishment to a ward complement of patients and staff, to each team of three or four members on each working shift. As part of the body it was helpful, if not absolutely necessary, to fit in and to join in. You wanted to survive, to be liked, and didn't want to miss out on all the perquisites that most others were enjoying? There were the inevitable occasions of initiation into something not previously encountered. For example, the slightly inflated supplies of fortifying alcohol such as Guinness, used for patients with anaemia, or as a dietary supplement, were a welcome staff refreshment on a hot afternoon and there was never a specific monitoring of patient consumption, in any case. Someone or other equipped me with the skill to snap off the lid of a bottle if a bottle-opener was not available by striking it with the hand while clamping it against a hard surface. Something which all the staff had learned, I had no doubt. If you botched the first blow a gurgling, foaming dribble would ensue, making a sorry mess of the whole procedure. It was one of those indispensable little crafts that would always be of use wherever your future took you.

There were other compromises which tainted the integrity. But, no sooner had the ink settled on some small, moral outrage that might have been noted about the general care toward patients than it was smudged by the insistent elbowing need to get along, and be on good terms, with colleagues. There was never a swearing in ceremony for staff loyalty, nor were you indoctrinated into an institutional philosophy that forced your thinking, feelings and behaviour into conformity. It wasn't even as if, like a rustic fence of young willows slashed and broken across each other, you were so intimately bound in strong friendship to those around you, that you could not entertain that very closeness being jeopardised. Over and above personal ties and friendships the very core of staff loyalty arose, essentially, from two precepts of self-interest. Firstly, that despite having little respect for some of the staff, and avowedly disliking the odd one or two, protecting your mutual interests at critical times helped to ensure the protection of your own interests. Secondly, the fact that staff loyalty and self-interest were considered occupationally expedient was predicated on their rights being considered distinctly separate from, and superior to, those of the patients. And all staff had a stake in this. Basically, personal integrity in an institutional setting like the mental hospital, necessarily involved a measure of conformity, and compromise, and this was not altogether disagreeable. Nevertheless, this did not preclude taking a lot of things seriously even if you were not sufficiently motivated to challenge them full on. There was the manner in which many individuals used the institutional routine to mask their lassitude; the limited efforts at interpersonal therapeutic measures; and the lack of interest in questioning the psychiatric method, per se. In some circumstances, it was possible to be incensed at the lazy indignity to which some patient care was subjected and the casual incompetence of some colleagues. It was none too surprising to note the strong association between the seasoned, feckless type, with a lack of ambition, and an abysmally low level of initiative, and the quality of their general character. One thing was for sure. I never suffered from a general lassitude and would baulk at those occasions when, on arriving for duty, patients were discovered to have been so poorly kitted out by the staff from a previous shift that you would spend the early contact completely redressing some of them. Shoes that were, in any case, hardly ever cleaned by any of us, might slop about bereft of laces; items of socks, vests and underpants may have been ignored; shirts, minus several or all buttons, might casually adorn bare chests; or torsos might be constricted by corset tight, shrunken jumpers; obvious soiling with stains, or cigarette burns, might be apparent; and outsized trousers might have had to be clutched, by hand, in order to keep them from slipping down in the absence of belt or braces. Just occasionally would be the gaping crutch, with no fly buttons and no underpants, through which the owner's hairy occupant flashed in and out like a marsupial infant. As a measure of the long stay patients' limited capacity for social graces, they would have been little perturbed by such self presentation and the knowledge that their scrotal area was now in the public arena. But this was just how advantage could be taken. While there was some merit to the argument that paying *too* much attention and detail to patient dress code was merely the staff enforcing their own standards, and preoccupations, such glaring examples of neglect did not pass examination. Patients were not permitted access to the store cupboards or their clothes supplies and certainly would never have had a view of their personal stock. Chronically damaged patients relied for their presentation, for every single article of clothing, for decisions about its cleanliness, and whether, and when, it should be changed, and its state of repair, upon their allocated ward staff. Similarly, there would be the days when the "Desperate Dan" bristles masking the jaws of some patients revealed that the staff had taken a day off, or three, from the shaving routine. The bath book might reveal that, contrary to the reasonable habit of spreading the bathing schedule over the consecutive days of the whole week, no patient had actually received a bath so that it was left for the staff at the latter end of the week to complete the entire contingent... or not! As often as not, such incontinent practice became its own habitual practice. For myself, my slightly obsessional trait prevented me from adopting such a casual attitude. Neither could I ever comprehend the flagrant gall of some senior staff who would casually disappear from their own wards for hours at a time, maybe to play a game of snooker on another ward, or languidly doze in a dayroom chair, or pop over to the clubhouse for a surreptitious bevy, quite oblivious to the risk of visitors. I suppose they couldn't have entertained such ventures if they *had* expected to be visited. Yet, who was I to speak when I indulged my own predilections?

My patient contact had soon assuaged me of earlier prejudices, fears and reservations about the terror, wildness, uncontrollability, inaccessibility, and malevolence, of which I may have previously considered them capable. I discovered, in the main, that these were without justification. With only a few notable exceptions, patients just did not have the personal resources to fulfil the derogatory reputations that they inspired and struggled enough, within themselves, simply to get through each day. This did not necessarily mean that they could always contain their frustrations that were sometimes detonated among the company around them but they were seldom openly threatening or dangerous. For whatever reason, there was no doubting, though, that you became desensitised to other aspects of the patients' lives – to their resignation, to their powerlessness, to the absence of any personal authority or control over any aspect of their institutional lives, to their lack of any real possessions. On the latter issue, rarely were relatives available to replenish clothing, supplies, or personal accoutrement. No one owned, let alone wore, a wristwatch, or neck chain, or pipe, and no married man could be identified by a wedding ring. The dormitory lockers – which held no handkerchiefs, no alarm clocks, no photographs, and housed no more then overnight clothing for the following day – were but a statement of administrative intent by the hospital management. Conversely, and not unlike the discrete powers of other State occupations such as prison officers, police and probation officers, the psychiatric institution's medical and nursing powers were implicitly unlimited. The virtually enclosed way of life cut adrift, as it was, like a small craft gently floating along a mellow tributary away from the rigours of the churning, storm driven oceans of the economic market, protected it from conspicuous examination. Consequently, over the following twelve weeks on the long stay ward I acclimatised to the circumstances which were encountered as I eagerly shadowed my new colleagues, shared the protracted tea breaks, the buckshee meals, cigarettes and beer, the gossiping, the institutional vernacular and prejudices, and the casual disregard for close patient contact. During one afternoon shift, I even managed to skip off to play in an inter-hospital football match and return to complete the shift. In short, I allowed myself a steady assimilation into the occupational informality and social apartheid of the hospital.

*   *   *

'Have you joined a union yet, Mr. Burrow? You know there's a good prospect that there'll be some industrial action, soon, don't you? I hear you are not a union member. It's about your pay and conditions, you know! You don't want to be one of the odd ones out, do you?' asks one of the most respected male nurses in the hospital who is a Charge Nurse of one of the infirmaries and who confronts me on the corridor, en passant. It is astonishing to be accosted like this, as if I've been singled out, and all the more perturbing because of this guy's superlative reputation and ability to scowl like a bear when he chooses.

'I'm not sure of the need to belong to a union, myself,' I stumble, with more self-consciousness than conviction.

'So, you're happy with what you're earning, are you?'

'No, I wouldn't say that, but…'

'So how do you think you're going to get a decent income for your future? Do you think the government's going to hand it on a plate? Can you really see any improvement without taking some form of action? It's a democratic right, to be paid decently,' he spits, his narrowed eyes seething contempt. 'Anyway, they're there to protect your interests. You can't say that about much in life.'

'Well, I suppose I believe I'll deserve to earn more by working my way up the ladder.'

'Very laudable. Pull up the ladder, I'm all right, Jack, is it? Let's put it another way, Mr. Burrow. If the union membership manage to secure a pay rise through industrial action you'll abide by your principles and forgo it, will you?' The Charge Nurse gloats back, nodding his head in studied condemnation. It's not pleasant feeling the perturbed arsehole that I'm feeling right now. Such an implication has never occurred to me, irrespective of its impracticality. Why, exactly, have I resisted union membership? Is it because I associate it with being working class, but believe myself to be more self-reliant, that I'd prefer to progress on my own meritocratic worth, and all that? If that is right, where does it stem from? There's the family background: father a manager, worked his way up from secondary school and a door-to-door insurance salesmanship, apolitical, owner/occupier; paternal grandparents, lifelong working class Tories, council tenants, voting for Conservatives who were a better breed of person; and mother from a working class family of builders, and through and through Labour voters. Conversely, my own grammar school education where I was intravenously fed notions of individual advancement and middle class aspiration, punctuated with the imperious mantra 'If you don't get your GCEs, you could end up sweeping the roads!' Then, there's always that intuitive isolation that normally precludes me from joining any association. And, am I really that bothered when I've been so grateful to have found an employment which is way off the common track, the rewards for which might have to include a little material sacrifice?

'I thought the government were promising a percentage pay rise?'

'A percentage of nothing is nothing!' is the emphatic, glowering response. The tone and expression are now quite seriously challenging and the next question is delivered beneath a thick brow of disdain. 'Is union membership beneath you, Mr. Burrow?'

'No, I don't think so!' acknowledging to myself that there's some truth to this.

'Well, what will you do if a patient makes a complaint against you? Do you know how much it costs to hire a lawyer if you have to go to Court?' the Charge Nurse thrusts at me.

'Why should a patient ever do that, I'm not going to harm anyone?'

'You don't need to intentionally harm someone. *I* don't expect to harm anyone but what if I make a drug error and there are irreversible repercussions for the patient from which they may never recover? What if the patient's parents haul me through the courts? I might do the same thing! Anyone can

103

make a drug error, even years down the line!'

'Won't the hospital help?'

'Well, there's no guarantee of that, and they'll expect you to have union representation, anyway. Forgive me for saying but I think you're a little naïve, Mr. Burrow! You need to think, again, maybe. Anyway, when you do reconsider, as I've every confidence you will, don't get taken in by the bleating Royal College of Nursing. They're virtually all women who tend to work in the general nursing field, who are more interested in their respectable image as pink and fluffy things, than addressing their conditions and, in any case, their income is often secondary to their husband's. Well, that doesn't help us fellas much. Respectability doesn't put bread on the table. You need to join something with teeth, like COHSE or NUPE – doesn't matter which because we'll all be acting as one. They're concerned with their members as employees, people who have realistic issues of wanting a proper standard of living for their families. Don't tell me you're not interested in all that?' In fact, I was fast appreciating the wisdom of a pragmatic climb down from this superior stance, knowing that I would never forgo any wage increases that industrial action might deliver. I was no idealist! I begin to understand for the first time how much a threat it might be to working relationships, and personal standing, if a show of such affiliation should be sacrificed? The Charge Nurse shrugs an indefatigable departure as his remaining words circle like a portentous vortex.

'Remember, Mr. Burrow, you could be very compromised if ever there was an industrial action called! You'd find yourself having to cross a picket line. Not very nice, not very nice at all!'

* * *

Another ward allocation in my training commenced – the disturbed ward area. In the past, there would always have been units designated as "refractory" wards for patients considered to be of a pugnacious, resistive, uncontrollable and fractious disposition. The "disturbed" wards of today, still gender-specific, were the inevitable destination for patients whose behaviour was problematic or gave some cause for concern elsewhere within the institution. Though this certainly included wilful outbursts of serious, or above average, violence it could, more often, involve a wide range of other challenging conduct which created more of an inconvenience and disturbance to all of the other wards. In the present, the disturbed male patients far from conformed to a stereotype of imminent violence or dangerousness. On the whole, they were more notable for degrees of intransigently difficult, socially awkward, and antisocial behaviour that were manifestly linked to their psychiatric pathology. In short, it constituted a generally pragmatic utility for a variety of social and psychological "inadequacies" under the descriptive headings of wanderers, absconders, incidental arsonists, the vulnerable, and the sexually deviant! For some like Freddie, for example, to have placed him anywhere else would have required a considerable amount of individual observation on his potential absconding, accidental arson, and a rumoured history of having an interest in little girls. Whether substantiated, or otherwise, his potential in this area was still suspected. A minority of patients had a non criminalised history of genital exposure or other unsolicited sexual interests, while others were vulnerable to sexual or emotional exploitation due to their immaturity. On the odd occasion, some could rage against the fixtures, smash a window, tear the curtains, break a chair or wardrobe door, and injure themselves in the process. Alcoholic intoxication or other detected drug abuse would be other admission criteria but there would be irregular demands to accept the occasionally violent individual. At that time, psychiatrists were legally responsible for treating drug and alcohol abuse, and sexual deviance, as mental disorders. Ideally, patients of the "disturbed" variety would only require a brief sojourn before returning to the initial ward following the subsidence of the disturbance. Nursing staff might just accept a patient swearing at them, providing it wasn't too hostile, but would tolerate only the meanest level of physical aggression. In practice, having acquired a reputation for deviance, most of the current complement were likely to remain indefinitely. The understandable priority was to eradicate any risk at all costs and conventional wards did not have the staff complement for this.

The small dayroom was the impoverished forum of the 20 unoccupied patients who milled around the stapled lines of heavy armchairs all facing toward a television altar from which perpetual noise aggravated the atmosphere throughout the long day. The dayroom also managed to cram in the dining area where, outside of the meal times, the disconsolate could collapse their tortured foreheads upon the table surfaces. Over and above the two staff observers of the dayroom, the two others of the remaining staff complement generally adjourned to the office for jokes, gossip and tales. Freddie was a prematurely aged, chronic schizophrenic of about 40 years of age, with the maturity of a young child, who retained but a rim of thready, hand swept hair. As if his mind was not ravaged enough, the deeply sallow skin, which hinted at his Jewish origin, was sprinkled with the blight of psoriasis. Short, and slightly built, always with shaving nicks to his jaw, he was constantly mobile, flicking out his legs in long, hanging, aimless strides during the incessant tours of ward space, all the time muttering incomprehensively to himself and gesturing with steady, controlled shakes of his clenched fists. Now and then a cry, or laugh, or smile, would momentarily leap out of his solitary rumination – surprising others' attention – before drowning beneath the coating of his preoccupation. Freddie was incapable of rapport but not of comprehension. He responded to instructions and clearly understood everyone else's words, but rarely spoke coherently. Little of the behaviour he displayed was sufficient to warrant what would be called social initiative but there were a couple of characteristic gestures which came close to being so. Like all patients deemed to be dependent, Freddie was not entitled to hold onto cigarettes, matches or lighters and depended on the vacillating goodwill of the staff for such access. When he tired of the endless, senseless delays he was forced to vocalise one of the few comprehensible sentences of which he seemed capable.

'Can I have a cigarette, young man?' he would ask in a faint deliberation that belied his normally childlike avoidance. Never missing an opportunity for fun some staff would roll off the predictable rejoinders.

'I beg your pardon, Freddie, what do you say?'

'Can I have a cigarette, *please*?' replies Freddie, intimating an apology.

'That's better, Freddie. Now, again?' For the briefest of moments there is a stab of defiance in Freddie's eyes but he is well acquainted with the ritual of jibing and, just to avoid the slightest confrontation, steps away, as if scolded. 'Come here, Freddie. Stand there. Now, what was it you wanted?'

Freddie has spun into reverse and approaches the staff member with his childlike compliance, a sceptical frown wrestling with his hopes, and raising his appealing, psoriatic hands, lest he has dared to offend, now gazes into his detractor's eyes and repeats in a quieter, confiding tone, 'Can I have a cigarette, please?' He rests his hands on his hips and looks plaintively into the face of his tormentor as there is nothing else he dare do.

'What will you give me if I get you a fag?'

'I'll give you a good punch,' Freddie may respond with innocuous candour, but leaving the tormentor quite satisfied.

'Alright, Freddie, let's get you a fag, young man.'

'Yes, hurry up, young man,' Freddie replies in a raised, excited tone which would amuse all within earshot as he follows the member of staff to the office. Even then, amusement might not have ended, for Freddie had his unique smoking style and not only inhales with such a snorting forcefulness that you could anticipate an anal plug being dislodged, but swings his legs from side to side in some form of preoccupied dance-ecstasy.

Freddie's second dabble with social initiative involved him sauntering up to an individual, at times perfectly innocuously, at others with a mildly threatening air, leaning to within a metre of that individual's face, fixing them with a dedicated and expressive eye, and mouthing a barely audible script until his eyes would narrow and his voice descend even lower until you felt drawn toward him to catch his fading efforts. It was then that Freddie's fists would be raised as if to strike, and while you would blink and start at the unexpectedness of it, they would merely punch the air in a brief, whirling indignation before he turned away oblivious of the threat he inspired. When more agitated, the fist shaking might culminate in a gentle, psoriatic rap on the bystander's nose or chin but never went beyond this. And there would also be that submissive gesture of holding up his arms and unravelling the splayed, nicotine stained fingers as if anticipating and quelling an incendiary reminiscence that he fears is bubbling to the surface. This is how he spent his days, on the cusp of an inexorable inner rage that hardly dare express itself and always restrained from being converted into actual violence. He was never more than a potential threat and so it had been for as long as anybody could remember. There never existed anything more threatening than the halitosis condemned to serve out its sentence around his rotting, stained teeth that no one ever bothered to examine. If Freddie's behaviour epitomised the somewhat low-key nature of disturbance on the ward, then the playfully goading stance of the staff was not entirely unrepresentative of the ward regime which had long since surrendered all pretence at therapeutic care.

On this disturbed ward, the Charge Nurse's presentation – a paragon of calming and responsible influence for his younger staff – was a professional parody. His degree of commitment teetered on a calculated disinterestedness but he would, beyond doubt, furnish all his staff with some unrivalled memories and tips and, for that, he was excellent value. As students passed through their practical training and experience on the wards each new activity or procedure was registered in a little red book entitled *A Record of Practice*. This would indicate to the professional body who supervised the training schedule that the student had undergone appropriate professional exposure. When I had handed my own copy of this *Record* to the Charge Nurse, for him to complete on my behalf, he had scored off that I had satisfactorily accomplished a "vaginal douche" as a procedure – somewhat difficult to justify on a male, disturbed ward! 'Er, sorry Ted, but you've made a mistake. How could I possibly have done a vaginal douche on a male, disturbed ward?'

'Oh, I always do that for my students,' Ted smiled, with callous disregard. 'Keeps those examiner buggers guessing! In any case, I've never known a student have to explain it away, yet.'

'Thanks for that, then. Supposing I'm the first, you sod?'

'You won't be but, if you are, I'd love to be a fly on the wall. Anything else I can do for you?'

* * *

The daily lunchtime "handover" was a habitual forum where the morning shift handed on clinical information, and any other untoward events about their patients, to the afternoon shift who had just arrived for duty. Sometimes, this meant selecting a trained member of staff to take on the responsibility on behalf of the whole of the preceding team. It was a pretty unstructured affair and would only include matters of concern, or something out of the ordinary. It would by no means involve a studied appraisal of every patient – after all every member of staff was well acquainted with the fraternity. Most of the personnel from both morning and afternoon contingents would be spread about the office and discussion would soon progress to hospital gossip. Ted, when he wished to get down to some juicy titbits, would have his own inimitable style of handover. Keen to get on with it Ted, reclining back in his chair with his feet plonked onto the table, would raise himself just sufficiently to yank the bunch of ward keys from his white coat pocket and, with a twitch of his wrist, send them clattering across the table and onto the opposite floor. With excellent comic timing he would decree: 'There's the fucking ward keys. There's fuck all doing, so don't ask no bleeding, stupid questions! Understood? Good job! Now where's that bastard tea? Right, get your tea and bugger off, all of you, 'cos me and him have got some nattering to do,' pointing to his opposite number, and to the unanimous enjoyment of the whole assembly.

* * *

There has been a patient admission direct from a police station which was a pretty rare occurrence. It transpires that a male in his late twenties had been arrested for a breach of the peace, having been stopped by a traffic cop for his dubious driving and subsequently having been embroiled in an alter-cation with the police officers. After having been breathalysed, and found to have exceeded the safe drinking limit, he'd been taken into custody and placed in a cell overnight. Whilst in the cell, he had complained of ongoing depression, of wanting to kill himself, and had threatened to harm himself in custody, in between periods of withdrawal and uncommunicativeness. The police surgeon, after examination, had taken the safe option and had him transferred for psychiatric observation. The Senior Registrar on the disturbed ward agreed to him being sectioned under the Mental Health Act and had him transferred for observation on account of his current symptoms.

Because he was an unknown quantity and had not been processed through the normal rituals of the hospital, such an admission generally stirred the ward community into a modicum of vigilance and apprehension. To begin with, and unlike most of the damaged patients, he looked healthy, well-groomed, relatively clean-shaven, thickset in build, and not psychotic. His diagnosis was yet to be confirmed, but the staff who had already observed him, and taken into account his recent history, had indicated that he was heading toward a label of "psychopath". The patient was reported to be an articulate, confident lad who, they guessed, was quietly weighing up the ward environment and its personnel. He was dressed in smart flannels and shirt, a sports jacket, stylish leather shoes and, with the exception of a small paunch, was quite athletically put together. It didn't need to be said that he would be a lot more of a handful than the standard patient if he kicked off. A great deal more was to be gleaned from the ward team interview that was now taking place a couple of days after his admission. Introductions are made through the person of the Senior Registrar.

'Good morning. I'm Dr. Benton, Senior Registrar; this is Mrs. Carlton, the Social Worker, and you already know Student Nurse Burrow. You are Mike Briers, is that right?'

'That's right.'

'So tell us about yourself, will you?' Mike unravels his story. 'So, you went to university. What did you study?' asks Dr. Benton, for whom I have a lot of respect since he's intelligent and diligent, sympathetic toward the patients, and has a less imperious, inter-personal style than most psychiatrists I've met. Not that I've met that many because there are so few in the hospital. Maybe it's simply that he's younger and less indoctrinated by the distancing superiority of the *ancien regime*. More to the point, he's respectful of me as a mere student.

'English,' is the guarded reply.

'I like Chaucer, myself. Did you do any Chaucer?'

'A bit, yeah.'

'So what could you tell me about Chaucer?' quizzes Dr. Benton.

'He was a fifteenth century poet,' Mike informs him without elaboration. There is an expectant pause. 'He really wasn't my thing.'

'Mmm. Did you finish? University, I mean?'

'No. I got too mixed up in the social life, especially all the great groups that performed, and the women, and a few extra-curricular things. In the end, decided I was more interested in making money. So I stopped studying, sold a few drugs on campus, and did that for a while until the university threw me out,' he says, carelessly.

'What work have you done since then?' asks the Senior Reg., raising his eyebrows.

'All sorts, mostly salesmen's jobs.' For some reason, I scan his hands and notice the fiercely chewed nail stumps.

'Are you still working, then? Do you have some work to return to?'

'Not really. I lost interest in my last job and waited for them to sack me. I'd like to try something else.'

'Okay, is there anything you want explained regarding your transfer to this hospital? I mean, are you aware of the reasons for being here?'

'Well, I don't much care, really. I may as well be in a loony bin as anywhere. I'm in big shit, right now. I'm over the legal limit and likely to lose my licence. That just about says it all for me, right now, and I'm not in good shape mentally. Perhaps it's time to get really sorted out, Doc!'

'I understand. You also had an altercation with the arresting officer?'

'Yeah, well, I just can't abide the fuzz. How can they do a job of work that sets out to make everyone else's life miserable?'

'A matter of opinion, that. You're not of the persuasion that we all have a need for them at some time or other in our lives, then?'

'Well, all right, granted and all that, but they butt in when you don't need them and I just want them to keep as far away from me as possible so's I can get on with my life without their interference. Look, there's any number of blokes out there driving all over the place without tax, insurance, MOT, pissed to the eyeballs, probably on drugs. Why should I be one of the mugs to conform, and play by the rules, while they're all taking the bloody piss? At least, I know my limits.'

'It's a pragmatic question of having to take the rough with the smooth, to coin a phrase. Police interference, I suppose you could argue, is the price we pay for being protected from those who don't play by the rules, don't you think? Regarding drink driving, there's a law about what the limit is to safeguard all of us. If you respect the rules then being stopped and breathalysed is merely a matter of inconvenience.'

'Isn't that precisely what every drink driver would say?' interjects Jan, the Social Worker who started off inclining forward as if to get inside the skin of this character but has reclined back into her chair with her arms folded.

'No, I wouldn't say so. Most of them rely on pure luck and that they'll get away with it! I don't think you have to come over all moral about it. There are lots of things in life like that. You take's your chances, that's all.'

I'm left wondering how much we've gleaned of Mike's illness, as opposed to what this all says about personality, while an air of bristling outrage for such calculated rationalisations palpates around our little assembly. Dr. Benton, deliberately permitting a protracted pause in order to convey his disquiet, pushes on, at a noticeably quickened pace.

'Well, let's be clear. You've been transferred into hospital because of threatening to harm yourself and being depressed. Can you expand on that for me?'

'I told the Doc at the police station about losing my job and getting more and more depressed since I broke up with my girlfriend and having nowhere to live. I'm NFA at the moment. I'd moved into her pad with her and we were getting along fine, but after I'd started drinking a lot, we started having loads of rows, and then, she threw me out. I've missed her a lot since then. Didn't know how much I would.'

'What do you mean, rows?'

'The rows with my girlfriend? Oh, we had a few scuffles.'

'Were they just verbal or did they get more aggressive than that?'

'Well, I didn't push her about, if that's what you mean. I suppose I was just too up and down and she'd had enough, but I missed her as soon as we split. I've sort of fallen apart since then.'

'The relationship gave you some stability?'

'Oh, definitely.'

'So, do you have any other supports in your life?'

'Well, I don't have anything, really. Let's be honest, nobody gives a shit about you in this world, do they?'

'Are you saying you have no friends, family, anyone who you're close to?'

'I see my parents, now and then, but I don't really trust people enough to have any close friends. Everyone's on the make as far as I'm concerned.'

'Sounds like you're drifting.'

'Yeah, I'd go along with that. Seems I've drifted into some agreeable company, for the time being, though,' unashamedly staring in the direction of Jan, who is an attractive woman.

'Okay. I see from your notes this is your first hospital admission,' interjects Dr. Benton with barely disguised disdain. 'Have you had any kind of psychiatric treatment before?'

'Depends on whether you think attending an AA group is treatment. I did that for a couple of sessions, but that was all too religious. Oh, my God, we only needed a few hallelujahs and we'd have been in church. It was all a bit too black and white for me – as if you'd sinned. Not my cup of tea, at all.'

'Presumably, you still have a drink problem and you're not managing it? Sometimes things need to be set in black and white.'

'Yeah, once an alcoholic, always an alcoholic, and being told you can't make it without help and a belief from outside of yourself. It's all intended to make you feel guilty and dependent. It was for losers, man, just too depressing! I wanted to be able to drink without getting off my face and they couldn't do that for me.'

'Well, I see you've been put on antidepressants in the past. Do you think they've helped your depression at all?'

'Well, I have to have something to help me out, doctor. I can get very uptight, you know. I don't want to get into any more trouble while I'm here, especially if I'm not drinking. I can't get hold of a drink while I'm in here, can I?'

'Sounds like you still have a dependency, then?'

'Wouldn't put it that way. Alcohol helps deal with my depression, though, definitely. I don't know how I'd manage it, otherwise.'

'Am I right in assuming you've taken other illicit drugs?'

'Most people who go to university do, don't you think?'

'Well, I didn't for one.'

'Neither did I,' spits Mrs. Carlton whose expression conveys sympathy tinged with disguised distaste.

'Blimey. Well, maybe you both missed out! I think you're in the minority. I and all the rest have tried most things, really.'

'Ever injected?'

'Yeah, I've done some of that.'

'When was the last time, would you say?'

'Couldn't rightly say. Not recently, anyway. If you don't believe me I'll show you.' With that, Mike slips adroitly from his jacket, briskly draws back his shirt sleeves, and presents the inner aspect of both straightened arms before the medical scrutiny which scours the line of major veins.

'Okay, that's good. Well, I'd prefer to monitor your progress before prescribing any more medication, all right?'

'You're the boss. But just something extra would be a big help.'

'Let's keep you on these and see how you go, for the time being. In terms of your stay here, you'll find this a lot different from the admission ward so you'll have to knuckle down to the way things are done here and try and curtail that temper, okay?'

'Yes, doctor. Can I have some ground leave? I understand you have to ask permission to get off the ward. Only I don't want to be cooped up for too long. I can't see myself having much stimulating conversation with the patients here.'

'Well, that will depend on your progress and how well you adapt here. You're not ready to have it quite yet. Let's just see you settle down, first, shall we?'

'Okay, doctor.' But Mrs. Carlton intervenes.

'So you wouldn't have a home to go back to when you get discharged?'

'Nothing at the moment, no.'

'Absolutely nowhere you can go to!'

'That's right.'

'And what about work? Are you anticipating returning to work and do you think you'd manage a job in the near future?'

'I really can't say.' I am aware that, though Mike has been coherent and responsive, there is a marked darkness of mood that colours his presentation. He half rises, as if he realises the interview is over, and checks with a questioning nod in the direction of the Senior Reg.

'Yes, that's all for now,' by means of dismissing him. Mike leaves the office and I rise to close the door to discuss the conclusions.

'I thought Chaucer was a fourteenth century poet, and much else, besides?' sneers Dr. Benton under a sceptical brow. 'I don't know that he stuck university for long. Fancy throwing away a chance like that, and for drugs, too!' We all nod in agreement before Jan affects a sagging posture in her chair.

'Oh God, I can see some difficulties coming my way. What do we do for people like this who somehow jeopardise everything without any thought for the consequences, or their impact on others? I admit it's terribly judgemental, but the more he said, the more he hung himself, and you feel your sympathy being totally compromised.'

114

'"The more he hung himself", eh? Hum, very Freudian comment if ever I heard one!' For his troubles, he receives a light slap on the arm from the Social Worker, who has leaned across in a surprising display of informality, and appears not too put out by the patchy rash of embarrassment splashing her cheeks and neck. This enlightening interaction is truncated by Dr. Benton, in his role as the psychiatrist and lead clinician, as he orchestrates the clinical conclusions and strategy.

'Okay, so what have we got? Lawbreaking, antisocial, irresponsible and aggressive behaviour, lack of empathy for others, inability to maintain relationships, disregard for conventions, and drug and alcohol abuse. That's more than enough to be going on with. I think we're getting closer to one diagnosis but I'm happy to go along with depression for the time being. He clearly has been depressed, that's for sure.' It is the first time I have observed – and I'm hazarding a guess – that he appears to dislike a patient.

'So, is it the depression that's played the major rôle in his failures or is his constitution the more significant factor?' I ask, wanting to clarify the competing shreds of information.

'In all honesty, Steve, we're never absolutely sure of diagnoses and have to consider some differential possibilities. You're right, the depression is the main presentation for now but how much treatment would be compromised by his basic personality is impossible to assess in the long run. It's the personality that seems to have the detrimental effect on his goals and his inability to sustain his efforts at anything. Mind you, the girlfriend situation is mildly hopeful. He seems to have held that together for a period and that relationship worked for him *and* kept him in work while it lasted. That's a positive sign, at least. Other than that, if he had succeeded in selling drugs, and could have afforded to go on abusing them, and indulge all his dodges, he'd be as happy as Larry. No, I'm not going to settle for a diagnosis at this stage. Let's see how his behaviour unravels. We may not have seen the last of his hand.'

'I feel so frustrated when facing the problems these guys raise. Ideally, they would benefit from a thorough social education and habilitate that they never seem to have had. But, how's that going to happen?' The Senior Reg. returns a wry grin while I note the candour which the social worker has dared to reveal.

'In the absence of such a creditable resource as you're suggesting we'll manage him for as long as we have to. If his case comes to court, I may have to provide a psychiatric report. Okay, my hunch is that he'll be with us for a while.'

* * *

There are many inevitable dilemmas which crop up in the psychiatric field and, although some seem insignificant, they may have the most surprising consequences. Unlike the usual complement of unfortunate patients on the disturbed facility who demanded and expected little interaction from each other or the nursing staff, Mike challenged the mode. His personality was outgoing and his social skills were intact. He was an intriguing and stimulating exception and, no doubt encouraged by the personal interest shown in him, he shared with me the uninhibited observations of a pretty unscrupulous, yet likeable, individual. Listening to his exploitative attitudes was a little disconcerting but it was flattering that he seemed to seek me out for such conversations. At the same time there was, among the staff generally, an increasing unease about his over-confident extroversion. Having kept his nose clean for a couple of weeks, it was difficult for anyone to eventually contradict the recommendation for escorted, then unescorted, ground leave which he took on a regular, and reliable, basis for the next couple of weeks. Then one lunchtime he failed to return for lunch and the afternoon hours progressed with no news of him. Being the locked, disturbed ward, this was not taken lightly by the staff who were more used to patients keeping within the constraints of their privileges. As the late afternoon arrived the decision would have to be made as to whether a hospital search would be instigated and then, if the police should be informed – which was standard practice. When the ward bell rang to announce his return, well into the early evening, we were all very relieved not to have to be hauled out for a search of the grounds, which would have been the first step in recovering him. But it was immediately obvious that, quite apart from being physically unsteady and jocular, Mike was assuming that his re-entry would be an unquestioned formality. 'Do you realise how much time you've taken up, this afternoon? We nearly called a hospital search!' is the simmering greeting of a Nursing Assistant who glowers with disapproval.

'You don't have to hold my hand, you know, I can look after myself. I'm not like all these halfwits,' taking in the ward with a brief sweep of an arm.

'You've overrun your ground leave limit by some time. Why are you so late?' demands the Nursing Assistant, nodding his head so as to indicate that the patient should follow him. 'God almighty, how much have you drunk? You must have been drinking all afternoon to stink like that?' Mike stops to lean on the wall with one arm, baulking at the reprimand.

'So what! Nobody said I couldn't have a DRINK!' he suddenly bawls back. The patient's eyes are a watery, bloodshot swirl and his focus sways about like a pitching lantern in a ship's cabin. He continues, belligerently, 'Who's going to stop me, anyway, you? Come on, then, any of you, what you going to do about it?' and glowers about the dayroom. This is sufficient provocation for the staff. We take this show of belligerence none too politely, an outrageous effrontery which defies our position, our responsibility and authority, so that we feel irresistibly drawn toward the challenge that is being thrown in our faces. No one is going to tolerate this language and general behaviour for long.

'Oh, we'll stop you all right. You can say goodbye to your ground leave for a bit, that's for sure!' the Nursing Assistant responds steadily as he assesses the readiness of the support around him.

'Well, stuff your fucking leave,' rejoined Mike, lurching threateningly toward the assembling staff. The situation deteriorates rapidly.

'Right, get into the dormitory, you need calming down,' directs the Staff Nurse in charge for that shift, who has arrived to take over operations. 'I'm going to give you some medication to calm you down. I'm not having you swearing at staff. Get into the dormitory area.'

'Bollocks, you cunt! I'm not taking any of your bleeding medication,' and Mike turns to the door with the intention of exiting the ward and reaching for a handle that is non-existent. The direct use of verbal abuse toward a staff member is nothing short of a personal and professional offence that no one would tolerate. If an individual did tolerate it, uncomfortable explanations would be demanded of them because it would set a precedent for undermining the authority of all the other staff in the future. Ascertaining that a struggle is in the offing, the Staff Nurse elbows the glass pane covering the nearest of the ward's panic buttons and the shrill urgency of the alarm is activated

117

throughout the ward and the entire hospital. Assured of imminent back-up, he calls in his troops.

'Okay lads!' and this was what all the team had rapidly prepared themselves for as they closed around him like a tightening knot. I and three other staff members pile in to grab a part of Mike's struggling frame before he is levered, pulled and tripped until, as a water buffalo mauled by the relentless grip of lions about him, he can only bear the weight for so long. Mike is on the floor. As with all such incidents, when the anticipated aggression of a patient is converted to the lightning thrust of physical contact, it was an intensely exhilarating moment. To swiftly move at another man, gripping him with all your power, forcing another's muscles, pressing, pressing, pressing until the other's strength is locked and battened down, then feeling the bulging, reviving resistance swell again, only to be forced back, and to hear the taut, gasping breaths, and the quivering chest, and the smell of sweat as all lay conjoined around the writhing victim beneath.

'Fuck off you bastards. Aaaah! That hurts, aaah! You fucking cowards, I'll take you all on, one by one. I'll fucking smash you, you see if I don't.' Recruits from nearby wards are, by now, bursting through the door to assist their colleagues but the alarm is still pealing and disconcerting.

'Are you all right, lads?' calls out the first arrival as others, having made it from greater distances, come lurching in, in various stages of breathlessness and excitation.

'Would you like to hold still, now, or do you want a bit more discomfort?' threatens the Nursing Assistant, leaning over the patient with his full weight, for good measure, causing the patient to rage back at him.

'Get off me, you pint-sized twat!' His eyes are a blazing, blurred firmament and it's clear that he's displaying far more aggression and strength than the staff usually have to deal with because he's younger, fitter, and more streetwise than the regular patients. It strikes all of them that this is not the first time that this patient has been in this situation for he's not in the least intimidated. In fact, it's as if he's weighed us all up and concluded that this mob is not up to much. I have a knee pressing heavily across Mike's upper right arm, ignoring the knowledge that it's painful for him, while nailing his hand to the floor with both of my own. There's no manual for this and no one's been taught how to physically restrain violence properly. How could it be written into a nurse training document? But that gives everyone an excuse to use whatever means they know. Everybody is making up their own holds. With the Duty Doctor already called to come and review the incident, the Staff Nurse in charge instructs the others.

'Right, get ready to lift him up and take him to a side room.'

'Don't you dare get putting me in one of them stinking, fucking side rooms, you bastards,' is the screamed response which peals around the walls. By this time, a belligerent forearm is forcing Mike's cheekbone against the floor so that he is now looking straight at me. Then, as if noticing me for the first time, he lowers the pitch of his voice and in as threatening a tone as he can muster growls, 'And as for you, you fucking Christian, this is the real you, is it? In our full, bleeding colours, now, are we? Well, I shan't forget you, sunshine!' with a glare that would immolate me in a moment, if it had the remotest opportunity.

'Who said I was a Christian?' I reply cantankerously, disappointed that this unpleasant side to his nature has been exposed and that our convivial association seems to have evaporated for the immediate future. For now, it is also important that I am solidly with colleagues and, besides, there's no particular reason for standing up for him, right now.

'Well, why do you fucking act like one, then? I've listened to all your bullshit, all that pretence, how much you enjoy your work, how worthwhile it all is, all that crap,' and he puts a last, fierce effort into wrenching free from the restraint so that each of the staff tighten their holds and increase the discomfort to their antagonist. 'Aaaah! Aaaah, you... sons of bitches,' and the staff's communal satisfaction gloats over his discomfort. He is not hauled to his feet, which would give him back some advantage. Instead, everyone tackles all four limbs in a rough, untidy lack of coordination and hoists him to a side room whose door has been opened in readiness, where he is shoved in and pressed without consideration onto the floor and where they begin to peel, tear and rip away his clothes, oblivious of wounded dignity. They are halfway though when the Duty Doctor arrives, which is pretty amazing since they seldom respond to staff emergencies promptly as a rule. As with most of the Registrars and Junior Doctors, he is an Indian and speaks with a pronounced accent. This one's not been seen before by anyone but he has an air of restrained confidence.

119

'May I have a quick word with the patient, please, if you could just stop for a moment?'

'If we let go of you I'll expect you to behave yourself, understand?' demands the Staff Nurse in charge of Mike. The dozen or so extra staff back away from the side room door but retain a proximate vigilance ready to launch themselves to the doctor's rescue.

'Got you,' is the surly reply. He is now sitting up with dishevelled hair and red markings to his body. The immediate restraining staff, of which I am one, stand back against the walls.

'Can you tell me what happened this evening?' the Registrar asks, in that superior tone of the classic professional while looking over the patient's written notes that he is holding.

'Are you talking to me or shall I wait till you've read those notes?' The doctor looks back to him, fleetingly, and resumes glancing through the notes.

'Can you tell me what happened to you this evening, please?' he repeats, unperturbed.

'I was perfectly all right until I returned to this shithole, thank you,' is the glaring snarl of response. 'Your nursing staff doesn't have the right to tell me what I can and can't do if I'm not doing anyone any harm. I got back here before the night staff come on duty. I'd had a drink but I was perfectly sober. That's not unreasonable, is it? Then your nursing staff start pushing me around.'

'Well, were you sober, in fact?'

'I've just told you, haven't I! You do speaky the English, don't you?' The eyes of the Registrar narrow with an accustomed, covert loathing for British prejudice toward him and his kind.

'It's not reasonable to return to the ward drunk and swearing, is it?' he asks the patient, assertively.

'Who says I was drunk? That's just your opinion. So what? Anyway, it was him that was abusive, not me. Wound me up as soon as he opened the bloody door. He was looking for trouble.' The staff become favourably disposed toward this foreigner as he is clearly unhappy with the obstreperous insolence before him. The assembly decide to give him a chance before they step in to advise him, which is the usual routine for strangers.

'Can you stop shouting, please?'

'No, I can't. Clear off if you don't like it. I didn't ask you here. Go back to Packi-land, you *Packi*!' The Doctor has heard it all before but no one would guess from his quietly determined expression and composure just how hatefully his emotions have been stirred until he ends the interaction by turning fully about and speaking through his departure in an act of calculated contempt.

'Right, you'll need to take some medication to settle you. Can I see his chart, Staff?'

'Like fuck I do. Like fuck I D – Ooo!'

'Give him haloperidol – 20 milligrams intramuscularly, okay?' As he turns to leave the seclusion room for the office to sign the medication chart that will authorise the extra injection, Mike kicks off again as if the water buffalo that has been held down by a lunging pack of predators tries to regain its feet so that they have to re-engage their efforts. Those that can, snap at a flailing arm or leg, one wraps their arms around his head in a full-nelson, and from several acute angles others press as much of their weight onto the major muscles for maximum discomfort while the Staff Nurse withdraws to draw up the prescribed injection in the adjoining clinic room. Mike is now so clamped down that he cannot speak his defiance and his breathing comes in short, desperate bursts. No one is even pretending to calm down this patient now. As a team, there is only one unequivocal goal and that is to show this nasty character that he's overstepped the mark and he'll be punished for it. No one is even thinking of illness to excuse him. This is, categorically, behaviour beyond the pale, and for now it's the only issue on the table. The injection is hovering over the scene and there is a need to access the necessary site, namely, one of the patient's buttocks. Now extremely short of consideration for the patient himself, the Duty Doctor instructs the injection holder:

'Don't let's struggle with turning him over; just stick him through his thigh.'

'Okay, lads, get those trousers off.'

'No, don't wait for that, either,' and taking the injection needle, he bends down to send it though the trousers and into the thigh. Staff catch each other's surprised looks. None of them has done that before and definitely not spotted a doctor daring it! Will it set a new trend? More than that, this doctor, one imagines, is smarting from the patient's disrespect and insults and he's taken it all highly personally. But they are grateful because it confirms the doctor's attitude is congruent with their own and helps justify their own indignation. Experience tells them that they do not, yet, release their grips until either the drug has had some short spell in which to take a minimal effect or the staff remove themselves in a smart and orderly withdrawal. For a few more moments they are content to continue the cumulating discomfort for the patient. A vice of retribution is ringed about his vituperative presence. He is released in controlled stages only so that the remaining clothes are removed without them losing their grip. Leaving only his underpants on, the patient is crumpled into an excruciating flat-pack so that, when the staff let go their holds, he will be too constricted to leap at them, and nodding to one another in silent comprehension, they leave their positions until the last of them springs backwards and through the door, which is slammed shut and locked. Mike is now in official seclusion and the staff have the right to keep him confined for as long as necessary, and until they determine that he presents them no threat. From behind the heavy, steel covered seclusion door Mike has not yet yielded.

'I'll have the police informed of this, and my solicitor, you see if I don't, you wankers! Cowards, the bloody lot of you! Couldn't you get any more of you to wipe me out? When's my next beating, then? Make sure there's enough of you, won't you?' The haloperidol injection will subdue an elephant for a couple of hours and no one will have any more trouble for a while. The panic alarm has been rendered with a fresh glass cover by the maintenance staff, a Nursing Officer is being told the story, general activity is calming, and the patients resume their customary habits and reveries. There is an air of minor celebration as the tense grip of confrontation slides into the limp relief of boastful chatter sweeping around the nursing assembly.

'What the hell was that about? Why does he have to go and muck every-thing up for himself? Anyway, confirms my doubts about him,' says the Staff Nurse in charge. 'He's got it in for you now, all right, Stevie boy! Serves you right, you shouldn't have got involved.' The admonishment is meant pleasantly enough but there is a sense of culpability, nevertheless.

The seclusion room was integral to the institution's life and served many purposes. It was, in the main, a punishment area. A separate appendage which, though physically integrated into the residential rationale, conceptually lay outside of the treatment zone. Any number of contraventions could lead to a patient's ejection from their place in the hospital community to a limited confinement. Frank, psychological disturbance of an exceptional order might count. There was a certain rationale to this: detaching the patient from the environmental stressors; enabling protection from other patients; preventing further exacerbation of symptoms while the medication had time to take effect; prevention of danger to others, such as fire setting or assaulting behaviour; prevention of self harm by excluding access to destructive means; and the hope that it might just nurture silent reflection, reconstitution and contrition. There was free licence to use this sanction and any inordinate indiscretion by a patient might induce a nurse's recourse to seclusion. Because of its history of abuse and the raving images of padded cell, chains and straight jacket all the previous safety elements had been excoriated, leaving no padding and no protection for patients, who could now freely hurt themselves in a space which was more or less transformed back into an ordinary room. Now, the seclusion room was much less of a specially prepared controlled area. Rather, it was more noticeable for its lack of preparedness! It shared the same grey brown, dingy unpleasantness of every single, male side room in the hospital with the exception that it contained only a mattress, sheets and pillow stuffed into a corner, and a stained, plastic, urine bottle. It was a space. An objectionable, stale, damp penetration of urine had hosted all its temporary residents for years and never abandoned them in their hours of need, and was considered part of the punishment. On the inside of the one window a wooden shutter would be drawn across and locked to protect the panes of glass from damage, when in use, so that it also served as a blackout and if the room light was switched off from outside the door there would be no light source other than that which seeped around the edges of the door; also part of the punishment. Staff never actually used the word punishment but it was implicated in all their narrative and intentions. Staff made use of the facility with few qualms about the reason, the patient experience, or the duration, and the sole rationale behind checking on their progress via a small peephole in the door was to ensure they still lived. There was another unspoken rule for certain older members of staff. The decision to remove the patient from seclusion was expected to be left to the person in charge at the time the seclusion was instigated. You would need a pretty good reason to step across this line of etiquette without incurring outrage. The use of seclusion to control a rebellious patient was a fundamental and indispensable part of the nursing repertoire and, though not resorted to with any great frequency, was utilised without undue occupational introspection. The staff's overriding objectives were the need to protect themselves, to quell any disrespect for their status and authority, and to be reassured by a patient's reformative contrition.

I would have been hard-pressed to justify ownership of a highly principled attitude toward the patients. Whether, for example, by working in this field I believed I was combating the general stigma toward the mentally ill, or contributing to their moral sanctuary just as the church had protected criminals and debtors, I could not claim any such high-mindedness. The issue took on some piquancy during what had developed into an unusual compact with Paul, an Occupational Therapist, whose current assignment happened to be the locked, disturbed ward on which I was working. Paul's job was to occupy this group of patients who were subject to more or less continuous containment and were not allowed off the ward for their occupational therapy. He was tall, willowy framed, youthful looking, with curly blond hair, and a pockmarked skin that was taut across prominent cheekbones; a reserved and enigmatic beacon who gave an impression of alertness and sensitivity. The refined pitch of his voice issued from beneath an intelligent brow and vigilant, scanning eyes that beamed into every crater of the ward interactions. This tight alertness belied his attempts at a relaxed, outward presence and he was an altogether arresting contrast to the machismo egotism of many of us nursing staff. As I was to discover, when he had confidence in your company his innumerable observations would spill over you like a continuous larval flow.

Capturing, and maintaining, the patients' attention for a couple of hours has to be a relaxed affair but Paul indulges his wards. I happen to be on hand to watch Freddie coat a large paintbrush with consecutive blue, then red, and then black paints in response to artistic encouragement. Paul and I await his next move but Freddie has just resolutely dumped the brush into a water jug, having suspended it indeterminately over his creation for some minutes without making further impression.

'Oh, Freddie, you built up so much suspense, there,' encourages Paul. 'Were you thinking about anything in particular?' While Paul is hovering over Freddie's raised, innocuous eyebrows and imminent response everyone's attention is derailed by a fracas that has erupted in the patients' bogs, to which you are obliged to attend.

'Get out of there you dirty little bastard,' can be heard as, with all the ward nursing staff, I rush to the bogs where Ted, the Charge Nurse, is standing on a toilet seat and hanging over the dividing wall that separates it from the adjoining, closed toilet. 'Get that bloody door unlocked, one of you, quick as you can. What have we got in there, a fucking paedophile?' And turning back to the toilet's inhabitant, 'Open that bloody door, you, if you know what's good for you.' He doesn't normally get this upset. He invests so much activity in what might be called a sardonic laxity that it's a surprise that he has the energy for outrage. One Staff Nurse prizes the exterior lock with a coin and Ted is down off the toilet to rip open the door. Craning to look in with everyone else, I am taken aback by the presence of two patients facing their onlookers. One, a middle-aged, scruffy man who looks as if he's lived rough for some time and has only been admitted to the ward the previous day, with a diagnosis of chronic alcoholism, and of no fixed abode, is seated on the toilet seat, fully clothed. The other, Derek, a late adolescent patient with a mental age of about six, is standing with his erect penis protruding from unclasped trousers that the other is trying to pull up after engaging in a fellating act with Derek. The latter stands with a smile on his face, clearly unaware of the seriousness of the situation. The younger of the two is hauled out while Ted agitates a path past me to reach the other. Ted's back obscures the initial contact but it is clear that he is demonstrating a vigorous encouragement of the patient to come out. The perpetrator clutches the toilet seating in an effort to resist him.

'Okay, okay, keep your hair on, nothing much happened,' says the older guy with disarming casualness.

'You bloody liar, I bloody saw you!' screams Ted.

'He was willing, he didn't mind. Ask him! Ow, there's no need for that, you're not allowed to push me around like this, OWWW!'

'Shut your mouth, you fucking useless wino!' Tugging alongside them, after Ted and another staff have unceremoniously peeled him out of the bog,

I help to haul the perpetrator across the dormitory to one of the seclusion rooms where he is, equally brusquely, instructed to strip down to his underpants. He seems to know the score. As each item comes off one of the nurses kicks it across the seclusion room threshold into the dormitory.

'Mind out. What you going to do with those?'

'That's not your worry. You've plenty else to worry about for now!'

'You can't accuse me of doing nothing!' wails the patient.

'Can't I, you little bastard. Do you know how old he is? Any case, that don't matter, you were taking advantage of a kid, you pervert!' Ted is struggling for his breath, half from the physical effort of the confrontation, partly from exasperation.

'He's not a kid, he's got a right to do what he wants!'

'Mentality wise, he's a kid and you know that fucking well!'

'How am I supposed to know that?' Ted can hardly contain himself.

'Don't fucking try to explain yourself to me, you piece of shit! If I had my way you'd be straight down the cop shop.' He turns aside to the rest of us. 'Better still, I'd chop his fucking bollocks off for him!' For all that the sexual exploitation of a young lad is a shocking scenario for the staff, you have the impression that this older patient has seen it all before. For despite some nervousness, he's managed the situation with a surprising calmness and some little aplomb. The seclusion room door is slammed shut. In the first place, there is the homosexual issue and it's probably true to say that none of the staff have the slightest sympathy with this proclivity. That an act of fellatio has taken place in their midst is a crime, even though Derek is unlikely to complain that a young patient with a low mental age has not been protected from becoming a victim of sexual assault. An ardent discussion ensues about the issues involved. Should the perpetrator, for that is the common view, be referred to the police. The nursing staff would like to make this a police matter but, because of the mental illness issues, there will be little hope of the authorities taking this further. The *Mental Health Act (1959)* specifically refers to sexual deviation as a basis for admitting people for psychiatric treatment. Sexual deviation is not spelt out, though. That the staff have failed to protect him, and the implications for his care for the future are more than mere inconveniences. The staff have never really considered his sexual vulnerability before. Are the staff missing other homosexual acts on the ward, and what action should be taken if they come to light? Surprisingly, these matters are governed more by personal attitudes than official policy but something will have to be sorted out Irrespective of any hospital policy, how long should the perpetrator be kept in seclusion; should he be transferred to another ward; or be discharged altogether because he's simply abused his hospital stay? What would the parents of the young boy have to say, and what action would they wish? Should they even be informed? In the unlikely event that the matter should reach the attention of the local press, life could be made just that little bit more difficult than, perhaps, it need be. If it should emerge into the public domain then it may be explained as the mentally ill behaviour of a patient who is not in full control of his faculties. If the decision is not to cause unnecessary heartache for all concerned, then the institution can spirit away the whole incident, if it so wishes. But, administratively, the hospital has a problem. How does it record and manage the incident? As much as anything, the incident has undermined the authority of the staff, as if they've relinquished some control, that patients have not only blatantly ignored their authority but actively "taken the Mickey"! That cannot be allowed. How could this newly admitted patient have had the audacity to do just exactly what he wanted, oblivious of the presence of the staff, and irrespective of the consequences? One thing is certain. The perpetrator is in for quite a time of it for every move of his association will be scrutinised from now on.

I return to Paul's company and the occupational therapy table where the three or four patients have remained seated throughout the kerfuffle. It is impossible to calibrate how much this sort of commotion affects them but the presentation gives little away. Paul pins me with a studied glance.

'Well, never a dull moment here, then. What was all that about? Something none too pleasant, clearly!'

'Oh, that new chap; none of us have taken to him, anyway; must have lured young Derek into one of the bogs and performed fellatio, and who knows what else, on him.'

'Oh dear! Well, that could be illegal. How old is Derek? Old enough to give consent to a private, homosexual act?'

'I don't know. How old do you have to be?'

'Don't look at me for an answer! We're blissfully ignorant, aren't we? But, the situation's got real implications if, as I understand it, consenting

127

adults should be allowed to have homosexual sex in private. The toilet may be considered private.'

'Are you kidding? What, on a psychiatric ward! In a hospital! That's not private! We don't even permit heterosexual sex in private! It couldn't be classified as private, not in these circumstances. Even if it was, we still wouldn't allow it, that's for certain.'

'Suppose not. But it's not really about that, let's be honest. The staff object to it because it's homosexual and that's the truth.'

'Yes, you're right.'

'It's not just homosexuality, either; it's got all those other connotations of cottaging, and glory holes, and what they call rough trade where young males will be paid to fellate blokes who pick them up.'

'Yeah, and as I understand it, some of those people don't even consider themselves to be homosexual. Same thing for prisons.'

'Sexual deviance, homosexuality, perversion, it's all the same thing in some people's eyes, eh, Stevie boy? Oh, ho! And none of the staff ever perform an act of sexual deviation, eh?' Not that Paul has given any indication of his sexual orientation but, in light of the liberal comments on display, I choose to watch my footing.

'When you open out these sorts of issues you realise just how much we try to avoid even thinking about them. The truth is, we don't even avoid such issues as this, it's taken for granted what is acceptable behaviour, and what's not.'

'Behaviour which, incidentally, may be illegal one day and legal the next! Take homosexuality. Illegal in 1967, then legal in the same year, I do know that much.'

'Excuse my ignorance but I didn't know that!' Paul turns side on to the table, with one arm over the back of his chair and the other resting on the table edge, and scrutinizes the ward personnel in the day area. He is partly shielding himself from the sunlight that has beamed a block of light across their table for some time. There is little fresh air in the day area owing to the limited extent to which each of the windows can be pushed open. 'When Doc. Belton was informed about the incident, just now, he raised the issue not only of Derek's legal age, but of his mental competency to agree to have sex with another.'

'Nursing staff probably saw that as supporting their case for protecting Derek, I don't doubt. Still, you know as well as I do it's got nothing to do with allowing, or preventing, or judging their competence to have sex with each other. Plainly, we don't want them to be out of our control, doing what they like without asking permission! I bet you that if they did ask permission to do something dodgy it would be granted half the time!'

'We'd take the line that if you're ill enough to need to be hospitalised then you are, ipso facto, not fully competent to make certain decisions such as that, and need to be protected,' I try to rationalise. 'After all, male staff can be criminalised for having taken advantage of a patient's vulnerability by having sex, so, presumably, patients can also be preying on another's frailty?'

'But you'd be criminalised only because the Mental Health Act has specifically legislated against staff having sex with their patients *and* because it's unprofessional. That hasn't come about by accident. I bet it's because male staff have perpetrated that too often in the past. There wouldn't need to be such issues in the Act if the government could depend on the staff not to take advantage of the patients.'

'Does the Act have anything to say about the patients' competence to have sex?'

'Not that I know of. In fact, I'm pretty sure it doesn't.'

'Perhaps we can assume that patients have the right to have sex within the hospital precinct, then?'

'But why should we be asking that, even?'

'Because, it just wouldn't be allowed, would it? When you think about it, we take it for granted that their illnesses incapacitate them so much that they're not sexually interested.'

'Just listen to yourself! Why shouldn't they be interested?'

'I hear you. What about rape, too, then? We don't really take the whole sex thing seriously, when it comes down to it. I think we hope it doesn't exist.'

'I honestly think it's because the staff and the authorities don't feel patients have a sexual entitlement in an institutional setting.'

'Well, it's not a recreational facility, nor a hotel. Is it a home, even? The issue must have cropped up before, surely! I've not seen any formal policy on the matter. Even if there was, or if the Act had permitted it, it's not

129

going to happen in the hospital buildings. Out of sight, out of mind, maybe,' I flounder.

'It won't be in the Act, or a hospital policy, because it would mean recognising the problem and having to take action such as putting safeguards in place, protecting people. More likely, legislators don't want to be accused of punishing patients by stopping them having sex, nor do they want to be seen to be encouraging it. Then there's the pill, other precautions, abortion, unwanted babies – a total minefield. Far better to ignore it, along with a whole range of matters that are better left to the professional discretion of doctors or local management. That hands a hell of a lot of power to a pretty conservative group of people to make decisions over very important issues.'

It was quite mystifying that so much that went on in the hospital environment seemed to readily conform to standards, or rules, which were not formally set out anywhere. Whether psychiatrists, nurses, OTs, or anyone else, all were expected to make reasonable decisions on behalf of patients on a shared understanding about what was appropriate for both patient and hospital. As if, by being exposed to the internal environment, you kind of absorbed the values of a status quo. The fact that such powers were brought into effect emerged on the basis of the major fault lines that ran through the institution, dividing competent staff from incompetent patient – essentially different classes. The dominant staff class was empowered to control the subservient patient class. Patients could ameliorate this demarcation by showing qualities akin to the staff, most crucially, social skills and occupational skills (intellectual ones were curiosities but not saving graces and may only have signified a superior level of craziness) but never effectively crossed the divide. The only patient competencies that mattered were those economic tasks that would fit them for a useful purpose within the institution. If they could work, be it only washing up on the ward, or cleaning, then they were credited with some status. If ever a contentious situation arose whereby the patient disagreed with the staff line, it was the latter's task to persuade the patient that it was in their interests to comply with what the staff wanted them to do. The clearest example was when patients would query their continued acceptance of medication or electroconvulsive therapy, when, conversely, the staff only questioned why the patients should not accept it, irrespective of awful side effects, and ignorant as to whether it would positively work for their benefit. Alternatively, medication refusal could open up a really dark set of issues culminating in the forcible restraining, and forcible injecting, of an uncooperative patient so that this scenario could always be wielded over the client as an ultimatum. At the very least, it was a matter of credibility and egotism that patients could not be permitted to "get one over" on the nurses and doctors – as if the patient was defying and abusing them. There was no point arguing that these were matters of *bad faith*. Staff had to be pragmatic. They had their job to do and if they couldn't persuade the patients to do as asked, they weren't accomplishing their duties. Individual patients could not commandeer the time of a staff member who was at the vortex of a myriad tasks. Patients were in no real position to argue. To do so only confirmed their illness or their recalcitrance. If a patient asked for some favour or other, the staff could fob them off with an assurance of dealing with them later, despite there being little prospect of complying with this promise.

'What is the absolute crux of our job? I mean, what is it we all share in common working in the mental illness field? Fancy a stab at that, then?' Paul prods, provocatively.

'It isn't that straightforward, is it?'

'Why shouldn't it be?' I'm being tempted into a veritable minefield, I can see that. There are too many competing factors.

'If I had to take a stab at it... let me see... um... it's hard to say... um... when it comes to a bottom line I'd say we all... help patients to understand their illness and to live a productive life within its constraints, even within the hospital setting,' I mutter with no huge conviction.

'Not bad! Do you really believe that?'

'Um... I suppose I do... to some extent.'

'What extent?'

'Well, to the extent that it's relatively realistic. Like I wouldn't have said that we're expected to cure them of mental illness. I've seen precious little of that! What do you think, then, smart arse?'

'I don't want to sound pretentious but the absolute crux of our jobs is to safeguard patients' interests and exercise ourselves for their benefit and that includes doing our utmost to get every one of the poor blighters out of here.'

'Are you serious? How many would manage? Where would they go? Most of them would be back in no time at all, don't you think?'

'We don't know that and who says they'd be any worse off?'

'I'll grant you that I'm probably assuming that when patients, chronic ones especially, leave the hospital they will return to the very conditions and stresses that brought them here in the first instance, and undoubtedly lead a solitary life, so why not remain where they're being looked after and have more than a minimal standard of living?'

'And where they can forego their right to have sex, you mean?'

'It seems there has to be a bit of a trade off, doesn't it?'

'A *bit* of a trade-off! When GPs and Psychiatrists agree to a patient's admission it's not just treatment they're offering; they're subjecting their patients to the whole institutional package, limiting their freedom, having every detail of their day scrutinised and accounted for, and probably determining their whole future. What about their patients' rights, their individuality, let alone promoting better food and clothing and improved conditions to live in? That's what I'd want them to do for me. But these are the head jailers! Look around you, man, hospitals can't exactly be in the patients' best interests. It's not much changed since they were Medical Superintendents, I'd say!'

'I'd say they've enough responsibility to cope with and are happy to leave everything else for others to deal with. Not that I'm defending them. But why should they make life difficult for themselves by challenging the hospital management, the commissioners, and the government, ultimately? Why should the nursing staff, for that matter? We've our job to do, too. We have to run the wards and the patients and that's enough in itself! '

'Then we're back to square one. Staff help to take away patients' freedoms after admitting them, virtually take complete control and then dispatch all other responsibility to other parties. It's the personal attitudes of nursing staff on the wards that really decide what is acceptable patient behaviour, and what is not, and psychiatrists are happy to leave it that way. Whether people like it or not, there has to be an issue about whether, in a hospital setting, the staff can act as judge and jury over someone else's behaviour and on what basis they can claim to represent normal, everyday standards. Where are these standards, anybody know?'

There was no escaping the unequivocal fact that, for a great many decisions in their working lives, nurses relied as much on personal judgement, and a shared, informal code of expectations, as on their formal training, or the influence of the hospital as an organisation. The formal training represented a crust of universal principles, but overlay a deep filling of local hospital culture, built up by the views of individuals, and precedent, and overriding hospital policy. Hospital policy offered the necessary guidance on what were thought to be a few major issues that were regularly encountered but they constituted only a fraction of a number of contentious scenarios. Taking into account the previous incident, if the staff had had to rely on what could be termed an ideal nursing role, or their Nurse Training schedule, how could they have managed such a situation that did not send out the message that they were required to be in control of events? Irrespective of nursing ideals was it not necessary, even vital, for there to be a capacity for muscular policing of patients' conduct when necessity called? It was easier to rationalise when the patients' deviant behaviour muddied the waters between what was sickness and what was badness but, even so, it was still only a rationalisation. Policing the patients, protecting them from one another, watching over the staff safety and your own, was a big factor in the job even though nursing staff were rarely subjected to outright assault. And, though experience taught you that patient violence was frequently precipitated by obstreperous staff behaviour toward them, this did not explain every eventuality. There was always room for what might be called spontaneous patient eruptions which were impossible to predict. Therefore, a preoccupation with controlling the patients as a body remained a big deal. In the face of the complexity of psychiatric problems, the asylum organisation, the wealth of diagnostic description, the dearth of effective treatment, and the disproportionate patient numbers relative to the complement of staff, it was the muscular policing that was the ultimate resource to damming back any breaches in acceptable behaviour. Muscular policing was the last line of defence and, without it, it was feared there would be no control. It set out parameters, brought immediate results, generally resolved the issue, and bestowed a measure of control over matters. It employed an informal, unwritten consensus to differentiate sickness from badness, and sifting out what was considered the deserving residue of patients whose mental illness drew on your sympathy. Paul breaks in on my distraction.

'I'm sorry, you guys, I feel bad that I've not been concentrating on you enough. It's this bloke here, he's a bit of a natterer,' cocking his head in my direction. Paul has turned to the few patients remaining at the OT table in a genuine apology for being distracted from his purpose.

'That's all right,' says Troy in a predictable show of conciliation.

'That's big of you, Troy, it really is. I hope you don't mind if we try and finish off this chinwag then I'll promise to make it up to you tomorrow. Is that okay?' Troy nods, while the others look on with a surprise that they've even been considered, in truth. 'Assuming, of course, that Stevie boy wants to continue nattering?' I can see Paul keenly raking through the revealing coals of my expression. 'As I was saying, it is so self-evidently perverse to allow a complex world like psychiatric care to be handed over to individuals who simply have to act on their personal attitudes. As much as it is a derogation of official scruples, I think it must represent a lack of clarity about the nature of the job that you're expected to carry out, you know? In terms of protecting yourselves from future problems it seems to me that nursing staff need all the official help they can get, actually.'

'On the other hand, if we were tied by greater official correctness I doubt if we would be supported in the stance we just took on that unsavoury little episode back there, do you? We'd be left even more impotent, totally without any control. Okay, a lot of what we do does seem arbitrary but it is that very arbitrariness which affords us some slack to adapt to different predicaments. I can make the case even stronger for you though it sounds perverse, I grant you. I would say that, apart from the fixed daily nursing routine, not only is there no real consensus about what we should be doing, but there is no real alternative that we can resort to. It comes down to the predilections of the person in charge of any particular shift who determines how much leverage there is. If you don't happen to agree with a superior then that's just a tough lot of shit because you've little room for manoeuvre until you reach a position of responsibility yourself.'

'Yeah, I grant you the human factor will never be eradicated. That's all right if there are sufficient checks on those whose choices dictate the game, that they're not bending the rules for their own purposes, and that patients are getting their just deserts.' You could only wonder at the massive implications for the service if Paul's ideas were to be officially systematised. The implicit accountability would be disconcerting, even overbearing, if justifiable.

'That would be to suggest that that horrible little man, back there, would deserve to have even more rights than he already enjoys,' I propose in a half-hearted criticism.

'Well, I'm not suggesting that what he did wasn't wrong but do we take a judgemental stance on him in hospital? I mean, exactly what's he been put in seclusion for, right now? He's been caught and we're going to be more vigilant, so he's hardly going to do it again, is he? He's shown no signs of being actively dangerous, I mean; he's not going around thumping people! He's in seclusion because Ted has objected, in a very personal way, to what he's judged to be unacceptable. Should he be given licence to do that? Does that constitute being professional, when it comes down to it?' For the first time in our morning contact Paul's tone, like a chameleon slowly transforming his colours, has gradually acquired the hue of a quietly angry man. 'I don't know that I'd be having this conversation with many of the staff, Stevie boy, but you appear to have some respect for the patients.'

'Nice of you to say so.' But, in truth, this came as a surprise to have been so adjudged.

'So, how far would you go to ensure their rights are protected?' he asks through a grin of disconcerting frankness. 'Come on, let's have it!'

'You've got me there. I've just got to admit that I don't see it in quite those terms. I believe I'm conscientious and I want to do a reasonable job of work, and I would like to help patients with their illness. If I could be working more closely with their thinking and motivation I'd be delighted but the training doesn't provide that. Yeah, that's it, really. Bottom line? I'd want to protect the rights of some patients but I'd turn a blind eye towards others.'

'Yeah, okay. A bit wishy-washy like, but okay. Protecting patients from illness is more like a skill than the *principle* of safeguarding their rights, though.'

'I know. I'm admitting that. I just don't see that that necessarily comes within my remit.'

'Interesting.'

'Well, I think I'd be a damned sight more useful to them if the training and the practice permitted me more therapeutic capacity. I'd be happy to leave it to others to determine whether their rights were being safeguarded, frankly. Take that fracas we've just had, for instance. I don't know that I'm

135

too concerned about whether that bugger's interests are being served! I admit, there are some patients I don't care for, who don't deserve to be treated on an equal par so, no, I can't say that I've got hard and fast principles that hold across the board. Having said that, of course, I've acclimatised to what's expected of me, I realise that. No one can be immune from the influence of his colleagues. What we actually end up doing is partly down to the formal training, partly the vague consensus of everyday practice, and partly down to your personal input,' I root about, unconvincingly.

'Frankly, I don't much see the point of your therapeutic skills if patients aren't treated as equally deserving, equally relevant, fellow human beings. Better they be left to wander free in their madness, don't you think? Not if they're dangerous, and not if they're suffering, I grant you.' I cast a concerned glance to where nursing colleagues are located, as Paul continues. 'What's just happened in that incident proves to me that personal morals dictate the nursing practice. I mean, where's the sympathy, the sense of fairness and fair play, the morality? It shouldn't have to be like that. It's just made up, contrived!' He raises an amused and sceptical eyebrow.

'Well, you just mentioned *morality* but that isn't an absolute, is it? In this game, one man's laziness in not carrying out proper care is another's abuse of their responsibility. And *morality*, well…. Does it extend to that, I wonder?'

'Uncomfortable, is it? I think it is uncomfortable and unfashionable, but I take your point. I don't give a monkey's if people treat human welfare like any other old job – basically turn up for the money in return for as little work as possible – but I care that patients are not treated with dignity and, more to the point, that it can't be guaranteed if confined to a mental hospital. What's needed that would hit the button, that's what I want to know?'

'I'm wondering why it's so important to you, personally?'

'Oh-ho, oh-ho!' raising his voice to a low crow of sarcasm and leaning back, defensively. 'You mean do I over identify with the patients? Of course, that's my problem, I see it all now!' he says sarcastically. If Paul is unsettled by this he manages to skilfully bind it into his humour which, I have come to realise, he uses like a foil. 'Well, maybe I do, maybe I do. What do you think?' with a huge, but more self-conscious, grin. His long, manicured fingers are twitching out a rhythm on the table. Paul's composure is not quite as poised as he fidgets but I admire his conviction. Sparing us both embarrassment, I decide not to go there, but the implications of Paul's comments are clear.

'What I am pretty sure about is that I couldn't actually report someone for foul play. I might be unhappy with their actions, have a word with them if I thought they'd gone too far, and I wouldn't wish to work alongside them if I thought they'd been unreasonable, but I doubt if I would ever shop them. In fact, I could be certain of that.'

'You mean you'd never whistle-blow?'

'What, you're saying that whistle-blowing is the answer? I don't think so, no. Shocking notion, anyway!'

'So, if you saw something distasteful, having a quiet word in the person's ear, or moving them to another area, is going to change their behaviour, is it? You going to have a word in Ted's ear, then?'

'I know, it's not easy. It might not seem possible to alter someone's stance but imagine the fall-out from whistle-blowing on your own colleagues?'

'Ah, now we have it! Let me put it another way, then. Having the bottle to expose ill-treatment! If more people were prepared to do that it would soon put paid to unsavoury treatment, another check and balance.'

'But look at the repercussions. All the parties would be marked for life: if upheld, any perpetrators would lose their ticket, their career, their pension, and the accusers could say bye-bye to any trust from their colleagues for their disloyalty and treachery, which might follow them to their professional grave!'

'What an indictment that would be, that so-called professional carers would be capable of ostracising colleagues for doing the right thing! I just can't respect people who are capable of doing that, seriously.'

'You know, the way you talk, I could believe that you were on some sort of mission. You can come clean, your secret's safe...'

'Funny you should say that,' nodding his head with a ponderous determination but seeming to shake the idea from his thoughts with a short grin. 'Only joking, though.'

'Well, if you *were* on a mission to report people, you wouldn't want to hang around in your job for long because it would be made unbearable for you. I'm certain of that.'

'You're dead right, I'm sure!'

'You're going to think I'm rationalising my way out of this, but, let's put it this way. You're an OT and we'd be expected to come to your rescue if a patient attacked you, as with anyone else. You'd expect us to rescue you no matter what it took, right? And I'm telling you, I'd do whatever was necessary to rescue a member of staff even if I disliked them intensely. Sod the consequences. Well, that's a bit of bravado, but their safety would be the priority, you know.' Looking directly at him, I lay down a defensive card. 'No one's beyond reproach, Paul. I know I'm not.' As the discussion has progressed, it feels as if the issue of patient protection is an elusive, silky fleshed fish flapping on the sands between the lines drawn between two protagonists and it is not one I want to reach out to salvage. We share an awkward silence before Paul's irrepressible mischief re-surfaces.

'Done something wrong have we, then, Stevie boy?'

'Bound to have done! And if every staff member that I've worked alongside was highly moral then I might have been reported before now! Logically, there'd be no one left to do anything other than the one person with the very highest moral credentials sitting in the middle of a sea of protected patients. I don't think so!' We both laugh aloud. 'You see, you're not exposed to the same rules of patient contact. Your rôle prescribes a wholly therapeutic engagement, but we're compromised by having to retain a modicum of good order and sometimes the ground rules have to be elastic.' Paul sits himself down and hunches forward, confidingly, onto the table that lies between them.

'Well, you know as well as I do that elastic ground rules may not comply with *morality*. You're only confirming my point, whether it's individuals acting as watchdogs, or whether people are prepared to speak out against staff that mistreat them, without one or the other, patients can only be left vulnerable to abuse. No getting away from it. So, these cigarettes, here, are theirs, not mine, not anyone else's. If we don't look out for their interests we might as well be guards for all the good we're doing. And frankly, irrespective of whether I have a *formal* duty as an OT, I just consider it so *personally* insulting when I spot the patients being taken advantage of. Their freedom and choices are limited enough. They don't even get the chance to select their own food or serve it up for themselves – throughout the hospital! I'm saying they don't deserve the environment they live in and it's the hospital's responsibility to keep on top of it. Seems to be an assumption that because they're patients they're unable to appreciate their conditions, and that their mental condition is not worsened by an impoverished environment. Well, I would say that if I can be affected by it then so can they. I'll tell you what this is really about, shall I? It's about the discrimination against people who are tarred as undeserving citizens who squander our taxes and live off the State! Actually, it fucking enrages me because it assumes that my view doesn't matter, that it's taken for granted that I'm going to accept all the unspoken rules, that I'll be compliant.' The grin is being swathed in a more serious disposition and the foil protrudes with some vehemence, now.

I hold back from the automatic explication that I'm tempted to give: that the patients' level of disturbance contributes to setting the rules of engagement; that the minimalist ward environment has deteriorated because they don't, or can't, appreciate their surroundings, will actually destroy them if left unmonitored, and that there's minimal potential for materials being used as a weapon! That, if it had a makeover, it would rapidly deteriorate within no time with the cigarette ash dropped, the holes burned into the furniture, objects getting thrown about the place. Even the TV has to be built into a wooden box; it would last five minutes if it wasn't protected. The justifications would be spurious and the automatic pragmatism just doesn't stack up against a more studied protectionism. I know that the staff are a lot more interested in their annual pay rise, and the overtime, than in the patients' environment, and the same applies to me, if truth be known. Where do any of us stand when it comes down to dividing up the health service budget – service increases or pay awards!' Paul turns away to the OT participants.

'What do you think, Troy?' Paul has included one of the patients who always joins this small group activity. 'I'm sorry, Troy, we've been neglecting you this morning. Been having a very interesting chinwag.' Troy had attracted Paul's attention by leaning across with a dog-end of staff-discarded, tobacco titbits, wrapped in a scrap of toilet paper that he has put together from the ward ash trays.

'Can I have a light, please, sir?' asks Troy while Freddie looks enviously across at Troy's prize.

'Look, you don't need to do that. Have a proper one, here you are,' reaching across with the packet to dispense a fresh fag to each of the party, followed by a round of lights.

'Thank you. Have you had a good chinwag, then, sir? That's good,' and he settles to contemplating his cigarette, and his inhalations, with a careless air.

'Have you been listening to what we've been talking about, Troy?'

'Just a little, sir,' he replies, with hardly an inflection.

'What have we been talking about, Troy?' I ask, doubting that he's taken in anything among the barrage of his preoccupations.

'P-p-p... pardon me?' as if he has, indeed, been stirred from a reverie.

'Tell us what we said.' Troy lifts his head and stutters an answer.

'You said that p-p-p... patients are not looked after properly by the staff, that the hospital should be improved, and that the Council doesn't care about people, either. I was brought up in a Council flat, sir, and now I'm in a mental hospital. Am I mad? My mum says she doesn't want me home because she couldn't manage. She said I never helped her out much, but I thought I did. Why can't she manage, sir? If I'd had a different mother I could be out of this place. It's not fair is it, sir? Just because my mum can't take care of me, I'm locked up in this asylum! Do you think I'll ever get back there, sir?' His face, though hinting at an appeal, is crystallised with the disillusionment of years of hospitalisation.

'I wish I could say, Troy, but I just don't know,' I say without relish.

'Okay. Is that enough, sir? Can I have another cigarette for later, please?' Paul and I look on in appreciation. 'Can I be quiet now, please?' Troy returns to his fag, closes both eyes, and sinks his head toward his chest in a show of retraction. Paul raises his eyebrows in mock concern.

'Oh dear, Steve, I've really shocked you.' The OT suddenly relaxes with the customary smile that reveals his exceptional teeth. I am considering the implications.

'Well, I'm wondering how far you take this, Paul. On behalf of society, we're expected to control some of our more difficult citizens against their will, to oppose their predilections, suffer the hostile repercussions of that exposure, while also leaving ourselves vulnerable to reproach by doing so. I think we should be allowed some slack over the ethical niceties in the more extreme circumstances. Meantime, in most other working fields, questionable practice, with impunity, seems *de rigueur*. I was only reading the other day of a pensioner who approached a bank for a loan to buy some new furniture for his house and sits down with a bank employee who processes the application. Now, because he's on a standard pension, and he's old, he's not a good risk so the system rejects his application. Fine and dandy! But, opportunistically, the bank employee tries to sell him a house contents insurance for the property he does own, because she needs to meet her personal work target for the month. Now, apart from being downright callous, you might call that unethical, not fulfilling a duty of care to that customer, but it's probably permitted practice. I feel we're so much more vulnerable to criticism than most occupations, that's all.'

'I don't know who of us has less faith in humanity, you or me. I wouldn't assume any human enterprise would act faithfully to its aims irrespective of whether it's a private or a public company. I assume that it will try to take advantage of the customer. But if that bank wants to make its money that way, that pensioner has the choice to walk out of that bank and never to go back. He need never deal with another bank again. The same applies to everybody else. But, for our blokes, they have no choice. They absolutely rely upon others acting in their best interest.'

'You'll be saying, next, that staff should have a vocation to work in our sort of field.'

'Um… not really, no. The trouble with vocation is that it suggests exceptional qualities which are almost religious, that it implies that you've sacrificed all your worldliness by surrendering your life to God. No, for me, vocation has an ulterior motive; it's not about a basic diligence toward the job in hand. There's nothing exceptional about looking after the interests of less fortunate people. It's common decency. It's totally beyond my comprehension that patients, deprived of their full capacities, should not be treated with care and respect.' It occurs to me that I've encountered precious few Christians, or others with a religious persuasion, working in this field – a perfect context for a contemporary vocation. Unless they were hiding their light under a bushel, it would seem that they reveal no earthly difference from anyone else – doing any old job that permitted them some advantage in the economic game. Or, maybe, they would argue that they applied their vocational orientation to any employment, irrespective of a humanitarian context, or otherwise. 'I'm possibly too biased. I'll tell you something that I came to realise about myself,' continues Paul in a confiding tone and with a drop in volume. 'I really craved a spiritual dimension to my life, for a long while, mainly because of its certainties which would save me from having to grind away at every bloody philosophical issue I was contemplating. Trying to find an intellectual shortcut, so that I could get on with living, if you like! And,' he emphasises this with a mischievous grin, 'that it might give me more justification for all the things and the people that I disliked. Okay, what I realised, for myself, was the absolute impossibility of making that leap of faith, or having to believe in the supernatural, of taking the risk of being completely wrong. It was like having to yield yourself up, to be obedient, to surrender control. I mean, what's the point of being given a life if you have to hand it over in total obedience? Just nonsensical! Nope, there's no way that I could possibly be a Christian – I don't even credit those that are. My personality would never live up to what was expected. I would always be defeated and compromised. I absolutely know that I am incapable of forgiving some people for the harm they cause me or other people and would far sooner go on harbouring my resentment. I feel I've earned it! I'm just far too egotistical, man! So, there is no earthly point in setting myself up for failure. Ha, ha, ha! While we're at it, what about that old chestnut about loving your neighbour? I don't know that I love myself, let alone others. I don't know that I even love you, Stevie boy, but I do like you!' and he rises from his chair to stand akimbo, in a camp pose which has one limp hand in an exaggerated clasp of one hip, which he dips to one side, while bending his knee.

'Bugger off, you bleeding queen. So, what's your poison, now, if anything?'

'I decided no belief system was a fair trade off for giving up thinking for yourself. I don't want to hand over that freedom, that responsibility, even if things go wrong for me. When life get's too much I hope I'll have found more feasible ways of coping than asking for God's intervention. I certainly don't want to be riven with guilt for whatever I do.'

'Religion's out, then,' I disgorge with an amiable goading. Freddie has spent quite a bit of his time at the table looking from one to the other of us with his plaintive innocence while keeping an eye on the cigarette rations which are supplied to the occupational group. From time to time, each of the therapy group will rise from the table to take a turn around the ward, which allows us to continue with our small discourse.

'Paul, I can see a contradiction in your stance on conventional beliefs vis a vis your conviction about psychiatric practice. You're freeing yourself from the constraints and demands of conventional beliefs, in your private life, but not prepared to permit that same freedom from the constraints of working life! Is there a difference, in principle?'

'You see, I knew I wasn't wasting my time chatting with you, my man! You nearly made a very good point! But, here's my answer. Even if I can't respect people who submit themselves to a total lifestyle around their beliefs, the ideals can't be ignored, and they haven't survived this long without being indispensable. I don't make arbitrary decisions about my life without a moral reference. Neither should the staff when their decisions have such implications about the rights of others. So, I'm all for supporting personal attitudes and idiosyncratic decisions if they're representing patients' rights and especially if they're breaking out from conforming to institutional limits, no matter how long people have survived with it. We need ethical values to be civilised. So, it's partly from within, partly from without.' He gives me enough time to consume all this before his next launch. 'There are plenty of precedents for all this, you know. I've been taking an interest in this spate of official hospital inquiries into abuses of patients that have been taking place over the past few years. Some end up not just as inquiries but as criminal proceedings. I take it you've heard about one or two of them?'

'Well, only snippets, really. The view is that if the staff of a hospital are silly enough to get caught out then it's their problem, and doesn't apply to our own situation. Which is pretty amazing in itself! You'd think this hospital, every hospital, had a vested interest in circulating this sort of event to the hospital staff as a sort of warning.'

'And it's nurses who are most culpable, you know!' Paul interjects.

'Oh, that's because we have the most contact and virtually run the places. We're bound to be targets.'

'From what I can make out, these places that get investigated don't seem any different to here. Let me see, there's Whittingham, Rainhill, Farleigh, Brookwood, St Augustine, South Ockendon, Normansfield – heard of any of these? All mental hospitals. Absolutely outrageous what gets dredged up. As if the notion of a hospital is simply not taken seriously at all! That they're still perceived as nineteenth century madhouses and the staff feel immune because what they have practised for decades was protected behind closed doors and would have remained so for as long as it took for somebody to take a stand!'

'Who, exactly, does take a stand?'

'Well, there is definitely a pattern from what I can see. Although patients, or their relatives, may make complaints about nefarious goings-on, they rarely make any headway. It is not until complaints get instigated by staff that matters are taken seriously because they give first hand accounts, presumably. I'll give you an example of one that I read about. It was an Inquiry into a place called Farleigh hospital, ever heard of it? No? It started with a husband and wife team who had both recently commenced working at the hospital – wife was already qualified, husband a new Student Nurse in training – and who reported the staff to higher authorities. In any event, the whistle-blowers have not been embedded long enough to have been absorbed into the local culture, it seems. They manage to retain some sort of perspective on what is, otherwise, insider behaviour.'

'Well, as individuals, they may not have been accepted by the staff for some reason and this was their revenge, perhaps?'

'May well be, but for the Inquiries to have been instituted there must have been good grounds for proceeding and there invariably are, seemingly. Anyhow, a stack of nurses were investigated; I think about nine were charged, six ended up in court, and three of them were served with prison sentences.'

'No! Prison sentences! Nurses! It's hard to believe in one sense, but it could happen to any hospital, surely?'

'Totally agree. It's what it tells us about any hospital, potentially. How can the institutional operations be so out of sync with working principles and plain human justice, for that matter?'

'Christ! Prison sentences! Should we look to our laurels with you about, then?'

'Nah, what you talking about?'

'I think I'll steer a wide berth from you from now on,' I add, good-naturedly.

'Don't talk trollop,' is his assurance. 'I'll tell you what, though. That Mental Health Act helps give the staff the false impression that they're bombproof when it comes to facing allegations about their conduct. You know – that section that specifies that no proceedings will be taken against any member of staff unless their actions were done in bad faith or without reasonable care.'

'Yep, I've heard of that. It's quoted like a mantra.'

'Done in bad faith or without reasonable care takes a lot of proving, mind you!'

'It should do if it's protecting someone's honourable intentions, though. Even for mistakes, quite frankly! Since you've obviously sorted this out, what's the bottom line, then?'

'The bottom line, my friend Steve, is *conscience*, plain and simple. Individual conscience and the responsibility that flows from it! It's about acting according to what your conscience is telling you is right and not abiding by majority opinion just for an easy life. As far as I'm concerned, at this moment, it's about sticking up for people who don't seem to have many rights or freedoms, something which I value more than anything. Personally, the bottom line includes my avowed pessimism about people's ability to free themselves from conformity, and my belief that no government legislation, no hospital inspectors, no hospital policies, will ensure that the patients' rights are safeguarded. You can't escape your own conscience if you believe you should stand up for people who can't stand up for themselves. No question. I don't have any pretensions to a moral crusade or having a missionary zeal. There are things which you just instinctively know are right or just plain wrong. I get very bloody hacked off with how these patients are treated and, if I choose to do something about it, then I hope the authorities would back me up. I'm not saying I am going to, like!'

'Doesn't sound like that to me. Seems we all need to watch our backs!'

'No, no, don't get defensive, now. No, I'm not going to do anything drastic but neither am I going to pretend to accept anything which shows a blatant disrespect toward those who, through no fault of their own, have to rely on others. Neither should they have to accept the appalling bloody conditions that they have to live in 24 hours a day – it's a fucking disgrace. You wouldn't want one of your relatives living here. If it's got to be a home for them, then make it a home of sorts, not a pigsty! We don't have the right to deprive these people of a decent life, a decent environment, and certainly not to ill-treat them. No question,' looking about the ward and its personnel with a shiny beam of amusement. 'Otherwise, it don't seem to add up to much shit, like.'

Needless to say, I was not wholly surprised when, several months down the line, Paul approached me and others with the aim of garnering support for a complaint that was taking shape. He had enlisted two male nurses as further witnesses and fellow complainants and, together, they instigated allegations of wrongdoing which came to involve a police investigation, in time. With respect to specific incidents which were alleged to have been perpetrated, I was relieved to be able to say that I had not been party to, nor present at, their commission. Furthermore, neither did I feel able to support them in their more general complaint about poor patient treatment.

* * *

As the plated lunches arrived and all the attendant, bland aromas of institutional cookery dispersed across the dayroom area, the OT group dispensed with the artefacts that had briefly distracted them while Paul gathered and stashed them into storage. Looking back on the equivocal mix of the foregoing encounter was sobering in the extreme: a dissembling of institutional morality; the uncomfortable implications about personal responsibility; flattery that Paul had risked sharing his zealous preoccupations; and the conceivable motives to which Paul might apply his uncompromising cynicism. In poking through the occupational film that lay across my equivocal rationalisations, Paul had assumed the part of an alter ego. Alternatively, I had the option of dismissing Paul as a contentious malcontent who flourished on resisting things, being non-compliant, being contrary, that his protestations were rationalisations of one who did not fit in, who was only committed to exploiting the convictions of an individualistic outsider. This done, it would not dissipate the import of what had been said, of what it would demand of my own insight and development, and I was discomforted not to be able to reach the same unequivocal conclusions that he had. It certainly would have been comforting to believe that people in the job of caring for other human beings shared a predisposition toward protecting others' interests. That they were self-selecting on this basis. Then, I was only too aware how partial I had sounded, how unconvincingly I must have cherry-picked a path through my occupational responsibility. That I did not really have a strong opinion as to whether people whose job concerned human welfare should possess a higher degree of moral integrity than would be expected in other commercial or industrial sectors; whether there should be an expectation that each of the staff valued and internalised basic moral principles such as respect for their patients or of acting directly, or indirectly, on their behalf without fear or favour. What should count as either ideal, or of necessity, or of sufficiency? Was an innate morality something that I and my nursing colleagues shared or was it rhetorical? What, if anything, was a common basis for our work? I dismissed the idea that there was much common ground other than the economic pursuit of gainful employment and accepting the maximum available overtime. Achieving overtime was probably the most discussed subject at any single moment of the staff calendar. Naturally, there was a modicum of shared skills in people management, crisis management, therapeutic intervention, and adminis- tration, all functional competencies arising from the formal training and working experience and yet even these could only be calibrated individu- ally. There were some who positively despised the work, minimised any patient contact, maximised their self-interest. For most, a general sympa- thetic attitude could be expected. Others could have been dealing with their own much loved family and, perhaps for that reason, somehow managed more than a measure of empathy. But the ideal commonly held by an awed public, that the psychiatric worker had to possess a vocation, perhaps with the slightest religious tint of personal sacrifice, was certainly an illusion. There may have been those with a secularised variant of sacrifice toward their job, but they were not numerous. If, on the other hand, the occasional individual took the risk of broadcasting their avowed religious beliefs, particularly in the context of their work, then they could invite a spec- trum of responses from polite derision to being deemed to be a misguided crank. How could it have been otherwise when the staff emanated from the same common stock as the general public, importing into the insti- tutional culture the same scepticism toward psychiatric patients, thereby remaining virtually indistinguishable from their social origins? More than this, it would seem that close proximity to the psychiatric experience only reinforced previous prejudices rather than ameliorated them. Neither was there much evidence that a public sector group of occupations had attracted those with a socio-political commitment to public service, and that this was considered more morally creditable than working with the private sector promotion of self-interest and self advancement. There was no more reason to believe that nursing staff would have a self-selecting predisposition that would suit them for caring for the mentally ill, than anyone else. Far from vocational, it would seem that the psychiatric nursing occupation was, as with any other occupational group, an instrument for pursuing a modern, consumerist lifestyle. In fact, the working climate was awash with industrial unrest and the generic unions of the Confederation of Health Service Employees, and the National Union of Public Employees, were deemed to be more representative of the economic interests of mental nurses than the Royal College of Nursing.

As for myself, I suspect that I had never possessed any particular conviction that the patients' lives should be uncompromisingly prioritised over every other consideration. And any such semblance at my hospital inauguration had undoubtedly been scaled down during my stint in the institution. The protection and advancement of the interests of the staff and the organisation over those of the patients, was taken for granted. A moral climate that placed too much emphasis on prioritising patients' rights could not easily take account of the need for organisational "good order" when it came to the management of difficult and unsavoury incidents and, sometimes, dangerous incidents. At moments of aggression and violence, the staff generally held patients responsible and employed an uncompromising set of responses which temporarily suspended those rights. If staff, themselves, were victims the response was particularly unequivocal. The caveat was that responsibility could not be expected of the patient who was clearly mentally unwell and staff were not incapable of differentiating such incidents on this basis. Contradicting this was the vociferous claim that institutional authority and discipline over the patient contingent was interpreted as undue control and constituted a step too far and was totally unpalatable.

Some considerable latitude was granted by staff for the disturbed, psychosis-induced behaviour of patients, but most other aberrant or anti-social conduct was viewed as contraventions of acceptable behaviour and swiftly denounced and sanctioned. This was the case even if the patient had been subjected to a "wind-up" and baited into arousal by either staff or patients. There were no clear rules to guide decision-making, and practices and sanctions could be spontaneous and impulsive. The most immediate intervention-cum sanction, was the use of extra medication to dampen any disturbed behaviour. It was, in part, viewed as a punishment for reprehensible conduct in equal measure to its beneficial potential. In those circumstances where the patient refused the increase, and resisted its administration, it was administered on his or her behalf via an injection in the buttock, having first restrained the individual in what could often descend into a free-for-all scuffle. Invariably dispatched to the seclusion room in an undignified sprawl, the patients underwent the indignity of being stripped of clothing down to their underpants. Perhaps, not surprisingly, the longer term patients revealed hardly a smidgeon of shame or self-consciousness, presumably having become accustomed to the total lack of personal privacy within the hospital environment. Thereupon, time was a pliable commodity. For seclusion was considered an indeterminate affair, sometimes stretching for extensive periods, and being terminated at somebody's whim when the patient had shown sufficient improvement, or contrition, or given certain assurances. Very rarely, release might only be granted by the individual who had initially secluded the patient! Other sanction options included confining patients to the ward without ground leave, or access to hospital activities, recreation haunts or general privileges. What all this amounted to was that the nursing body in the county asylums became authors of, to say the least, highly compromising, heavy-handed scenarios in which some either participated, directly observed, or of which they had unquestionable anecdotal evidence. None of this was difficult to invoke, justify or authorise. But, in terms of hospital vernacular the phrase "boot therapy" that was sometimes invoked to describe the masculinist control that was dished out, owed more to hyperbole than a literal enactment.

So it was rather fatuous to assert that your prior regard was, without reservation, the inviolable protection of your mentally ill patients, their predicament, their potential, their future. Was it a part of the working remit to concern yourself with returning patients to a productive life, to gainful employment in the community? Did it matter that they might spend the rest of their lives in the institution especially since few seemed intent on being rehabilitated? If most of the patients were either successfully returned to their origins, or relocated in alternative housing provision, what would be the implications of the closure of the hospital for the staff careers and our own community relocation? Institutional experience acclimatised you to the necessity for efficiency in the routine and to the fact that when it was interrupted it could create a deal of irritation and confusion for staff and patients alike. That this diluted and compromised the care that you invested in the management of the people you were paid to look after was indubitable.

But together, time, evolution and retrospect are unforgiving historians that rewrite the past. As institutions, asylums had their physical proportion and boundaries, their defined rôles, their manifest and latent cultures, and their own definition of time and reality. From the vantage of their castle like entrenchments, tribal loyalties, subjugation and superiority, the psychiatric casts played out their performances and, as their own critics, opted to ignore the conventional audiences beyond their precincts. They leered out of history, rooted in the functional purposes of their origins, and many of the players considered themselves immune to the major political and social changes that swirled about them. For "insiders", the social boundaries virtually held the promise of a total community life which, though it did not permit them to be completely independent of the outside world, allowed them a substantial insularity. Unlike the shapeless anonymity of a mass, outside audience they were theatres with their own resident scripts and, even if everyone was not a star, they were at least valued extras. Within this social confinement arose a landscape of localised myths, assumptions and intentions.

It is tempting to think of the asylum as a place apart, a special place, a container for therapeutic engagement which helped people on their psychological journeys. True, for those wishing to take refuge from an uncomprehending and condemning society, it offered some sort of habitation and inclusive resource that defied the drift into complete anonymity. But if this asylum was also political and psychiatric space, it could neither guarantee the alleviation of psychological pain, nor the acquisition of mental health, and hardly any approximation to a cure. And this would not have varied from one institution to another though more variable outcomes could be anticipated from smaller, specialist units. Conceivably, a patient could be processed through this entire psychiatric space once they had entered it. Starting at the acceptable frontage of the admission wards they would be bedded in around the main entrance, replanted into the rehabilitation wards, then more intensively supported in the psycho-geriatric wards, before being deposited onto the composting mound of the mortuary and, thence, to an obscure pauper's grave. As a social creation, inadvertently or otherwise, the asylum amplified the deviance, stigmatisation and marginalisation of the patients it was expected to treat. In this sense it was akin to criminalisation where, however justified the "guilty" judgement following a trial and conviction, the subsequent prison incarceration magnified the consequences of the criminal act and the condemnation of the perpetrator. If asylum was to mean anything, if mental health care within the context of asylum was to mean anything, it required some basic contractual preconditions: that the class of people who exhibited disorders, and their very illnesses, should be respected; their right to appropriate care should be indubitable; their rights as citizens should remain sacrosanct. None of these could be guaranteed without further expectations; that individual practitioners and their hospitals were sufficiently self-policing to be left to their own devices, in large part; that this be supported by the adequate preparation and continuing guidance of professional bodies; and that external monitors maintain an adequate supervision of conditions and practices. Was nursing, in particular, as one of the major mental health professions, sufficiently professionally competent to override, or modify, the perverse predispositions of individual practitioners? And would it root out those whose non-fulfilment of these obligations invoked the determination that they were unfit to practise? None the less, assuming that these ideals had been played out as insistently as they might, I fear that very few of us would have remained immune to fault and condemnation. Nursing care was a suitable enough notion for describing the inclusive task of managing the patients' physical, social and psychological dimensions, but at a profoundly superficial level. Nursing observation was not so much a formal, evaluative prescription as a casual, impressionistic informality. These were of a relatively superficial order owing to the logical progression that started with a demonstrably limited training, from teachers who had not themselves acquired more extensive skills, because there did not exist the political or professional will to pursue and establish skills training, in itself, generated by the belief that there was not likely to be significant patient improvement. The effect was that professional decision making about patients' behaviour was as much dictated by normal social judgement as by occupational expertise. Conclusion? Nursing care was an unsteady hammock swinging between the opposing pillars of locally entrenched precedent and professionally educated evolution.

CHAPTER THREE
TREATMENTS

THE BUDDLEIA THAT ROOTED ITSELF IN THE hospital estate could easily be underestimated, if not disregarded. After all, was it not just a wild bush? Though enjoying an early flush of acknowledgement following its importation into Britain from China, it was not a highly rated species, presumably, and would not have been associated with prestige or grandeur, or been the subject of a deliberate planting strategy. And since it could not compete with more illustrious species, or afford to wait on horticultural invitations, it resigned itself to settlement of the most unpromising scraps of land where it could flourish in undisturbed obscurity. Buddleia became notorious for colonising the most inhospitable plots of ground. It was a feral, gypsy breed that became established wherever the land was left vacant, on wastelands, on bomb sites, on derelict lands, places that were aesthetic eyesores at the margins of cultivation and civilisation where, over successive years of growth, the over extended limbs reached through, and over, any neighbouring species in a competing display; anywhere where the roots could reach into even the meanest of earth. The roots flourished and adapted to any soil, humidity, heat, drought and moisture, hardy as could be, and then launched their lean, woody, unattractive stems.

People and establishments also owe their existence as much to chance and opportunism as they do to rational and conventional proceedings. Even when established they have to fight for the right to be noticed, not to be undervalued, not to be isolated, not to be desecrated. Both, in their separate ways, have an existence and internal organisation that is more than the present, whose existence and relevance reach way back into their histories to give explanation as to who they are, and what they are.

* * *

Medical training meant medical power and this was the most defining element in the psychiatric firmament. The psychiatrist held the legal authority to interview the mentally disturbed, to officially record observations, to confer patient diagnoses, to enforce admission against a person's will, to allocate that person to a hospital ward, and to follow this with medical treatments and prescriptions against the patient's will, if necessary. Doctors proposed all, nurses applied all, patients received all, in a class differentiation commencing with the omnipotent, through to the relatively powerful, and ending with the completely powerless. The nursing profession ensured that medical supremacy was made operational through its own legitimate powers on the wards. The clinical phenomenon of medication held a particular symbolism for the relative status of the professional groups within the psychiatric fraternity. Nurses' powers did not extend to the vast range of pharmaceutical prescription. Yet, it was this general management of medication, strangely, which was one of the defining tasks and one of the most potent symbols of nursing authority and behaviour because it was their exclusive, clinical domain and no other's. They ordered the drug stocks from the appropriate inventories, received and safely stored them, then dispensed them to the patients, much as a shop assistant would operate between a businessman and the customers. This clinical authority was slightly embellished by having to be conversant with the indications (uses) of individual preparations, their side effects, and with memorising the dual names of drugs. Drugs have a proprietary name, and a trade name, and each must be known. Medication had become the pre-eminent psychiatric treatment for mental illness since the advent of a pharmacological concoction called "largactil". Largactil was designated the wonder drug that was said to have revolutionised psychiatric practice during the 1950s owing to its anti-psychotic qualities but was often referred to as a major tranquiliser because it substantially diminished disturbed behaviour. It reduced acute and chronic symptoms of psychosis, helped to make the patient easier to manage, and contributed to the removal of the straightjacket and padded cell

There was a special emphasis given to the medication round in the mental hospital that stood out from the other procedures to the point of being almost sacrosanct. Firstly, the ward atmosphere was hushed and the radio and TV were turned off to minimise disturbance. In this quietness, the dispensing nurses set themselves up with a seriousness that may not have manifested itself in other respects. Generally after meal times, as the dining room emptied, there would normally be two members of staff who would issue from the clinical room pushing a portable white metal cabinet, the medicine trolley, from which were dispensed the patients' medicines. Pills, tablets, capsules, liquids, drops – everyone received something – very rarely did a long stay patient not receive some drug at some point in the day. Like most rituals it was not a single act but an elaborate procedure which all staff adhered to diligently. In effect, two nurses stood shoulder to shoulder as an insurance against medication errors which could have serious professional consequences if perpetrated. While one read out each separate prescription from the patients' charts and signed for each item given, then checked every step taken by his colleague, the other located the named medication, dispensed the appropriate quantity, and passed it to the correct patient, either directly into the hand or into a pot which was then handed to them. Both pairs of eyes scanned the movement from the patient's hand to their mouth and if the scrutiny was not satisfied, there was a demand for the patient to open their mouths so that the eyes could sweep the oral interior for any sign of medication secretion. For safety's sake, the patient's hand never crossed over the medicine trolley, thereby avoiding any opportunity for medication to be stolen. For those patients who had a history of non-compliance, they were poured liquids rather than handed tablets in the expectation that it was nigh impossible to remove or stash the medication. The medication keys were a crucial element of the ceremony and needed to be located at every juncture; never left in, or on, the trolley or placed anywhere but in a nurse's pocket or on a chain. When the trolley opened, a state of high alert operated and nothing took place casually. All this exceptional diligence lay only partly in avoiding the potential adverse reactions to patients and a scrupulous commitment to ensure each patient received their full treatment regime. Professional self-interest and the need to avoid the ignominy and sanctions from making drug errors were the more motivating. It was also more than just fulfilling the responsibilities of the job because, in fact, it was a peculiarly defining task of the nursing function. It served to help define who nurses were – to other staff, to patients and, no less relevantly, to nurses, themselves – for in health care, virtually nobody else administered prescribed medications other than medical staff. It carried the corollary of an exceptional power over other human beings. It also carried the responsibility of knowing that to give the wrong drug, or incorrect dosage, might seriously harm, if not kill, a patient. It was also a quite daunting responsibility to be expected to detect any side effects in a patient issuing from an administration of medication and then to know its correct antidote.

When the medicine trolley was wheeled out it set in motion a discrete ceremony that, at its core, induced a vague hope among most of its celebrants that something almost miraculous was promised. Medication was not given out haphazardly, or to suit the particular whims of individuals at different times. This was a formal community event that kept to a strict time and procedural schedule that was nothing less than a "Pharmaceutical Communion". The "host" was unlocked and brought before the supplicants, who lined up in a queue as the service dictated so that the giving and receiving of the "living body" and the "living blood" could be effected. The host was offered up in the "body" of the psychotropic pills, capsules and liquids, followed by the "blood" of the jug of accompanying water with which to swallow them. After receiving the wafer and wine, the supplicants quietly turned and sojourned to whatever inner world they had come from. Most of the assembly were, it seemed, true believers and with varying degrees of faith believed that something redeeming, something curative, or something healing and transforming, might be happening. Why else would most patients willingly line up as often as four times a day if not in the belief that their minds could be improved, that their very own medical officers really cared for them and had assured them of the benefits of their treatment? Surely, without this belief, every patient's treatment would have needed to be imposed and physically forced upon them? This was not to say that all patients submitted themselves voluntarily all the time, or that it was never necessary for enforced medication to occur, but so ingrained was the belief that the ritual produced patient benefits that for one of them to decline the offered host was to confirm a perverse and sick state of mind, a lack of reasoning, a lack of insight tantamount to a lack of belief! Treatment, *ipso facto*, was all the more necessary! It then became necessary, in the short term, to have the administration of medication enforced but when the patient eventually submitted, even this had several implications. It was evident proof of its benefit; to begin with; the patient had now acknowledged their transgression; the staff could now forgive them their transgression; and it confirmed that the staff's assumptions were correct. The patient could now re-enter the communion body. Even Captain, restlessly brushing his neighbours up and down the gallery like a scourge, approached when called, stopped abruptly, took the doses in his hand, tossed them into his throat, hurriedly swallowed a small water draught with which to wash them down and, all the while, fixed his stare on the face of the dispensing nurse until he finally spun away.

Faith must have been at the heart of this. What else explained how the supplicants continued to share the host when, for these long term sufferers – even if the very worst of symptoms may have been dampened down – no identifiable transformation had returned them to the person they once were, even though most of them had taken the psychotropic communion for years? This was no less relevant than the incurable trudge of bodies and minds on the annual pilgrimage to Lourdes in defiance of the evidence of past failure but incurable hope. Faith must still have lingered even though patients may not have had a visitation from their psychiatrist for some time. They were generally only re-examined if the staff or patients reported some untoward side effects and, even then, it was likely to be done by a Registrar. So, once prescribed a drug, the patient would wait on the promise of a cure, or just be satisfied with a dampening of the worst symptoms. That is, until the very medication prescribed was directly responsible for the gross, iatrogenic side effects such as tics, tremors, agitation, restlessness, photophobia, contorting muscular spasms, and occulo-gyric crises that the patients must endure as the cost of their faithful journey. But the medics had all the bases covered and there was medication for these side effects, too, or the drug could be changed to another! So, each patient could acquire quite a chemical portfolio over the years!

That this was, ostensibly, a ceremony for the mind rather than the body, was illustrated by the lapsed behaviour of the staff when it came to dispensing remedies for less serious physical problems. A more acute condition such as an infected eye, for example, might have secured more vigilant compliance with treatment but a more chronic condition, such as psoriasis, was as likely to be missed as adhered to because it was simply an inconvenience to fulfil the application. No harm could come of the minor physical complaints so treatment required less vigilance. It was the epitome of the inequalities between two groups of people that the group with power and authority could not only impose an activity on the other, be it therapeutic or otherwise, but that they could do so with consummate bad faith and deep scepticism for the efficacy of that activity.

*　*　*

It is possible to isolate certain initiatives in the mental nursing repertoire which could be accounted as more self-consciously *patient treatment* rather than *asylum management*. One somewhat nebulous introduction, for me, emerged among the quiet constancy of the long stay ward which was intermittently ruffled by the visits of the unit Nursing Officer, a bustlingly energetic, ebullient, middle-aged man of short, lean stature, whose heels clipped the linoleum, whose expression bore the pugilistic hallmark of a seasoned veteran, and whose suits were cut as trimly as the best dressed patients. He would march his twitching torso and keen eyes along the gallery, prodding cursory greetings and nods to any bystander, exchanging brief notes and high-pitched rattles of laughter with the person in charge, before jerking his way to the exit. Apart from accomplishing a daily errand of instructions, and dispensing overtime opportunities to the staff, his visits served no noticeable purpose. As I was discovering, this applied to most of those in a similar rôle as they roamed the hospital byways in search of some purpose other than booking people for overtime. A purpose that the recently implemented *Salmon Report* – a well-intentioned managerial career structure for nurses that effectively scuppered the validation of clinical careers in favour of managerial advancement – singularly failed to deliver. Whether or not it was my protruding trail of disdain for him that tripped the Nursing Officer's attention, was not possible to say, but I imagine my cautious contact registered with him. Stung by this little man's obdurate lack of acknowledge-ment, I rewarded him with my own brand of insolent silence. The effrontery obviously proved too much for him and, one afternoon, a time unusual in itself for such a visit, he stopped right alongside his quarry and asked me to accompany him to one of the ward store rooms where a private tuition was to be imparted! With a practised and barely camouflaged glee, this superior briefly probed my subordinate comprehension of the long stay ward regime to which I had been exposed while on the ward. But he cut me dead when I started to elaborate the ideals of "rehabilitation" which was very much the prevailing *zeitgeist* of the current training ideals but, admittedly, absurdly out of step with the clinical realities.

'Yes, yes, that's all a very nice theory, Mr. Burrows, but what we can best do in this real world of ours, with this type of patient, is to "habit train" them. Habit training is what we're about! Now, do you know what that is?' with a sneer that slipped from his eyes and draped itself across the entire length of his cackling jaws.

'I thought habit training was for the psycho-geriatric patients,' I replied, truthfully, with just sufficient restraint to hide contempt for such a sugges-tion, and smarting at the indignity of being personally challenged by this little man. As I've already mentioned, habit training was meant to be a constructive, preventative procedure for sustaining some common routines and orientation for psycho-geriatric patients subject to the dementing process. In reality, it was a phrase that conjured up nothing more than the batched "toileting" of the incontinent, in a bid to avoid having to change urinated and defecated clothes. If it was not implemented, it didn't matter, because disposable pads were stuffed into their underwear to catch the seepage.

'Well, it is, but chronic schizophrenics who are as damaged as these can quickly deteriorate over their self care. Something that we all take for granted in our lives. Stick a few years on them and, hey presto, they're psycho-geriatrics, too. Anyway, I'm interrupting; you were saying?' he adds, waiting for further opportunities to catch me.

'I was about to say that I haven't heard "habit training" mentioned on this ward!' 'Really, well you surprise me! Ask yourself, Mr. Burrows, what have these patients got left to live for? Ask yourself how you'd cope if you were in their place. Can you tell me? '

159

'I'm really not in a position to say…' The Nursing Officer, like a swaying, inscrutable cobra, is quietly relishing an inner reflection, gently nodding his head in anticipation of his own striking rejoinder. His attack is to embark on tuition with eminent conviction for his stand and an uncompromising disdain for my defaulting. I am not so much listening to as curdling with pleasure at the contorting, agitating right shoulder, the twitching eyes, and the unconvincing show of confidence.

'They need regular routine, Mr. Burrows. They need some purpose now that their illness has stripped them of a life. They might not function anywhere other than in hospital, because they've deteriorated too far, and they're never likely to be rehabilitated. Getting them organised around a fixed timetable gives them something definite to stimulate them, even if it's not very much. It's something, and better than leaving them to themselves. If they were left to their own devices they wouldn't do anything; wouldn't get up, or dress, or wash, or cook, change their clothes, nothing. They have to be helped to pay attention to every detail of the day and when they can't help themselves then we tidy them up. That's why they're here, and that's why we're here. So, we train them with a daily pattern so that they know when to eat, when to go to bed, when to get up, when to go out, when to have a weekly bath, when to have their nails cut and cleaned, and we take them to the toilet at regular times, if necessary, and keep them in contact with their relatives. If they didn't get taken out on walks, or included in the Hall Party, or have coach trips, they would sit idle and vegetate. They'd certainly be more depressed if we didn't maintain that strict routine. It doesn't matter what type of schizophrenia they have, they all become detached from reality, withdrawn into their own little worlds, and it's our job to try and keep them in touch. That's why we still have televisions and radios on the ward – not for the staff entertainment.'

'I hear what you're saying but do all these daily routines that we put them through really amount to a treatment programme?'

'Why ever not!'

'Well, if it's so important, shouldn't it be more formalised so that we can assess whether individuals are really making any headway? I mean, it doesn't feel like treatment; just a very basic way of getting through the necessary stages of the day, really!' I'm only describing the ward routine and practice as I've experienced it. There is real, mutual contempt in this confined room among the dry-cleaned suits and overcoats hanging on long clothes rails with a musty odour of lack of use or of human presence. We are a couple of snakes sizing up one another's nonchalance, trepidation, ferocity, arching into each other's domain, deciding on either a vilifying submission or waiting for that moment to spring with snarling, clawing imposition. I consciously steady and calm myself in order to deliberately accentuate the other's unease, ask no questions, hover in silent contempt, and glare with a sullen acquiescence into the little man's face. There is an urge – only fleeting – to swing a punch, ramming into the horrid features of this bloody little man with the coarse manner and unshakeable conviction, but I anticipate that this seasoned pugilist has been in many a spar and the tumult would very much make his day. I dam back the leaking haemorrhage of outrage. Apart from the ward newspapers, which they don't read, and the radio and TV, which they don't watch, we are their only contact with the outside world. I wonder what earthly logic there is in crediting a standardised routine with a pretence of treatment.

'Have you ever tried sitting down with any one of these patients to encourage them to read the newspaper, Mr. Burrows, or ask them what TV programmes they want to watch?' A triumphant crease distorts his jaw and the excited shoulders are twitching so rhythmically that he must be loosening them up. It feels as if he's sniffed out my challenges. But isn't this all easy to say, idealistically, here, in this room? It's the staff who read the newspapers and then leave them in the office on the assumption that no patient is remotely interested in the world beyond these walls. They're not even curious about what happens in the hospital, or the ward! They wouldn't stoop to help a patient who dropped to the floor in front of them! But I have to accept that I've never tried too hard to stimulate a patient's orientation to the outside. I silently muse on how much effort this superior made in the areas he is pointing out and why I have not observed the Nursing Officer exemplify these notable ideals when he comes to the ward? But, to continue on the offensive is to feed the other's determination. By this time, the defence of the principles, the rights and wrongs of the situation, is draining away. It is more that the sharp thrust of criticism is puncturing my pride, and my ego, as I already know, is a vulnerable shield!

'One thing you'll learn, here, Mr. Burrows, is that patients are in hospital for a long time because they become institutionalised and progressively more

161

mentally ill, and being cut off from the outside world they gradually lose every scrap of motivation. The fact is, unbelievable though it is, they can lose all their basic habits! With habit-training we've taken all this into account and we go that one step further. You don't have to have Alzheimer's to be incontinent, as I'm sure you know. That's what we're up against. I've seen hundreds of patients go that way. It doesn't much matter whether the cause is years of being in hospital or progressive mental illness, Mr. Burrows, but when patients acquire these regressive behaviours it's our job to take hold of the situation, as parents do with their children, and help them to relearn, and this is the point, *relearn* the skills they once had. So, we set up a rigid timetable, just as you said, but not to do things *for them* but to encourage them to take responsibility for doing these basic tasks for themselves once again. We're re-educating them, you see? Now, I suggest during the time that's left to you, you select a specific task, doesn't matter whether it's bathing, dressing, feeding, going to the toilet, cleaning shoes, or whatever, and select a small group of patients with a similar level of deficit in that area. You put them through that task each shift that you're on duty, and gradually build up their skills again. You do the same thing every day with them until they take back the initiative, themselves, then you might be able to move them on to a higher functioning task. Now, do you think you could manage that?' I don't know whether I'm more incensed by the triumphal note in my combatant's manner or the fact that there's been no such intimation that habit training is the therapeutic model that will help to re-establish normal habits. On the contrary, the nurses have taken control of every task. No one gets *taught* anything. It would simply take too long! It's far more convenient for the staff to complete tasks themselves!

The private tuition is obviously terminated as the Nursing Officer edgily squeezes past, toward the door, while I resist the fantasy of delivering a knee to his groin, or similar grossness. Triumphant, the antagonist then strides past the Charge Nurse who is reclining in the gallery.

'Mr. Burrows and I have been having a little chat about habit training for patients. We left out the staff,' he chortles with the snapping jawed, high-pitched laugh, and the scuttling flanks of an engorged and satisfied hyena. Not that there emerged any necessity to exercise such swingeing passions as crushing this adversary's testicles, or spilling his ugly little frame down the stairwell, or fantasising about any other altercation during the remainder of my allocation. From that point on, a mutual unspoken avoidance of one another was the mark of our personal, not to say working, relationship. That it had been a confrontation, a provocative, even calculated, melodrama, up front and personal, was for sure. Why else had they been removed to a remote corner of the ward so that any fractious deterioration in relations would pass off unseen, informally, man to man, unreported? What was singularly offensive about the encounter was the Nursing Officer's rigid, and deliberate, reference to me by my surname. But when the pacifying embers of consideration and time had coaxed me away from a vengeful spitefulness, I was better placed to rationalise the feeling of being affronted by the episode and to draw on other considerations. Perhaps the guy had felt it necessary to impose his personal authority over what must have seemed the insolent scepticism and disrespect of a presumptuous student. And maybe it wasn't such a personal thing, after all! Perhaps this was some vestige of the Nursing Officer's pre-managerial, clinical creed that he couldn't let go of and to which he remained committed and believed he still had a duty to impart to subordinates. If it was about being indoctrinated into the tried and tested method of the past, then this was certainly a challenge to the current philosophy which advocated rehabilita-tion of institutional patients back into the community. That was understand-able, wasn't it? Wouldn't I have done a similar thing? And what about that little matter of "habit training" that had been so heartily dramatised? If it was a formal technique of timetable, group based interventions for the long-term care of major disability, why had we students not been taught to utilise it for those other than the dementing psycho-geriatrics? It could be surmised that the staff did not believe it was worth the effort to rebuild the severely deteriorated competencies of most long stay patients within their permanent confinement, because it was far too time-consuming, irrespective of whether the cause was pathological or institutional. You only had to review the passive lines of our charges waiting on their daily dosages in the medicine round and wonder what would have been gained by reversing the years of institutional organisation. Rehabilitation meant civilian status, the right to challenge the prescribing doctors, refuse the dispensing process, negotiate with the nurses about their current symptoms and progress, and to attempt all these within the handicap of their poor communication skills, often their mutism. No, nothing would conceivably change if the patients remained within the confining walls where the tasks of the day were drilled by a slick routine. But this was little more than convenience vying with inconvenience. What passed for long-term care was a casually routinised, expedient, common denominator for keeping "good order and discipline" across huge, chronically debilitated classes of illness – mainly schizophrenia, the general paralysis of the insane, epilepsy, alcoholism and manic depression. And, as such, it was a gross distortion of a formal therapeutic model that was supposed to deliberately target institutionalised de-compensation. The Nursing Officer's tetchy little message was, creditably, something positive and constructive even if it lacked the optimism of the ultimate goals of rehabilitation into the community beyond the walls of the hospital. Furthermore, as I had to acknowledge, someone had had the gumption to represent what he believed in.

But exactly what was the difference between institutionalism and the deteriorating schizophrenic condition, and how much did they overlap? Did it really matter to the staff? What was abundantly clear was that when the staff looked toward the long stay patients they perceived a body who were, in the main, simultaneously schizophrenic *and* institutionalised; any differentiation being irrelevant! In terms of social intercourse, the patients did not initiate conversation, or contact, with the staff or with one another. They would often be forced into close proximity because of the lack of space and yet seemed immune to the presence of others about them. They revealed no drive, no decision-making and no sexual interests; never read the newspapers, never enquired after their families, showed not the slightest interest in the past, present or future, and never helped one another. Truly, never, never helped one another. Like so much else about institutional life, the staff became quickly accustomed to what seemed to be a self-imposed estrangement of each patient from another; it became an accepted perception of the in-patient world, and slipped from a brief consciousness into the unreflective habit of routine. It seemed hardly possible but the patients gave every appearance of accepting their circumstances while having no enthusiasm for a return to their former existence. So, what was the schizophrenia and what was institutionalism? On this matter, you just knew that nobody really cared a flying fart!

*   *   *

'Good morning. Or maybe it's not!'

'Er, sorry about that! Good morning.' The new Nursing Officer has called across to me after having heard the fall of my obscene curses being dropped onto the courtyard below through the small gap in the lounge window. 'Just calling out to a friend, you know!'

'A little quieter and more discreet, perhaps? So how much have you gained from this allocation, young man? Have you learned much?' continues the recently arrived colleague, ebullience personified.

'Well, I believe I could make a good fist of a job that lies somewhere between a town crier and a shepherd of human beings. I've had a lot of practice in rounding up the flock and moving it from one task to the next, and calling out to everyone at regular stages of the day,' I reply with amiable sarcasm.

'Ha, ha, ha, is that so, now? Don't I know what you mean?' This new guy has wasted no time in orientating himself to his unit incumbency, of which we are one. He doesn't, exactly, trip lightly onto the ward, either! He's a tall, well-built, Southern Irishman, replete with deep brogue, a generously grandiose self-confidence, a beard of ostentatious topiary, and natty, wide-striped, bespoke suit, and in his mid-thirties. The light blue eyes are piercing and vigilant. He is the conjured antithesis of his predecessor with the sole exception of also having an abundance of verbal and physical energy. He's already made himself a reputation for outspokenness and for not gladly suffering fools. If I have read him accurately, he can hardly contain his contempt for some of the staff. It is not unknown for him to stop alongside a patient and tidy him up in front of a staff member, thereby sending out the message that someone's not done their job adequately. If he's unpopular with some, the sentiment is far from universal. Indeed, some like him a lot and, in their estimation, believe that beneath the self-importance is a man struggling for friendly informality. On most subjects this chap really warms to his theme. He engages me about the state of mental nursing. 'I consider myself very lucky indeed, you see. I trained at an old bin, Claybury Hospital, matter of fact. Ever heard of Claybury?'

'Certainly know of the name but not much else, no!'

'It's where a very famous psychiatric experiment was set up, using a therapeutic community, by a determined, unconventional psychiatrist named

Dr. David Martin. Just my sort of fella, got some balls, you know! When the Unit got established it split the hospital right down the middle; half saw him as a kind of saviour, half saw him as the anti-Christ. Ha, ha, ha! Now I'm a good Catholic so I couldn't possibly have seen him as Christ, but near as damn it, ha, ha, ha! It was only one ward but it shook the very foundations of the hospital, I can tell you. It got everyone talking about what psychiatric nursing was actually about, and it's about time we asked that. The book he wrote is a very famous text. It should be standard reading for all psychiatric staff. It's got only one flaw that I know of anyway... I'm not mentioned in it, ha, ha, ha!' The topiarised beard is spread wide by an enamelled portcullis of fine teeth that are joining in with the joke.

'Well, presumably this place would resemble the more traditional part of your hospital that was up in arms. So, could I ask why you bothered to get a job here?' It seems a sensible question.

'A very good question, my friend, a very good question indeed. You're on the ball there, all right! I mean, from what I've seen, this place could do with a dose of that model, I can tell you.' It is impossible not to be impressed by the energy that emanates from this guy. 'It's a matter of economics rather than principle, I have to say, young man. It takes a lot longer to gain promotion in those specialist units because the blokes in charge tend to stay in post for years. The plain truth is that if you want to get on, you come to backward joints like this one where there are a lot more opportunities and it's a good deal easier to make an impression. Those are the facts. But all is not lost, my friend, we can still do a great deal that's worthwhile. Ha, ha, ha!' He has a warm, indomitable spirit about him and he lacks the cynicism that has such an unfortunate prevalence among the nursing contingency, and he's never dull company. Or, maybe, he's not been promoted long enough!

'Now that's interesting, because I've only very recently been formally informed that, on this unit, we're all about habit training. Thing is, in practice, we don't even pretend to try anything of the sort because it's too inconvenient.'

'Habit-training! I don't believe what you're telling me! Where, exactly, did a bright chap like you get such unfashionable ideas?' he continues, hardly containing his amusement and a hint of frustration. 'I mean, has nobody taught you that magic word "rehabilitation"? If we don't at least try that we might as well all give up and go home. You've just uttered one of the most unholy of words, be Jesus, nothing but barefaced institutionalisation. The worst thing in the world is to stereotype our care of patients! They'll never move from here, otherwise. Ha, ha, ha, ha, I don't know, really! Other than sharing that load of drivel with me, how's your placement been?'

'Well, it's none too stimulating here, in one sense, but an experience never to be missed, in another. Overall, I'm just looking forward to being on an admission ward where there's some real optimism and activity, I hope, and moving on from all these chronic guys. I want some normality, really, but it's not these chaps' fault! If you don't mind my saying, this ward is so bleak, no wonder patients curl up inside themselves. I can take away a lot, I know. I mean I don't regret being here. I haven't hated it, or anything. The staff have been friendly and all.' Behind his startling eyes, my words are being turned over before his ponderous reply.

'Do you know what you can definitely take away from this experience, young man, eh?' he confides in a lowered, earnest tone and with a surreptitious glance across his shoulder to the gallery. 'What you can really take away from this is that when you become a Charge Nurse, this is exactly the sort of ward you want, where you can make an unbelievable mark because there's practically nothing that can't be improved. It's obvious, isn't it? That's why I was delighted, absolutely delighted, to have been given an old back ward when I got my first promotion. It gets you noticed if changes for the better can be put down to you.' His bleep sounds off and he fields the enquiry on the office phone and heads for the exit. He winks as he turns on his heel, head bobbing, deliberately, merrily, from side to side along the gallery as he departs whistling an air. He's enjoyed himself. 'Have to go. Anyway, see you. Ha, ha, ha!'

* * *

Of the many ironies of institutional language was the term for exposing incarcerated, disinterested, socially severed patients to occasional community forays under the guise of "the rehabilitation trip". In the case of this particular long-stay ward, it meant packing a group of the more predictable, fairly presentable patients, aged between about 40 and 70, into a hospital coach and driving them into the countryside for an afternoon trip. If you believed that such exposure would stir the party from their mute reveries, that there would even be the slightest eruption of enthusiasm and appreciation for the change in environment, you were in for an eye-opener! You really had to witness and marvel at how cleanly mental illness seemed to skin the very consciousness from its victims! Such a trip was on the current rehabilitation agenda for our patients and, despite being reminded of the occasion, none of the selected group seems to register any awareness of it on the day.

Surprisingly, Timmy never wants to join in these events and, in making his own contribution, reveals not just how long he's been inhabiting institutions but how fixed people's images can become. The party are lining up alongside the hospital coach. Timmy is on hand; no watch, as usual, but he has the uncanny knack of being there when anything's going down.

'All aboard the *charabanc*. All aboard! All aboard for the seaside. Everyone's going on the *charabanc*,' he chortles away to the assembly. 'I bet I know who's the driver. You know. It's that one with the fat gut. You know. Heeeeeeeee, he's my mate, he's my mate.' And, like a grotesque bird, he displays his unique ear-rubbing ritual. He is also displaying one of those recognisable traits of the mentally handicapped, which is that when something has been learned, it is pretty hard to unlearn. So, in addition to continuing to refer to coaches as charabancs he will, from time to time, speak of the C of E chaplain as the "Parson". The Chaplain's position has recently changed hands and the new incumbent and Timmy have been introduced. Timmy somehow knows that the Chaplain is a cricketer and we've been treated to his version of how the parson is likely to perform so he must have been an instant hit with Timmy.

'And d'you know what that Parson does on Sundays? You know, at the church service? All the patients stand up and go to the front!' Timmy has put down his bags and is adopting his rendition of a pious pose with his head turned upward, eyes closed, one hand apparently holding the Communion cup, while the other seems to be holding the Communion wafer.

'You mean the Communion. Yes. What does he do, then, Timmy?'

'They all have a sing-song then all the patients go up to the front and stand in front of the Parson. Parson says to the bucking patients "Open wide", then dips something in the cup and chucks it in their gobs! Yeee! Then he says "Bless you" and they all go back to their seats. Yeeee. Silly bastards!'

'What, they have a nip of whisky on the sly, Timmy?'

'I'll nip you in a minute, you bugger. Ha, ha, ha. I hope they choke on it!' This is relayed with a squeal of delight. 'Heeeeeeee, he's my mate, the parson.'

We, the staff, are leaning against one another, abandoned to gales of laughter, and part of this has to do with the incongruity of little Timmy attending the Communion in the first place. What religious awareness would he have? None whatever, probably. But the church services are just another part of the complete hospital timetable, a routine which he has internalised, without a watch or ever asking the time, where he can be a participant observer of any of its activities in the only world he has ever known. Perhaps someone in the establishment should have responsibility for educating and updating him but who would want to wipe out the world of pure nostalgia which he clings to? But I have a go, if only for the fun of it.

'You don't say *parson*, these days, Timmy. That's very old fashioned. These days he's called the vicar. Have you heard of that?'

'Yeah, I know,' he replies rather meekly, turning his head aside and diverting his gaze as he does whenever people are addressing him directly into his face.

'Don't ask me why they call it the vicar, but that's what he's called. So, can you remember that? Who is he?'

'Bicar.' As usual, I realise he can't even pronounce it properly with his missing teeth.

'*Good*. Now, say it again.'

'Bicar.'

'Vicar, *v-v-v*-vicar, *v-v-v*-vicar, *v-v-v*-vicar…..'

'He's bucking mad, heeeeeeee!' interrupts Timmy, looking toward the attending staff.

'Vicar, vicar, vicar, get it into your thick head, Timmy. Vicar….'

'Bucking mad!'

'No, go on, say it over and over.' Timmy tries it, slowly, concentrating and smiling.

'Bicar … Bicar … Bicar… Bicar.'

'G – ood! One more time, now, just so that we can be sure.'

'Bicar.'

'*Excellent*. Now, you go and surprise him next time you meet him.'

'Yeah!' Timmy ambles off, getting bored now. I want to gloat in front of my sceptical colleagues so, before he is lost from view, I call out.

'So, Timmy, who is the bloke in the church?'

'The Parson!'

'Okay, then, let's go.' All the staff are pointing at me, ribbing, slapping my back.

'That's very impressive, Steve! You'll have to share with us exactly how you did that?'

'Yes, yes, ha, ha, bloody ha! Right, come on, get aboard you lot.'

* * *

For the rehab trip, about 15 of the ward patients have been kitted out in their best clothing and are being escorted to the hospital coach, where they embark with an enthusiasm that they're being delivered to the gallows! Food supplies are shoved under some of the seats; we three nurses stretch out over double seats, and the hospital coach and driver make off for one of the local beauty spots, some 12 miles away. Only trouble is, no one has the slightest idea about what happens when we arrive!

'I think they should all stay on the coach,' suggests one. 'That way, we've got some control over them. Otherwise, they might just wander off every which way!'

'I agree,' says the driver. 'Nothing can go wrong if you keep them on board but it seems a shame, all the same,' smiling at them all via his rear-view mirror.

'But they're going to want to have a piss and then there's the food?' queries another. 'We can't dish it out on the coach, surely!'

'Well, I'll draw up by a public toilet, drop them off, and then you can march them straight back on the coach,' continues the driver, beaming with feigned contrariness.

'On the other hand, do we want to come out all this way on a bloody lovely day and roast inside this sodding thing?'

'Well, what are they going to do if we let them get out?'

'I don't know. Whose stupid bloody idea was this, anyway?'

'Management's, of course. Got to be seen to be doing all we can for the patients, haven't we?'

'Well, what exactly are we doing, can anybody tell me?' I remark. We look about the gathering on the seats behind us. No one has noticed any conversation between the patients, as usual, and many are not even looking out of the coach windows. We, separately, wonder if the patients are registering anything other than the sensation of the coach movement, whose hard suspension springs them over every rut and ridge.

'We'll adopt that tried and trusted maxim… when in doubt, play it by ear!' I add, facetiously.

'You'll get a bloody earful if you get it wrong,' quips the driver with a good-natured snigger. Kev, the driver, is a congenial, softly spoken, middle-aged man who is the most approachable of characters. 'Anyway, we're nearly there so what's your decision?'

'Oh, let's park up away from the public and let them get out. They can't do much harm, can they?'

'How about over on that big area of grass where nobody's sitting?' suggests Kev. 'I'll park in the middle, then they can get out and wander about near the coach. Anyone plays up, they can just get back on the coach. Easy.'

'Go for it!' The coach, its suspension in smithereens years ago, takes off like an out-of-control carousel, tipping its human occupants violently against each other as it rides the rutted edges of the grassed area and comes to a halt in the relative obscurity of its centre. In the vicinity there are but a few other small parties parked around the grass verges but this doesn't reduce the lingering anxiety of the staff.

'Okay everyone, let's all get off and take a seat on the grass. Do not go wandering off or you'll have to get back on the coach,' says the Staff Nurse in charge. Like a silent file of ageing monks, the contingent decants and, before anyone can stop it, Whitey, followed by most of the others, have undone their trousers and are pissing onto the grass without a hint of self-consciousness or an awareness of the surrounding onlookers. It is the innocuous way they then stand with hands in pockets, oblivious to any breach of social etiquette, that seals the moment. In the full view of the public it is the three members of the nursing staff who jostle to hide their embarrassment and giggles, huddled

171

between the patients and the coach, while the driver, who has remained in his seat, is leaning his God-forsaken head on the steering wheel and his shoulders shudder, uncontrollably, at the entertainment. The staff now have no idea what to do with their charges. How do they dare marshal them about this scenic hot spot with an example of their eccentricities already on full display? Lack of enterprise, and plain expediency, dictate that they all sit on the grass area alongside the coach and settle for the picnic. For the Nursing Assistant with them, the event is lacking a certain energy. He needs a small spectacle.

'I think I'll wind up Whitey. What do you say?'

'Bloody hell. You be careful. Somebody might complain.'

'No way. Just a patient behaving as a patient! Hey, Whitey!' Whitey has the self-possession not to turn his head as if he has a suspicion of what's to come. He has been quietly cogitating with himself. 'Whitey, who said you could take a slash on the grass, just now? Don't you realise you exposed yourself in public and could be arrested?' Whitey, who has been the epitome of relaxation, leaning back on his elbows, has heard. He remains poised, his head still and, though seeming to contemplate the comments, gives nothing else away. He is patently ignoring his agitator but he *has* heard. 'Did you hear me? You could have been arrested by the police. Well, what have you got to say for yourself?' Whitey's lips have started to move silently and a pensive glare has crept around his eyes which dart back and forth toward the nurse, in a succession of half-glances. 'Come to think of it, we could all be in trouble, Whitey. So, if you want another slash you'll just have to tie it in a ruddy great knot.' The half glances are speeding up and barely audible oaths are now tripping from Whitey's toothless lips and there is a calculating menace glowering from the frame that is now seated upright. 'What do you have to say for yourself, you old bugger?' The nurse lurches across and gently prods his target on the arm. The words of response are now clear as if the rules of engagement have been settled and he's preparing for conflict.

'The fucking bastard,' says Whitey in a clear but still restrained tone. As his head moves from side to side his brief, hostile glances lash across his agitator's face. 'Fucking bastard.' The agitator again leans across and prods Whitey's arm.

'What did I just say to you?' As if stung, Whitey struggles to draw himself to his feet and adopts the aggressive pose for which he is renowned among those that have managed him over the years. The only one standing, he looms over the gathering, both fists clenched, feet astride, in a boxing stance, right arm drawn back, ready to scrap, and is now bellowing his habitual script whilst staring at the ground but flicking his glares across to the aggressor.

'Get out of it. You fucking bastard. What d'yer think you're playing at? I'll fucking kill you, you bastard. I'll punch your eyes out. What do you think you're doing? Don't you come near me. Yerrrr… yerrrr…' and, though growling with apparent conviction, he gives no hint of actually throwing a punch or making any kind of direct assault. All the staff are enjoying the scene which is made more hysterical by the incongruity of the performance, the setting, and their own restrained chortling.

'Ah, now you've upset him,' interjects the kindly Kev with only a hint of reproach.

'Okay, Whitey. Thanks for that, mate. I'm only kidding. You can sit down, now.' Whitey has the extraordinary capacity to be defused with such a simple acknowledgement and, as always, manages it on the instant. He drops his pugilistic stance, replaces his thumbs through his thick trouser braces, and nods appreciatively towards his erstwhile agitator. Incredibly, he then bursts into a hearty laugh which whistles through his pursed lips and rumbles through his big shoulders.

'Ha… ha… ha… ha…. *Yeeees*,' dipping his hands back into his trouser pockets and shrugging with apparent content. It is the very knowledge that his stance is, with some calculation, nothing but empty threats that encourages anyone who wishes to toy with Whitey. Empty threats or not, the perpetrator and his audience are guaranteed a performance of ritual outrage in response to the "wind-up". This is a playful cameo which hails from the Victorian clockwork toy whose key is placed adroitly into its winding mechanism where it is turned, and turned, and turned, and turned, and turned, until it meets with resistance, when the hand is removed to release the charged energy that is now played out by the toy in a short, stereotypical performance until the coil runs its course and it slows, and slows to a halt. To the thrill of the audience, the toy will not move again until the player's whim is excited and the simple ritual is repeated. Between vigilant sweeps of the group I engage Kev.

'You didn't actually apply for a hospital driver's job, originally, did you, Kev?'

'No. I originally came up here from Dorset, where I was a farm labourer, to work on the hospital farm. Never dreamed I'd be doing this.'

'Oh, I've heard about you. Someone said you were an authority on this subject.'

'What, the farm? Well, I don't know about that.' He's delightfully self-effacing. 'Used to work a damned sight harder than I do now. It was a bit like those old American movies where the prisoners were packed off into the country to work in chain-gangs, only without the chains. Used to load up the patients on lorries in them days. They were encouraged to work, then, see. Blokes were used on the farm or the gardens if they weren't skilled tradesmen. Staff didn't need to be standing back to keep an eye on them. It was kind of accepted that they should work. Not many ever tried to do a runner in them days. They were generally pretty good workers, I'd say. Farm labouring was a damned sight more useful to them than sitting on their backsides on the wards, anyway,' he argues.

'Sounds as if the farm was huge. Did you have to travel far, then?' It was intriguing.

'Well, the farm was the biggest part of the estate then. Dozens and dozens of acres. I couldn't say, exactly. And we used to grow everything, including masses of livestock. Used to rear our own pigs – you know where the pig farm used to be, don't you, behind the Nurses Home – there's got to be a ruddy joke in there somewhere! Raised our own cow herd, and chickens too. We had our own horses, so that required a blacksmith, too. Oh, yes,' in reply to my surprised expression. 'Yeah, so I came up as a farm hand 'cos I see this job advertised and because jobs weren't as plentiful as they once were back in Dorset. Machinery taking over more and more of the work, see! Thought I'd give it a go and moved up here. It was an ideal opportunity for me.'

'So, presumably, if the farm was viable and useful for patients, how could the authorities just close it down, like that?'

'What we were told was that we was using the patients as cheap labour to keep the hospital running and we weren't helping them to get back into society. I mean, it was true, they didn't get paid any more than pocket money but, there again, they don't need no real money since everything's laid on. None of us could see the sense in it. Can you see any of this lot going anywhere, because if you can, you're a better man than me?'

174

'No, but these are extreme cases, I suppose,' I counter. 'You can see the argument, though. Say you're working on the farm. How exactly would you move on? If you worked well you're going to be recommended to be kept on. If you're kept on, you don't learn anything that will help transfer you into industry, or anything else. If you started kicking up a fuss, you'd either be sick or seen to be deteriorating and it's back to the wards where you'd have to start all over again, I suppose.'

'Anyway, this little number will suit me, now. At the end of the day, you need a job and I haven't had to uproot myself again,' Kev answers with genuine equanimity but you feel almost appalled by the fatalistic resignation at his lot.

'But with all your experience it seems like a huge comedown. How many years have you put in at the hospital, Kev?'

'Ooh, now you're asking. Umm, about 30? Yeah, that's right, 30 years this summer.' It seems that everyone – staff and patients alike – have put in their time!

On the return journey, my gaze settles on a favourite of mine, Charlie, who is seated opposite me. Charlie is a crumpled mass of dislocated looking bones, with lopsided shoulders, who has a crab like gait, and incessantly hoists up his trousers with his crooked left hand. He sits on his own on the seat opposite. Charlie's eyes do not move from the floor beneath, or the back of the seat in front of him, and he neither looks up, nor out of the window.

'How are you, Charlie?'

'All right.'

'Have you enjoyed the trip?'

'All right.'

'What did you enjoy most?'

'Don't know.'

'Is there anything else you would like to have done that we didn't manage?'

'Nahhhhh!' It is not that Charlie is uncooperative. Rather, he is being asked to judge something quite remote from his daily expectation and experience. Though not irrelevant in itself, it was none of his choosing, was a mere glimpse, was nothing that he could build upon, and simply did not warrant evaluation in his eyes.

'Would you like to do it, again, Charlie?' A non-committal grin dances around his jaws for a moment before he returns his gaze to the floor.

* * *

On the last shift on this extraordinary ward I make my way toward the door through which I had entered three months earlier and turn back and stand a while, to survey the patients. They are variously leaning along the length of the gallery, or sitting around the TV room, dishevelled, unoccupied, listless, a disconnected humanity. They seem to have gained a type of freedom and protection in their madness as if, by not being understood, they are defended against the intrusion of the sane world. Each stand within their own silent space like candles that have been set around the candle-stand of a side chapel. Each has his individual flame burning with equal power and significance, and each is cast with some resolution against the dismal recesses. As the even flames flute upwards, almost reverently, they are disturbed into frantic, stuttering flickers by the moody presence of Captain, who fidgets and glides amongst them in unholy abandon.

* * *

When proceeding to what was called the admission ward, in the next stage of training, I could have been excused the passing notion that the relatively flat tyre of the institutional atmosphere should have been inflated with some short-lived energy for a brief period. There were few monumental euphemisms of significance here, surely! Patients who were exhibiting signs and symptoms of acute mental illness were either cajoled by their doctors, or involuntarily "sectioned" out of society and they came into the reception units for assessment as well as treatment. I was to discover in some cases that if the patients had not entered voluntarily then the medics had assured them that they would have been compulsorily detained. Then, once admitted voluntarily, they could still be detained if they tried to discharge themselves against medical advice. Though psychiatrists had the power to implement this, the nurses were generally happy to comply. Anxious, as usual, at the start on a new unit, I dawdled through the milling, post lunch ward areas, trying to gain a purchase on the décor, the regime, the people. I was more than a little grateful for a warm, bellowing introduction that issued from the floral draped bay window of the day room and pitched itself across the introspection of five or six seated patients. Not from a member of staff, but a patient! Bill Farak, who may have been of a distant Mediterranean origin, was confident, articulate, curious, had fulfilled his admission requirements and was casually preparing for his discharge. The man was connected to all that lay around him, absorbed, helpful, extroverted, a temporary presence who would now go on to resume a full existence. Before we disengaged later in the afternoon Bill had acquainted me with a working induction of the entire ward routine, and managed to sketch his own biographical tale in between. In this small gesture, I was to be introduced to the tenor of the admission wards. True, the residents still retained the immoveable status of patient, but they had lives and interests, individuality, backgrounds, stories and relationships, and showed initiative and spontaneity. Patients liked to talk about themselves, their difficulties and preoccupations, in the most uninhibited way. There was also such a phenomenon as the patient-turnover that went some considerable way to ensuring variety and stimulation! You could return to the ward after a few days' leave and find a quarter of it unrecognisable. The ward routine included admissions procedures, discharge procedures, volumes of procedures; weekly, clinical rounds, interviews, discussions of observations, discussions of potential treatments, discussions of patients, discussions of progress! For the first time in my hospital experience – even taking account of the colourful individualism of the chronic, long stay patients and the favoured, hospital "pets" and "characters" – admission patients were, by and large, distinguishable from the processes that packed away the rest of the hospital community into congealed lumps. Even if they revolved with successive cycles of discharge, relapse, admission, treatment, remission, and back again – known as the revolving door syndrome – they generally retained an accessibility and the potential for interaction and relationships. This meant they held the status of an institutional undergraduate unless, and until, they crossed that threshold from acute disturbance into chronic disablement and dependence, where they could come and go no more. But if their progress faltered and a major diagnostic deterioration was detected, they would graduate as a chronically dependent case within the predatory institutional jaws which circled about them. Until such time, there was colour, there was material ownership, there was varied conversation, there was assent and dissent, family members, lovers, tears (all too often taken for granted elsewhere), fashion, make-up, deodorant, toothpaste, spontaneous bathing, humour, politics, religion and rock and roll. But no sex or drugs, please! They could continue in this vein and experience the staff's listening skills, the negotiation, the compromise, even sympathy, on the apprehension that they had been only temporarily displaced from an acceptable status to which most of them were likely to return. Provided, that was, they played the game along the way!

The admission ward was a psychiatric, accident and emergency department that took in all-comers as delivered from their homes by general practitioners or families, from off the streets by police officers, and, very occasionally, via the courts as an alternative to prison. Each new admission was swiftly scanned with the staff's informal, off-the-cuff, risk detector and classified into a basic psychiatric triage. The lowest level of risk would demand a general observation that would secure the whereabouts of those who gave no cause for concern, demanded only residual input, who were capable of looking after themselves and could all but be ignored. A middle level called for a fairly systematic prompting, guidance, knowledge of whereabouts, generalised encouragement toward progress, and low level discouragement of shortcomings. At the most acute level of risk, vigilance was required and patients were expected to be permanently visible to one staff member or another, were permitted as little mobility as possible, were granted the fewest possible privileges, and every action and communication was acutely scrutinised for signs of deviance, psychosis or danger. The highest priority within this rationalisation was accorded to those who presented propensities for violence toward others, property damage or a fire risk in the immediate environment; for self-harm and suicide; for wilful or inadvertent absconding; or for non-compliance with treatment such as discarding medication, etc. For all of these reasons, it was routine to assess such propensities by holding the newly admitted patients back on the ward, firstly by instruction, but also by ensuring that night attire and dressing gowns were worn until patients were considered safe and trustworthy. Any intention or effort by them to abscond into the wider hospital or community would immediately identify them, to other hospital staff, as being at risk and culminate in their immediate apprehension and return. Vigilance was, perforce, the primary skill on parade since the accepted practice was to have the ward doors remain unlocked though, according to circumstances, this could be rescinded by the ward Charge Nurse or sister. So, too, could a patient's individual rights to leave the ward area. In effect, the likelihood of a favourable or unfavourable nursing response to individual patients resulted from a matrix comprising three essential dimensions: firstly, the aforementioned risk/observation level; secondly, the diagnostic category to which the patient was formally assigned by his/her psychiatrist, or informally by the nursing staff; and thirdly, the degree to which the individual staff member actually liked, sympathised or empathised with, the patient. As with every other area of their work the nursing staff poured the diverse psychiatric harvest through the presses of their personal attitudes so that only the most worthy ingredients reached their occupational attention. Most were deemed worthy with no fault attached, while some were considered undeserving time wasters. Stranded among the compressed, undeserving residue were what were perceived as the self-inflicted indulgencies of drug addiction and alcoholism; even suicide attempts were sometimes met with contempt. And then there was the unrepentant animosity and elusiveness of the psychopath. All were treated to a minimum of sympathy and input unless there were exceptional circumstances which militated against taking a harsher stance. But, with the very best will, when 30 odd patients needed to be managed by three or four nurses during daytime hours, and two during the night, their input could often only be rationed by the foregoing rationalisation. This could mean that for some periods, sometimes hours, occasionally days, one patient might dominate the attention of the entire staff quota. The converse rule of thumb was that the least difficulties that were presented to the staff, the least input a patient received.

On the acute wards, a patient's background, biography, and the contemporary events around their admission were viewed as more pertinent histories and every staff member was to be found regularly scanning the patients' case files! Which also meant that their clinical case notes were live commodities, rather than museum artefacts! For the first time in my psychiatric experience the relevance of these documents went far beyond their medical authorship. And, piled high in the middle of the weekly ward rounds, they could hardly be ignored! Case files were the sole preserve – in terms of the hand-written entries – of the psychiatrist who summarised *his* observations, taking account of the rest of the team who would congregate for the ward rounds. But, for me, the files began to open up more than the clinical biographies of the extraordinary lives of patients and expound just as much about their authors. For example, the older case files had a passing resemblance to historical parchments written, as they were, on stiff, higher quality paper, in admirably legible, long hand fountain pen, and which recorded a mass of biographical information about the patient. The content spared no sensitivities but contained brutally candid descriptions of patients' diagnoses, propensities and general behaviour at the time of their hospital admission, as if written with an unimpeachable, professional impunity. Allusions were made to sexually promiscuous or sexually immoral, or lewd behaviour, homosexuality, drug addictions and alcoholism almost as if they were the Devil's own work! Something else about the style of the entries, and the identified diagnoses, seemed to suggest the personal predilections of the psychiatrists themselves. Most notably, among patients with a long-term mental illness that had required a bevy of hospital admissions, over time, each successive admission often generated an alternative diagnosis of the patients' symptoms because they had been ascribed by different psychiatrists. The diagnoses didn't even approximate to one another and could be as wide-ranging as schizophrenia, schizoid personality, drug induced psychosis, depression, manic depression and psychopathy… for the same patient! It was one thing to talk of possible "differential diagnoses" where the final diagnosis was not yet determined and awaited an evaluation of the different options. Had the patient exhibited all of these diverse syndromes and the associated clusters of symptoms, over time, much in the way a creative artist would exhibit the hugely contrasting styles of their career development in the varying products of their professional work? Could it be that symptom recognition and diagnostic deliberation was much more an artistic flair, swayed more by the subjective bias and opinions of individual psychiatrists, rather than a determining scientific objectivity? Were even the diagnoses an inappropriately convenient shorthand and over-simplification of the complexity of human behaviour? In short, I soon realised that the diagnoses, as a measured evaluation of an individual's mental illness and life difficulties, should be treated with a substantial scepticism. More to the point, a diagnosis was a life-consuming transformation that had treatment implications, social status and legal implications, residence and employment implications, that would determine not only the future life opportunities for that individual but their personal self-image and self efficacy! And it was very rare for patients to enquire about their diagnosis; they certainly never challenged it, and were generally prepared to accept the majority of the interventions to treat what they were told was their illness. Few showed any dissension, or sought any redress, and I was mystified by the compliance, and faith, and reverence shown toward psychiatrists by their patients. On the other hand, what choices did they have? Where could someone afflicted with mental illness turn for help in a world so alienating of their predicament and suffering?

The ward round – a misnomer in psychiatric circles since the medics and their entourage did not circulate round the ward at any price! – enabled each patient to be reviewed on a weekly basis. The team, such as it was, comprised the Consultant Psychiatrist and/or Registrar, the Ward Charge Nurse or Ward Sister, exceptionally, a Social Worker, and any one of the current batch of Student Nurses. The ward round on the admission wards – or acute wards, as they were also named – was a small window of staff/patient intimacy, or the nearest thing there would be to intimacy in a large hospital. To begin with, the ward office, usually an area of quintessential utility, was transformed into something resembling a confessional booth where the patient confessed their symptoms and past history to the clinical priest. In turn, each patient to be reviewed that day would be ushered into the office, and seated, door closed behind them, for the few minutes of the week in which they had the team's sole attention. While the eyes of the Consultant flicked between the notes and the patient, and the other staff partook of the tea they had been served, the patient waited upon his or her fate. As if by baring every intimate detail before the assembly they were availing themselves of a more potent, curative potential. It was a very public contrition and one that not one of the staff would be prepared to undergo themselves. Perhaps to have given up personal discretion was just another sign of the patient's malady. On the other hand, it was taken for granted by the staff, without any explanation to the patient, that their biography, history, and current psychological machinations were public property, whether they liked it not. Hidden behind the screen of professional status, the

Consultant heard the patient's confession, their privacy, deeds, thoughts and preoccupations, and intoned their medical judgement and treatment forfeits. The Consultant demanded contrition via an ECT schedule, or a change in medication, to assuage the patient's insecurities, guilt and self-doubt before drawing his audience to a close. Often, there was an indeterminate conclusion, no clear signs of recovery, no indication of prognosis, as if there was much that the confessor was required to fulfil before attaining forgiveness. The Consultant could always be seen next week, or the week after, perhaps. What to do until then! Suddenly, the door opened to the light of the ward, and the brief encounter with their own uniqueness lay behind them as they merged back into the communal timetable. It was, perhaps, its very brevity which gave it the illusion of appearing to be a precious, almost holy gift!

* * *

If anything was to be the cutting edge of the psychiatric endeavour within the large institutions, it was the admission wards. This was where new drugs or ideas might be entertained or experimented with – medical ideas, that is! Nursing staff had their procedures, and more procedures than were operational in any other ward! The "admission procedure", in itself, was a regimen of pure organisation and conferred a conviction of achieving something useful despite yielding only the most basic patient-information. It included a basic history taking, a clothes and possessions inventory, urine testing; bed allotting; ward introduction; form filling for blood tests and x-rays; temperature, pulse, blood pressure, height and weight measurement; diet ordering; and a bath. The bath procedure! There were basic health and safety issues: preventing someone intent on drowning themselves after having to suffer the trauma of a psychiatric admission; pouring the water to a safe level, and testing its heat in order to prevent scalding; and monitoring one of the few areas of privacy in the very public space of a hospital ward. The admission bath served a number of purposes. Personal hygiene could be assessed, thereby giving an indication of the patient's mental state and general lifestyle. Previous or current trauma could be detected by the presence of operation and accident scars, along with identification marks, birthmarks, tattoos and injection sites, or indications of self-harming conduct. Particular vigilance appertained to fresh abrasions which might hint at abuse by prison officers, police officers or ambulance personnel since the nursing staff – though not intentionally wishing to implicate other services – had no desire to be found culpable for acts perpetrated by others. Bodily rashes, ulcerations or communicable disease might be detected. The reason why all this could be effected was because of the presence of a nurse throughout the bath procedure. The admission bath was an invaluable, if intrusive, diagnostic aid and, as your experience developed, you discovered signals about the degree to which the patient was familiar with institutional life. Those that were not demonstrated every inhibition to being watched – embarrassment, disdainful looks, covering of the body, and the most guarded, attenuated conversation. The institutional "old hand", on the contrary, showed no such inhibitions, willingly exposed their nakedness, and talked as freely or in as constrained a manner as they wished. Something else which patients would have no choice about was the rummaging through of the clothing they had previously removed in the search for dangerous implements, drugs, money, valuable possessions, etc. For the time being, at least, any valuables would be bagged up into a plastic bag and locked away until later. Meantime, patients were handed a sample of the hospital night clothing – pyjamas, nightgowns and dressing gowns – that had been worn, laundered, and ironed a thousand times, by a thousand different bodies before. To round off, the patient's remaining possessions were openly displayed, registered in detail on the property card, valuables sent off for safekeeping, money banked away in the hospital bank, all articles that could potentially cause harm – such as scissors, penknives, ties and belts – locked away, and all excess property bagged up and transferred to the ward store room. In most other respects, the admission patients were no more fortunate than the rest of the in-patient fraternity. The hospital laundry was exempted from stocking the stained items that had circulated the other hospital wards. The person who entered into the admission ward was not a citizen in the full sense but had been redesigned into a patient.

* * *

The anticipated rewards of working in an admission unit, as a nurse, were realised to some degree but were no cause for particular celebration. If, in principle, you aspired to the acquisition of formal technical skills of a searching, psychological character it rarely happened in practice. The aseptic technique during the cleansing and dressing of wounds could keep you occupied with an illusion of professionalism. This procedure would follow from a medical assessment and prescription whereby pharmaceutically prescribed cleansing and healing agents were combined with a physical application to repair wounds and ulcerations. In fact, almost any formal clinical function a nurse performed was at the instruction of another professional group, or occurred in the capacity of assisting another professional enacting their particular clinical expertise. At a more prosaic level, nurses contributed to their own professional and clinical subordination by an ingratiating hospitality toward their superiors' appearances on the wards, such as rushing to make pots of tea or marshalling them through the intercepting patients who wished to speak with them. A cumulating resentment and frustration smouldered within me at this compliance with both the subservient behaviour and the inferior professional training which would ensure this state of affairs was perpetuated. There were, no doubt, many others whose critical faculties were hungry for closer access to the psychic adventures and the mysteries of the pathological mind rather than house management. Consequently, an increasing suspicion emerged that you were being cheated by the lack of opportunities in the training, the inferior labelling associated with a nursing culture, and the inaccessibility of medical culture. Inexorably, you were enticed toward paramedical insights about the patients and the human condition.

The paramedical professions, such as psychologists, psychotherapists (absent in our establishment), and social workers, had had the advantage of extensive academic and professional development, accessorised by personal intellectual qualities and superior educational schooling, and it was not surprising that their psychological assessments, individual and group therapies, and other treatments, that intruded into the fringes of the nursing syllabus, should have been so stimulating. The consequence of this was to ask, rhetorically, why these rich resources, ideas and experiences were not more widely available both to the training culture and to the treatment armoury of the hospital. Surely, the long stay characters would have had some chance of a better outcome, a proper life, if they had been exposed to the psychologists and psychotherapists? Why were there only two full-time psychologists employed by the hospital, and why not a single psychotherapist? Why did the psychiatrists visit the patients so infrequently? When had the ward's Consultant Psychiatrist last attended the long-stay ward? How could they be content to stick with only mundane physical drug administrations, aseptic techniques, and electroconvulsive therapy? It was a good thing, really, that I was not to learn until much later of the many similar hospitals where the psychology and psychotherapy departments thrived, along with day centres, group houses, parole hostels, extensive occupational and industrial therapy units, an established community psychiatric nursing service, and drug and alcohol units.

* * *

The most disciplined treatment available in the hospital, and most conveniently accessed during a student's admission ward experience, was the ECT procedure. Electroconvulsive therapy tended to be prescribed for endogenous depression – a depression understood to be generated more by an individual's internal make-up than by external, causative events – but was originally applied to people with schizophrenia. The very prospect made a huge impression on everyone, not least because our elders relished relating tales of "neat" ECT, whereby patients were strapped down, electricity was administered without the accompanying modern medication, but they were accompanied by many members of the nursing staff, who affixed themselves like limpets to the flailing joints of the victim patient. Patients would bite their tongues during the procedure, sustain fractures of the limbs, and become incontinent. But the treatment had been transformed to reduce these more barbaric images that it had acquired.

There was no doubting that each ECT treatment was a definitive event and taken very seriously. Firstly, the patient was starved overnight so that there was no risk of aspiration of stomach contents during the unconscious phase of the procedure. The patient changed into a back-to-front gown that tied at the back in case emergency intervention and access to the chest was required. All personal accessories and prostheses were removed from the patient. The event took place in a clinical room specialising in the task and prospective patients waited in a gloomy anteroom. When called, the patient

lay on a hard clinical couch – for the purpose of cardiac resuscitation, if necessary – and was then enveloped in staff, machines and paraphernalia that must
have terrified them. In what was termed a "modified" ECT, an epileptiform fit
was induced in the patient after the administration of an analgesic to prevent
any pain, along with a short-acting muscle relaxant to prevent damage to
the limbs on contracture. Images are still resonant for me: accompanying
the patient and helping them onto the couch; the anaesthetist administering
the intravenous medication through a butterfly cannula, applying the oxygen
mask to the face to oxygenate the brain when the patient slipped into sudden
unconsciousness, and inserting the mouth gag to prevent the tongue being
bitten; the ECT nurse holding the saturated electrodes against the sides of the
head while the Medical Officer throws the tiny switch on the ECT machine to
send an electrical current across the patient's skull; the clench toothed, deep
groan emanating during the seizure; the initial turning up of the patient's toes
and the contortions of the face; the toned arching of the back and stiffening
of the limbs; the cyanosed face, lips and neck, the following clonic rhythms
erupting across the entire body; then, after what seemed an age, the sudden
stillness; at the last, turning the patient onto their side to allow secretions
to flow out unheeded; and the recovering, shattered, helpless mass moaning its way back to consciousness and certain headaches. And the overall
impression was one of awe and utter helplessness, of giving over complete
control to an innocuous looking machine, dangerous energy, medication, and
the volcanic implosion within someone's mind and body. For all that, the
very substance of the whole procedure, its definitive quality, and its organisation, lent to the whole issue some gravitas. Whether the thing worked was
altogether indeterminate.

* * *

There was one additional social issue to deal fleetingly with because it
made its presence felt during this allocation. Male homosexuality among
the nursing staff was alive and well in the hospital though not widespread
as far as anyone knew. The male homosexuals were vociferously identified,
and surreptitiously scorned, by their heterosexual counterparts. One such
gay member of the teaching staff was widely respected for his teaching

commitment and made a noticeable effort to be liked by the students, extending his rôle into personal matters. Immaculately coiffured and clean shaven, with the finest buffed fingernails and shoes, sharply ironed white coat and trousers, he released aromatic squirts of campness to advertise his orientation. When in your presence he was as interested in gauging your reaction to him as in dealing in the professional matters as his critical eyes swept across your own presentation and sifted every flicker of response to him, hungry for acceptance. Meeting with him was not disagreeable but always tense, always apparently unfinished, and never void of the possibility of offending his sensitivities. During one of his clinical visits to the admission ward, he sat me down in the day room. 'Mr. Burrows, how do you think you're settling in here?' he asks, planting his unblemished hands on his crossed knees, his back bolt upright, and with a determined air.

'I really feel I'm learning a lot and getting a huge amount from being here,' I reply acquiescently, more intent on evading this contact.

'Settling in, then?' he adds in a measured but dubious tone, to which I peremptorily reply, 'Yes, no problems to date, I think.' The measured tone is now matched by a facial cast which is equally quizzical.

'Mr. Burrows, I get the distinct feeling that you keep yourself at a distance from me. You're friendly enough but you hold back, don't want to give away much about yourself. Am I right?'

'I'm not aware of that, really,' squirming in the knowledge to the contrary.

'Yes, I get along very well with all your group, but you're a little different, as if you don't want to allow me to get near you. Maybe you feel a little superior?' His effort to sustain a controlled tension seemed a determination on his part to appreciate my view of him, whatever the cost. He needed to know if I liked him or not and, if I didn't, to make me as uncomfortable about the fact as he could manage. But I was completely overtaken by the provocation.

'Why should I feel superior?' I hesitated.

'Well, I get the feeling that you make up your mind about people pretty quickly and don't give some of us a chance to share ourselves? Consequently, you don't get the best out of us.'

'Hmmm, get you,' I countered, with my own camp insinuation,

187

thoughtless of consequences. 'Well, you can't expect to be friendly with everyone, can you now?' I added with a limp shrug of one hand. The tutor took in the stance, the feigned intonation, the innuendo, and from a stony grimace weathered by years of other peoples' scepticism, one threatening eyebrow was slowly raised as if to deliver a decapitation.

'Listen, cunt, don't knock what you've never tried!'

* * *

Whether due to sympathy, curiosity or incredulity, for those of us that took care of them in large numbers, the institutionalised schizophrenics we encountered would be indelibly assembled in our memories decades later. However, there were also equally vivid examples of younger folk who sustained their first episode of hospitalisation, and others who teetered on the brink of chronic membership. The young Indian male, admitted during my acute ward placement, who described the resident viper in his throat that threatened to protrude every time he opened his mouth to speak. What reassurance could be given for such a disturbing, culturally symbolic belief in one who was such an inoffensive, retiring, neat little character who wandered in downcast, silent preoccupation round and round the ward but, when engaged, could be prevailed upon to shed the most captivating smile? Or the articulate, university educated English woman with lank, greasy hair, unwashed, odorous body, and lustreless eyes, aimlessly drifting about the corridors, smiling her generous Christian greetings, and believing that the 12 trees at the foot of her family's magnificent garden were nothing less than the twelve apostles of Jesus, each of whom she could name. And another young male who had graduated from university, subsequently revolving around the hospital's "admission" and "back wards" in an irredeemable social and psychological decline which could not conceal his clipped, middle class diction and sharp intelligence, and who had refocused most of his attention on acquiring cigarettes and bundling his thoughts into self-deprecating, sometimes suicidal, ramblings. What use was sympathy toward folk whose daily round was so utterly impoverished so early in their lives? It was not merely the devastation of their youth that disturbed but their irrepressible decline into separateness, the irrationality, the social and economic degeneration, the difference bordering on alienation. Their personal identities were utterly unique, for sure, but an indissoluble estrangement rumbled throughout every preoccupied moment. As nurses, we had not the occupational tools to understand this class of illnesses. For us, they were beyond comprehension.

* * *

In between the various ward allocations, the thrust of the theoretical side of the nurse training, such as it was, meandered an idle course through the backwaters of the elegant rooms of a former private house, set apart from the remainder of the hospital buildings, under the unruffled bowers of a cedar tree. Tending these gentle waters were the Nurse Tutors, fishers of information who lazily mused about the streams of knowledge, while shading in the overhanging arbours of a nurse training schedule that protected them from the rigours of academia, well-founded research, and personal learning. And reminiscing on their own distinguished elevation above the ranks of their ward based colleagues, while staring into the glassy currents, the fishers rolled out their vocational teaching qualifications on the arid banks and smiled contentedly. Then, after a profound sojourn, they proudly gathered up their parchments and sauntered back to grace whatever subject they were imparting and share with their hungry students the enriching anecdotes which represented their own former hospital experiences that had passed away some several years before. The fishers had satiated their desire to explore the well stocked waters for new knowledge and were content to supply a steady flow of needed recruits to take up their places on the hospital wards, thus fulfilling the modest demands for the national training of psychiatric students by their masters, the General Nursing Council.

* * *

'Would you believe that we have only one mental hospital in the whole country back home in Malaysia and that's for people who are mentally sick *and dangerous*?' our student group was informed by our Tamil-Indian, Malaysian classmate. 'Otherwise, you would be living on the street if not looked after by your family. There *is* no one else. There's no social security system, back

189

home, and there just isn't the money to spend on them. You wouldn't be off work for depression like all you lazy British,' he said while opening his mouth wide to let out a hearty laugh. He was a thoroughly gregarious bloke who, like many of the Malaysians, was as lean as a cheetah and around whose skinny brown wrist swung a metal banded watch like an outsized, iridescent, shiny bandolier. He had, during our acquaintance, made it very clear to the group that all this psychiatry was nonsense and would never be tolerated in his own country. As a consequence, he had some advice for me. 'Maybe you shouldn't take it all so seriously, Steve. How can you help these people! They're just mad,' he said of the patients, 'just fucking mad, *innit* mate.' The *innit* was a characteristic comment of his which was designed to mimic the poorly spoken English vernacular of our indigenous staff. It was delivered in a good-natured manner and unfailingly raised an appreciative smile from onlookers. 'In any case, do you realise that when I applied to come to England I thought I was being recruited to a general hospital? I could not believe my eyes when it turned out to be a lunatic asylum! I never ever intended to work with madness! And all this psychological bullshit, it's just a laugh. I prefer the real, practical work. It's far more useful, "init"?' Another burst of laughter from him and the rest of the group.

In keeping with all previous study blocks, our diminutive seven member fraternity is the only student group currently using the building which serves as the Training School. Far from a bustling hive of activity it is the very essence of tranquillity and, aesthetically, the setting promotes the atmosphere of a retreat. It is a former residence whose internal pretensions to grandeur have been masked over for the purpose of utility yet, as with all the rest of the centenarian hospital, the original exterior to the detached house has been minimally altered. The front door and lobby, when opened, throw a blind of light across a broad hallway laid to black and white, ceramic tiles and, leading off, are the several doors which would have led into vast reception, drawing and dining rooms but now serve as tutorial and clinical facilities. The rooms backing onto the garden grounds have French windows that reach onto a mossy lawn whose past, better days would have been cleared of the many pine cones and twigs that are strewn around the base of a moulting conifer. The yew tree is the embodiment of natural guardianship, seemingly satisfied that the house is still valued, still retains some semblance of its former dignity. Here, it is so easy to overlook the silence, the stillness, the seeming emptiness, but there will come a time when there will be no call for this building. The numbers of students are already falling. In time, there will be no suggestion of the nursing occupation that currently permeates the dwelling, no hint of psychiatry, or of academia, just history. This is an old dwelling in its dotage, living in the past, barely cognisant of the present, not wanting any more refashioning, and bearing a presentiment that there will be no other lease of life.

Though I had become frustrated by the wasted potential of both the nurses in training and the scope for therapeutic development in the hospital, it did not extend to the humiliating realisation that my fellow students and I might be learning our trade in a second-rate establishment, or worse. How could a situation persist that tolerated a level of expertise in mental health which hardly rose above the level of physical care and routines, and everyday sociable interaction? How was the establishment permitted to lag behind in so many areas so that nursing languished as little more than a prosaic procession of tasks – medication dispensing, escorting, valeting and housekeeping and facilitating the interventions of other professionals who worked on a more individualistic basis? We even have to appreciate the part played by industrial and occupational therapies as treatment, which takes up at least six months of our training allocations! Packing plastic pieces into plastic bags and making stuffed animals! All students are bored to tears when they perform their stint on either of these units but I managed to see some art therapy when a visiting therapist did some sessions for a while, and that was pretty damned impressive. Was this the sum total of psychiatric nursing? True, there was the modern theory of rehabilitation, and community care, but it could hardly be accused of extending practice, or of exercising the intellect, of anyone. Though these were politically significant strategies, in theory they were nothing more than an institutional relocation of patients and resources, in practice. On the other hand, the technical schedules and intervention therapies of psychologists, and the psychic archaeology by the psychotherapists, could acclimatise to any location. Even these disciplines were but a figment of institutional imagination because they were under represented in the hospital as a small department of psychologists and not a single psychotherapist in situ.

191

When returning for the study blocks at the Training School, my rising gall could only be exacerbated by the inconsistency of the individual sessions. While one Nurse Tutor would spend an hour and a half chalking up a diagram of a part of the body (anatomy) – remember, this was a psychiatric training – which was slavishly copied by the group, the following hour and a half might be passed with a Consultant Psychiatrist who composed a whistle-stop tour of common medical conditions that could have consumed weeks! Too bad if you couldn't capture the medical conditions, there was no time to tarry! And he was being paid, handsomely too! Meantime, the Principal Tutor – head poncho at the Training School – treated our group to a third rendition of the nursing management of epilepsy, a condition about which he obviously considered himself to be a specialist! This was the measure of it. Each Tutor had acquired one or two areas of expertise which had been derived from their personal nursing experience and they leaned heavily on them. The Principal believed that the epileptic condition epitomised, as well as any, the interrelatedness of the physical and mental symptoms of any psychiatric condition, otherwise called the psychosomatic. He savoured the historical perception that epilepsy was the archetype of what used to be thought of as spiritual possession, and that everyone should be intrigued by the cause and effect of physical and emotional changes relating to epileptic crises. Starting with the diagnosis of brain dysfunction, then the emergency management and safety considerations during seizures, he moved on to deal with the physical injuries and facial disfigurements, and the patient's compliance with taking medication, and the lifetime dependency and commitment to a medication regime. And then there was the tracing out of the epileptic personality and dealing with symptoms that could only exacerbate the physical vulnerability but were understandable in the circumstances. Self-centred, short-tempered, fractious, bolshie, uncooperative, sometimes aggressive, unaccepting of any advice from anyone, and regarded very much as "Loners". Put together, the drama of physically "fitting", along with their difficult personalities, made them a wary target for the public but it was clear that the Principal had nurtured a considerable sympathy toward this group of patients and he wanted to engender that in his students. It could be assumed that what made epilepsy particularly appealing to the Principal was the patently clear package of problem identification, disease progression, and nursing management, that made this a condition on which the practitioner could gain some therapeutic purchase. Conversely, the complexity and indeterminacy of most other mental illnesses afforded the practitioner but a limited measure of therapeutic viability.

'I'm sort of glad the epileptics are still around 'cos they take you by surprise and break up the monotony. Everywhere you turn there's an epileptic either fitting on the corridor, on the wards, in their dormitories, or even on a rehab trip!' This is from Cath, the older, English, female member of our student group.

'If they're fitting everywhere it kind of makes you wonder if they're benefiting from treatment and whether they'd be better off somewhere other than a mental hospital?' says Nat, the male Indian Malaysian.

'I wouldn't argue with you if they were destined for those epileptic colonies but they're oversubscribed. Yes, you heard me,' says the Principal Tutor, responding to the evidently astonished quorum. 'Shocking connotations, I know! But, you know, that's precisely what we've got here, isn't it? An institution is as much a colony as anything, when all is said and done.'

'Oh, scary, though,' says Cath. 'But quite appropriate, really. Colonies for mental lepers. That's how society treats these places, if truth be said.'

'Well, as you know, one of the main policies, these days, is to relocate psychiatric wards away from these institutions and graft them onto general hospitals. Everyone else will be found places in the community, if you can believe that. Ideally, there would be smaller units, with more specialisation, I suppose.' The only specialisation, at the moment, is based on whether patients remain on an admission ward because they are acute, are assigned to a long stay ward because they're chronic, or constitute a challenge which catapults them into "disturbed". Other than that, everyone's plonked together as if they're all one generic class rather than individuals with quite separate diagnoses. We argue whether, if different diagnostic categories were placed into different units, then treatments would be better differentiated and tailored for each category and the staff would become skilled in that particular area of mental illness. But what's the point of speculation when the only real therapy on offer is medical treatment? There are grounds for asking whether medical treatment, alone, does justice to psychiatric problems. However, there's no denying that, if nothing else, medication works if only to dampen down the more excessive symptoms, which is a blessing. Well, it's a blessing for the staff; who knows for the patients, themselves? The discussion produces an agreement that things will not improve on the proposed general hospital wings. They'll just be more disruption for the general hospital and they'll have to lock the wards, in any case. One concession, the only one, is that the patients will enjoy a more normal environment and not feel so geographically shunned. Cath has a no-nonsense, unpretentious view.

'Let's face it, it won't matter whether we're in the community or stuck here, we can't pretend that we do anything fancy by way of psychiatric nursing. You just don't have the time to adjust to their individual problems when you're managing between 25 to 30 patients. Most of your time's spent on just maintaining the routine, carrying out the ward admin, and managing the sheer numbers. I don't know how we avoid one crisis after another!' Kaur, the female Sikh Malaysian, has a gift for never being able to say anything, seriously, without collapsing into a charming giggle.

'Well, there's more, don't you think?. Because the admission patients don't have much contact with the doctors, we're the ones who get hassled with all their questions and problems. At least, on the long stay wards, the patients don't bother you all the time and leave you to get on with your job. They are less complicated, less demanding, *and* they do as they're told. Takes a lot of the pressure off.' There are nods of agreement round the group while she, predictably, unable to retain her composure, draws her long, black hair around her generous brown eyes in a fit of giggling.

'Anyhow, it may well not come to that,' ponders the Principal Tutor. 'These old hospitals have been threatened with closure for some years and here we are in the mid-1970s and nothing's happened. Personally, it would be a pity if it did happen.' The Principal breaks off in a brief reverie, as if sifting through the images of his own institutional collage, and re-engages in a confident tone. 'These institutions would be hard to replace, you know. Just think of the present convenience of concentrating all the patients, their problems, and the resources, in one place, then imagine the logistics of reorganising the services and redistributing the staff across various sites!

No I cannot see that ever happening. The mental hospital is here to stay. Asylums are forever,' chuckles the Principal with the benefit of historical precedent.

* * *

'You're not a happy boy are you, Steve? What, precisely, would satisfy you, do you think? Let me put it this way. What do you think would make you the mental nurse that you think you ought to be?' the Principal pointedly asks me during one day's plenary session, to the group's accompanying amusement.

'Well, that's a good question. I suppose I have issues about identifying with the notion of a *nurse*, to some extent. Admittedly, *psychiatric nursing* has less of a feminizing edge to it, and I admit to being more comfortable with that, but active nursing treatment is proving to be a bit too low key, not challenging enough! I suppose I'm saying that I'm not happy with the overall limitations of the rôle. It sounds a mite pretentious but I want to get closer to the person's mind, the motivations and the background influences on that person, not nursing the external symptoms so much. I don't feel that we're treating the mental illness. That's everybody else's department, it seems, while we deal with the mundane leftovers. I don't see why the rôle can't incorporate more of the in depth exploration of a patient's mental state that you associate with psychologists and psychotherapists, really.' As expected by now, the comments stir some opposition and a little exasperation in the group but I can't retract them now.

'Oh, come off of it. Some of us definitely don't want to go that far!' huffs Cath.

'We shouldn't hope to ape them, naturally, but there has to be some scope for taking on more of their rôle. After all, we know the patients better, we have more time with them, there are far more of us; it would make plain economic sense!'

Then Nat pipes up. 'Actually, I can just see Steve doing something like that. He's got that inquisitiveness. It would suit him.'

'Nursing's losing a lot of its mystique for me, right now, and I don't feel that should be happening,' I continue. 'I used to get quite a kick from telling people that I nursed psychiatric patients. You could see the promise of

195

mystery in their expressions, that they were cherishing thoughts of demons, chains, bloodletting and straightjackets. But there's also some expectation that patients are undergoing some form of psychotherapy or analysis with us and, to be frank, I'm left feeling a bit of a charlatan. I don't see why that should be a bit of a fantasy, to be perfectly honest.' I tail off a little limply, aware of having had a fair say and concerned that my complaints may not reflect those of my indulgent colleagues.

'I can't see why you think like that!' interjects Kaur doggedly. 'I just tell those I meet that I take care of unfortunate people who are mentally ill in the same way that a general nurse manages the physical complaints of their patients who can't look after themselves. I help get them through the day, do all the things they can't do for themselves, feed them, change their clothes, bath them, give their meds and injections, stop them from harming themselves, give reassurance and encouragement, take them out on trips, assess their mental state, link up with their families, help sort out their finances, deal with any problems that crop up, get them ready for their treatments, like ECT. I don't think any other profession does as much as we do, when you think about it. That's enough, don't you think? I don't want to do any more. I haven't even mentioned the madness!' The appraisal draws communal agreement as her features burst into ironic amusement. The whole group nod unanimously and steer a look of genial inquiry in my direction which I receive in similar good humour. I get along far too well with the group to want to confront them further, and what little exasperation shows itself soon subsides. Nevertheless, why should I feel so dissatisfied while they are so appeased? The Principal takes up a little of the slack.

'Well, it depends on what you think the job is about? Are you expecting more than it has to offer? I understand what you mean about the mystique but that's purely because the rest of society has no choice but to feed off the fear, and ignorance, and differences between themselves and the mad, because of knowing no better. The spin off for them is that the more they can demonise the mentally ill as having weaker constitutions, the more they can afford their own superior valuation as human beings who have the mettle, and the backbone, to tackle life's difficulties unaided. They cannot bear the prospect of having to accept their own potential for madness.'

Kaur expresses an unequivocal compromise. 'I agree with what Cath said. It's not possible, or necessary, to dig too deeply. Isn't our job simply to look after our patients as best we can, using the nursing skills we have? I'm happy with that. If that's not enough for some, then maybe nursing's the wrong way to go! Take my own people! Many of my Malaysian countrymen have no intention of remaining in nursing once they've qualified. Many are already preparing for other professions, you know! Sure. We're not a bunch of thickos you know! Ha, ha, ha!' She has a gorgeous chuckle and if there had been any trace of tension then this certainly punctures it.

'I know where you're coming from,' I have to acknowledge, almost apologetically, 'and I kind of admire that; that you're satisfied with what you're doing. For me, begging your pardon, I suppose I'm asking if nursing skills really amount to a whole hill of beans? Should we be talking about nursing *and* therapeutic skills? Why not therapy skills? Anyway, as I've said, the way the hospital's being swamped with the elderly there will be no opportunity for much other than basic care shortly.'

There follows a further discussion on the changing social ecology of the patient population. The pressure on admission wards to move on the elderly, if there is a whiff of dementia about them, has gathered momentum in the mental hospitals and there has been a gradual colonisation of whole hospital blocks by psycho-geriatrics whose residency is drawing across the establishment like an old quilt, and dimming the light of broader, psychiatric practice. The demographic changes in society, of increasing numbers of folk who were living to a ripe old age, have meant that the overtly demented seniors were being palmed off onto the State. Families wanting to retain their prosperity and minimise disruption while receiving little support at home, face the prospect of their relatives ending their days in the asylum. However economically and organisationally feasible it was to ship them in from the community it meant that an increasing professional focus was developing in the psychiatry of the elderly. In terms of working function it required plain hard graft, of moving from one physical task to another, a habit training, en bloc, of groups of elderly. There was seldom improvement but, there again, institutional staff were accustomed to that. As the hospital clogged up with more chronic, elderly patients, the main outcry coming from the student body was that a greater proportion of their allocated training experience was being diverted into psycho-geriatric placements than should have been allotted to them. The students were becoming alarmed that the reallocation of the patient estate would result in a reduced capacity to provide a sufficient psychiatric training. Psycho-geriatric work didn't demand too many *psychiatric* skills, and each successive psycho-geriatric placement meant a reduced potential for acquiring the craft to cover the wide range of disorders in the limited time available. Training specifications were not, in practice, the hospital's priority, which was to meet its own organisational needs, and the cynic would have said that the training of students provided the hospital with a supply of cheap labour. So, who was going to protect the students' interests? Staff were not generally prepared to go as far as to admit that psycho-geriatrics were not the real deal, nor that they were a professionally demoralising fraternity. But viewing the intellectual decline of individual characters, and what was prescribed as the ultimate human condition, provoked as much cynicism as sympathy. There was the additional fear that, the less exposed students were to experiential diversity within the limitations of their training hospitals, the more this would impact on future aspirations, job prospects, and ambitions. It was pot luck, of course. Each hospital could only work with the materials at its disposal and, whereas some hospitals did offer a few specialities – drug addiction and alcohol addiction units being fairly widely dispersed – many did not. Throughout the discussion, the Principal has performed his level best to field the complaints on offer from his student group.

'It seems to me that there has been a very unfortunate strain of thinking developing in the hospital for a while now, and this group is a microcosm of it, though I only make an observation, you understand,' proposes the Principal. 'Just tell me, will you, how a mentally ill person avoids becoming old? For that matter, any person? We have a responsibility to look after any patient that comes our way, you know. It's not sexy dealing with the long stay and geriatric, I grant you, but they can't be confiscated as being irrelevant, and whisked away somewhere else. When all is said and done, I have to say that there should be no less satisfaction from caring for a demented person than there is for nursing a florid psychotic, or hapless neurotic, or anyone else. They are worthy of our attention just because they're there. You are caring for your *fellow man*; for goodness sake, there's nothing more important than that! You must not lose sight of that! No skills are a substitute for plain care. I think you need to go away and think about that. It's worth you considering how much of all this complaining about the shortfalls in your training is more a rationalisation about what is, more honestly, a lack of sympathy for your patients, particularly the elderly. If I'm right, and I hope I'm not, you'll need to take a good look at yourselves and develop some self-awareness. I don't wish to sound too harsh but please take on board what I've said.' I, for one, am astonished by the immediate impact this has on me. Instantly shamed by the principle, and the so generous magnanimity of it, I am more surprised by the source from which it has emanated. Never being in doubt of the good humour, informality and plain good nature of the whole body of tutorial staff, this has not amounted to having respect for them. Now, a simple endorsement of human validation has laid bare my own callous disregard for the human condition.

* * *

One scheduled afternoon of the study block is dedicated to the visit by a small group of five residents and the accompanying three staff members from a nearby, and very famous, Therapeutic Community. Between them they share in outlining the rationale and treatment regime. While four patients make a vocal input, one of them has a hard time even remaining in the room. Each patient – known as residents in their Unit, by the way – presents a resumé of their individual problems and the reasons for attending the Unit. In a calmly rehearsed delivery the four confident residents dig up their potted pasts of children's homes, drug and alcohol abuse, self-harm, suicide attempts, criminal history, and difficulties with holding down jobs and relationships. It seems that the TC is a last resort for many of its patients, providing an opportunity to change their criminal life styles. The courts have given most of them an opportunity to be *diverted* from a prison sentence in favour of treatment. The difference is that the criminality is supposed to have been directly derived from their personalities so that they enjoy the distinction of coming within the psychiatric orbit under the diagnosis of "psychopaths". The atmosphere is surprisingly tense and virtually none of we students utters a word. As their visitors' stories unravel the students realise they are being presented with unprecedented patient histories that will do more than raise their eyebrows. These stories will pile on the already dubious reservations about being in the presence of "psychopaths" who have a thoroughly established reputation for difficult, manipulative, anti-social and frequently violent behaviours. It is the visiting patients, rather than the accompanying staff, who outline the structure, routine, and interventions of the community regime, alongside their potted biographical histories. The Director then breaks in to tell them that the theoretical foundation of the TC is "social therapy" whereby the group, itself, becomes the treatment intervention since it is the residents who best understand each other's condition and are in a more informed position to challenge one another. The therapeutic strategy is that the residents are the most effective therapeutic agent to bring about real change because they can detect the avoidant and rationalising bullshit of their fellow patients better than the staff can. When the bullshit is aired by one resident, it is therapeutically challenged in what is known as a *confrontation* and this provides its recipient with the chance to examine their behaviour, their ideas, their thinking. This is the radical difference between the philosophy of the TC and the traditional hospital. In the latter, when a patient acts up, or kicks against the traces, or generally gives cause for concern, it is the staff that make decisions on everybody's behalf to re-establish order and the status quo. For the TC it is the whole community who will address the deviation and the final solution may require a shift in the original status quo. To be able to facilitate this, the organisational atmosphere is much more tolerant of such things as swearing, dress, manners, and forms of "acting out behaviour" than would be the case in the hospital to which the students belong. The staff are equal partners in the treatment and help guide the residents through the "confrontation" process of being supportively challenged to examine, identify and justify feelings, ideas and behaviour that they exhibit. The use of medication is minimised and general behaviour can be very relaxed and permissive provided the basic principles are adhered to and each resident is made aware of the limits whose contravention will not be tolerated and which will exclude them, including the revelation that nursing staff have the same status, and make as equal a contribution as every other discipline. And all the disciplines join in the community, the group-work, and individual work, every day. And they have the whole spectrum of disciplines, including the somewhat exotically named "social therapists", psychologists and psychotherapists. Because the Therapeutic Community has always had to fight its corner against traditional organisational structure it has had to prove its efficacy in order to continue to gain funding for its service. The staff contingent, rather than being demoralised by their uncertain predicament and the constant need to justify their existence, seemed energised by the whole project. It demands that there is a continuous research programme of the treatment method and results while the large institutions can take it for granted that they need not bother. So the Unit has produced its own academic course to train both its own staff and interested outsiders, regularly contributes research papers and professional publications, and has an international network to support its development! As the session progresses the Director, whose fame and notoriety is utterly lost on our student contingent – and, no doubt, our tutor – asks his hosts what sort of treatment would be offered to patients with this condition in their hospital, and what comments they would have about his own Unit's treatment approach. As tactfully as she can the well-built Cockney, Cath, reproduces the rehearsed nursing and medical commentary on the psychopath.

'Well, as far as we've been led to believe, the jury's still out on whether the psychopathic patient is really mentally ill and should be given psychiatric treatment, or if they should be held responsible for their actions, and serve out a prison sentence, instead of being allowed to avoid their punishment.' The rest of us students can't believe she's actually said this but have to acknowledge that this is our common understanding of the debate. She's certainly showing some balls!

'Is that by way of saying that there isn't a plan of treatment for the psychopathic patient, here?' asks the cool, famous Director, looking around the group inclusively, so that everyone feels put on the spot. The question is rhetorical. He knows the answer.

'To be perfectly honest, all the staff I've spoken to wouldn't be happy having psychopathic patients on their wards and can't wait to see the back of them,' she continues. Bigger and bigger balls!

'Do you think it's right that the psychiatric professions perceive these patients in this way? After all, the Mental Health Act says they're ill? Do you think there's a certain degree of ignorance, perhaps?' Before anyone has a chance to reply, the tension is ratcheted up a few pugnacious notches by one of the visiting male patients – he could almost have been recruited for the purpose of confronting the student group – who takes this opportunity to elaborate his version of the malevolent treatment he has received in traditional mental hospitals, such as theirs, over the years.

'Why can't you accept that we have an illness like other patients, eh? What gives you all the right to judge us and treat us even worse than the other patients?' He's not really interested in answers. 'You all think we're shit! You don't get anywhere close. You don't even scratch the surface. You wouldn't know how. All you've got is power. You're not even smart; most of you; you don't deserve the responsibility you've been handed. I'm trying to change my life to the best of my ability at the Unit and you wouldn't be able to convince me that you'd have any idea how to begin helping me.' The gloves have come off. Sod informing, sod educating, sod influencing, sod theoretical challenging, and double-sod politeness! Politeness be fucked, this guy is sick of idling and his engine is running. He wants to cut through the crap and make some real impact, to lay down the benefits of his insights, to really connect with the group! See if you can handle it, you tossers! It's an opportunity for him to unleash a smouldering resentment that will maximise everyone's discomfort. It is noticeable that he does not check out his other colleagues who have been laudably constrained until now and his pointedly overbearing presence soon blunts any input from anyone else. The group is stunned by a mixed indignation and astonishment. The Director waits, looking cool. The students' tutor waits, looking distinctly uncool. The one female patient who had avoided any contact is now so desperately anxious she would give anything to be displaced from here! It is clear to all present that it is our nursing contingent in the room that represents the traditional system to their antagonist. We are the ones being characterised as the therapeutic equivalence of a political dictatorship, or religious theocracy that permits no individual liberties and pronounces on every shade of deviance. In contrast, the Therapeutic Community portrays a foreign country with exotic and seductive ingredients. It's all the confirmation I need to confirm the paucity of my and my colleagues' traditional experience. The tutor responds, thankfully.

'We must remember that in a hospital of this size there are so many different groups of need that they militate against determining a specific model of care. In your community, you're able to benefit from a special regime because you're small and dedicated to one patient group,' the Director counters.

'But it would be perfectly possible to set up a specialist unit within your precincts if that's what the authorities wanted. But there again, you might not think that there was a sufficient culture to support that.' This all reminds me of the discussions we've had in this training block about what, exactly, our job entails.

'I feel like I'm a border guard of the Soviet Block looking onto the liberated West; running our searchlights over the population that we're trying to contain, scrutinising people's conduct for deviations and protest, and ensuring no one absconds over the wall! There's no negotiation about anything. We don't have anything like a treatment model that we all adhere to. I'm feeling quite frustrated that our job is, well, passive, functional, not active in a therapeutic sense. We merely come on duty and work our shift. And we certainly don't have any research going on as to how effective we are. And definitely not by nursing staff!' Before anyone has a chance to comment, the initiative is taken up by the disgruntled male resident who unequivocally addresses me with a personal challenge. One of the pleasures of group settings is that the self is not so sharply demarcated, where the emotional and social tension between individuals enjoys a kind of fusion within a communal identity. Conversely, a belligerent confrontation can wrench open any conviviality like a tin-opener, levering open the protection to an individual, and spilling their personal content before the scrutiny of others. He focuses a cocky, self-assured pugnacity in my direction.

'I don't know who you're trying to impress by pulling this stroke, here. As far as I'm concerned, it's easy to say something like what you've said in our company. Why should any of us believe you? You don't have to impress any of us that you're waging your own private war against the system while condemning everyone else for getting it all wrong. Why don't you stop moaning about the system you're working in and actually do something constructive to change things, if you feel so strongly about it? And I don't believe you do.' His opinion is delivered grimly, and he leans back with every indication of maximising my discomfort, while the remainder of the group laugh, affably enough, at the sudden injection of vitality, albeit at someone's expense. I receive it as the smarting rebuke that is intended, shunting into my self-assurance like a betrayal. After all, I've attempted to support the guy's own assertions! Why should he have turned against a potential ally and undermined me with a personal attack? Unseen, wounded, bristling, I slink into a vengeful, ruminating silence, preparing and rehearsing a retaliation that will redress this disrespect. My attention has become consumed with getting back at this guy's ungrateful opportunism. Like an imperceptible, silently drawn bow I build up a momentum, awaiting the moment to spring back upon the discussion and rip into this target. This guy's in for a shock if he thinks that he will quietly retire from the field! A suitable moment arrives and, with my target in mind, but not staring directly at him, I release a reply, constrained, compromising and reasonable.

'We do have to change to meet the needs of some patients. That said, you don't have to be seen to be organising a one-man, underground revolution just because you believe there should be changes to the system.' The reply masks a deeper reproach. 'I'm merely suggesting how much more stimulating and productive it could be for everyone concerned if we all had a treatment model to focus our attention rather than the basic institutional routine. I, for one, would think it would give me more skills and make me far more competent. Do you have a problem with that?' suddenly focusing my gaze fully on him. The whole group maintains a tentative appreciation of the confrontation and anticipates a further antagonistic thrust from either of us.

'You just make it sound as if you're putting everybody else down but yourself. I bet your mates, here, feel great about that!' Christ, he knows how to get underneath your skin, all right! But the visitor has found his mark and leans away from the encounter, with his hands locked behind his head, in a satisfied withdrawal, knowing that it is not he who will have to lick his wounds. There's room, yet, for pushing in that blade just a little further!

'Well, I'm certainly not having a go at them,' first looking round the group and returning to stare into the visitor's face. His response is a shrug, at first. A shrug! The artful little sod!

'Don't interest me, mate. You can go on justifying it to yourself, if you like.'

'I don't think I'm justifying anything,' but I feel increasingly uncomfortable and wished I'd said nothing at all! How did I get into this position, anyhow? Having lost the initiative, I launch myself back at the nasty little twat! 'It feels like you've turned my well-intentioned remark into a bit of a weapon against me, actually.'

'You don't have to get upset with me, mate. If you think anything's to be done, just get it sorted.' He delivers his answers while assuming an air of unconcern. It's clever. Accomplished. Hit your mark with a confrontation, withdraw when the job is done, and watch the target compound their discomfort with their awkward justifications. The trick is to hold onto your own cool. Cath, the ballsy one in the group, makes a stand.

'Personally, I think people should be allowed to give an honest opinion, in a group, without being made to look insincere. Sometimes you just have to accept people on face value.' This is bold, very ballsy.

'Not if you believe it's bullshit!'

'And you have the right to make that judgement, do you?' This is very reasonable stuff, indeed!

'Course you do! Look, if the kitchen's too hot, get out! After all, you're mental nurses, aren't you?'

'Doesn't matter who you are. We're human, just like you.' Cath stolidly continues.

'Look, it's not my fault if people are too sensitive to take criticism. That's their problem. It's everyone's prerogative whether they want to challenge what's been said by someone else in a group. Comes with the territory.' Our friend has all the answers. Therapy has become a handy new weapon for him.

'Sounds a bit heartless, that's all.'

'They can always have their own therapy if the going get's tough, like,' the TC client says with a wry smile. The intentional irony of his remark is that, in the Therapeutic Community, the staff will be expected to have personal therapy as an integral part of their professional training and practice. But such an idea is pure anathema to asylum staff, such as us, where it is only associated with a sick person's needs, not a healthy person. From the ripples of movement around the forum this comment has the effect of racketing up the unease. Which is just as well, as I am not confident of holding my ground against this seasoned campaigner. The Tutor steps in.

'And at that juncture, I think it's time to draw the session to a halt and to extend our thanks to our visitors for taking the time to come and spread the word about the aims of their unit. I'm sure I can speak on behalf of the students when I say that the session has been very thought provoking for us all and we hope that you have also gained something from your time with us.' There were assenting voices all round.

*   *   *

Over a communal tea following the session, the malcontented visitor keeps his distance from the student group while I and a pretty, German accented "social therapist" discuss how much the TC veers away from traditional hospitals. She states that she is not in a position to comment on traditional psychiatric practice, not having been exposed to it directly. She says she has a psychology degree and is waiting to progress to a clinical psychology training. At an opportune moment, though, she quietly confides to me that she believes I should consider working in a Therapeutic Community following my conventional psychiatric training. She feels that the way I manoeuvred myself in the previous scenario has displayed a potential for handling the sort of challenge that would be encountered in a TC. The question is, should you take such an appreciative message as a reliable signal that there is a satisfying avenue ahead? But the gratifying strokes are sullied by my own awareness that what the therapist perceived as a therapeutic potential was, to be quite accurate, more of a retaliatory redress. The evidence was incontrovertible: the perceived insult puncturing my self-esteem, the affront to my integrity, and the knuckle of immediate retaliation and vengefulness and that I should give a good account of myself, only some of which has subsided now that the confrontation is concluded. That all I'd really done was to wrap an undetectable anger in the refined linen of apparent conciliation and therapeutic confrontation. I did realise that I had resorted to acting just like my adversary – wanting to attain some degree of payback for feeling slighted. Was this the price to be paid by susceptible personalities who must yield their inner pain like infected lesions on the emotional surface? When winning and defeat were uppermost, when argument was trampled and shattered by the efforts of opposing factions to impose maximum casualties at the cost of all accommodation, was the argument diminished, the ideas less rational, the outcome less honest?

Was any discussion anything more than a no-man's-land of opposition and counter opposition and, therefore, only worthy of the name if informed by the pain of its participants?

* * *

'Thank Christ I don't work in a unit like that,' says Cath, commencing the session's post-mortem after the visitors have departed. 'Imagine having to pussy-foot around, waiting for a whole group to make the simplest decision, with patients like that, all day long. Only being allowed to take control of a situation if a patient seriously steps out of line, like cutting their wrists, or cutting up! I mean, how can you justify offering psychopaths that sort of regime when they should have been in prison, anyway? It's just encouraging them to take advantage of people. You don't negotiate with psychopaths! You must be joking! It'd drive me absolutely bloody mad. I'd end up either wanting to kill myself... or them!' We all laugh. The general consensus is that this is definitely not how patients of the order of psychopaths would be managed in our type of setting. Marie, a female Filipino, another older member of the group, who is benign and retiring, voices more of the folklore that has been passed onto mental nurses through the ages.

'I've been told you're not to have more than one psychopath on any ward, if it can be helped, you know, because they're hard enough to deal with on their own and can be particularly nasty toward one another. And if they join forces... oh, my, my! Imagine a unit full of them!'

'You can't offer psychopaths the opportunity to run things the way they want. They'll run rings round you looking for every sign of weakness in the system and the staff. Then they'll manipulate it to their own advantage!' adds Kaur, who surprises everyone with a forthright opinion, for her. 'I think what that session showed was why these characters are seen to be so different and why there are questions about whether they have a mental illness. With other illnesses you feel sorry for the patients even though they can be difficult and, occasionally, aggressive. But I couldn't find any sympathy for those people in there, you understand me? I mean, look at the way that bloke went for you, Steve! There was no need for that and it was all so rational and calculating. How can that be mental illness? No wonder they don't get sympathy from people.' There is a communal hum of agreement. 'As if he was just waiting for a little hole to open up and stuff you right in it. I wanted to punch him one!' And she deteriorates into characteristic giggles.

'But you stood up for yourself and gave him a good answer, Steve boy,' says Nat. I appreciate the flattery, of course.

'Bang out of order,' Cath joins in. 'He was just having a right go at the treatment he's had over the years, that's all! Pity we didn't have the point of view of staff who had to manage him over the years. Can you imagine! He ought to be grateful that the health service saved him from being sent to prison, which is where the likes of him really belong! And did you notice how not one of those staff who came with them intervened in any way? I bet he leads them a merry dance.'

'I'll tell you what struck me most about them,' says Marie. 'They were all so unhappy, every one of them. And that did make me feel more sympathetic about their mental illness, actually. Not that that changes anything because you could never pay me enough to work in that sort of unit. I'll stick with our own lunatics, thank you!' Marie concludes on a salutary note, and unusually outspoken for her. This is the closest any of us have come to trying to get a handle on our visitors' lives, as they experience them. We've only shown a basic human reaction to a group of patients whose unflattering reputation precedes them, whom we neither understand nor care for. In fact, our experience confirms the received wisdom on this patient category. Our training and ward experiences have not equipped us to stand back from immediate reaction and we have allowed ourselves to become embroiled in the patients' emotions, rather than to consider the motivating background to the behaviour.

'You know what the prognosis is for these characters, don't you?' says Nat, through his white toothed, wispy goatee of a smile. 'They say nothing works until the psychopath burns himself out.' He is voicing one of the most firmly held tenets of the psychiatric field in that at about the age of 40 the psychopathic patients lose much of their worst traits, seemingly as a snake sheds a useless skin that it no longer requires, and emerge with a degree of maturity that most people have attained during early adulthood. 'Anyway, they're all fucking mad, mate, innit?' is his inimitable rejoinder. This meets with the conclusive approval of everyone and the group is visibly relieved that the whole business is over and preconceptions largely confirmed. And

that was as far as any analysis went. How was a short session going to recon-
cile two opposing philosophies like the hospital asylum and the therapeutic
community? And, hey! What's in a name? Indeed! A Therapeutic Community
was a radical, democratic psychiatric movement akin to a revolutionary break
from the Established Church or conventional political party. And we were not
ready for it.

*　*　*

Every Student Nurse in training in a bog standard mental hospital during this
period experienced a minimum of a couple of geriatric allocations during their
three years before qualification. Some were luckier than others, it must be said.
I found myself on an elderly male placement for long-term physical illnesses
and infirmity as an alternative second geriatric placement. It amounted to an
infirmary for elderly males. The bonus was that some of the patients could
dress and generally look after themselves. In terms of the absence of acquiring psychological insights and therapies, the experience was anticipated to be
unrewarding, yet it held its own very peculiar wonders. Urinal incontinence
was a big issue as patients' capacity to control their bladders declined. Other
problems included hydro seals, insulin dependent diabetes, amputations, post-
operative rehabilitation, while some became wheelchair bound and, inevitably,
there were the two or three who were permanently bedridden. Professionally,
its compensations were that it was an opportunity to develop more traditional
nursing procedures, such as introducing urinary catheters, and performing
sterile wound cleansing and dressing techniques. Its other compensation was
that the ward was run by a diligent, casually mannered, beneficent Charge
Nurse who hailed from Guiana and who was interested in teaching. The ward
efficiency was due, in large part, to his easygoing, and participative leadership.
I readily appreciated and adapted to the warm welcome and team atmosphere,
which was far from being the case in all wards.

'Of course you can join me. You'll have to gown up, though. Can't have
you flicking well contaminating my sterile area, you bugger, ha, ha,' is the
enthusiastic rejoinder of a strapping Welsh male nurse in response to my show
of interest and the information that this would be a new, formal procedure for
me. The muscular frame that was once drilled into shape on a hard, cold, gritty

coal face is about to delicately probe the tender limbs of a crippled bundle of humanity. To my eyes, the Welshman, named Keith, has proven himself to be a manically jovial lad, just a little older than myself, who is utterly incapable of silence and negotiates a skilful line between a worldly sense of humour without offensive smuttiness or swearing. We are ensconced within the dormitory area with broad screens drawn completely around a particular bed. Behind the screens, the scene is as technical as it gets in a psychiatric hospital. Keith is robed in a long white gown, white rubber gloves, plastic apron, and white face mask, and he hugs the glass treatment trolley bristling with plastic and metal instruments, dressing packs, and cleaning agents. He is embarking on a treatment routine to change the dressings of a chronically bedridden patient whose emaciated body still comes within the remit of pressure area care, but has the smell of a carcass. This is a chronic condition whereby the bed surfaces come into contact with the more prominent bones of the patient's arms, legs, ankles, hips, shoulders, heels and sacrum, wearing away the cover of flesh and leaving a series of quarried craters which exude a putrefied slough and offensively nauseous smells that need to be changed twice daily. Before the skin breaks down completely and peels away like a tin lid, the deadening mass of black ulceration that has formed over the pressure area resembles the leathery underbelly of a dead badger at the roadside. Before we start on the dressings there is the faecal incontinence to dispatch. Because Keith wants to retain as much sterility as is conceivable, he instructs me to wipe up the offending matter in the incontinence pad that lies beneath the patient's buttocks. I duly place the fouled pad in a plastic liner that is attached to one end of the sterile trolley! Keith begins by removing one of the outer dressings and then the underlying ones discoloured by human rot. Astonishingly, the patient is so incapable of communication it is almost impossible to establish the pain level despite the earlier morphine injection which the procedure requires about 15 minutes prior to commencement. Keith proceeds to scrape out the pits of pus with forceps and swathes of gauze and cements in the gaps with new dressings which are plastered with micropore tape to the precarious surrounding skin. But when he moves on to the sacrum it gapes like a pothole, a descending tunnel whose walls have been washed of all lining, leaving only bare rocks. As the onlooker, I marvel both at my colleague's thoroughness and due reverence despite the patient appearing to lie like a threadbare standard rendered almost unrecognisable by mutilating conflicts and explosions, yet still retaining some vestige of what he once was, some representation of his personhood.

'He must be in agony when that morphine wears off. Surely, this can't be right. Do we just carry on doing this till he's gone?' The remarks are as much rhetorical as expectant of a confirming answer and serve to express my personal disgust, discomfort and impotence in the face of this virtually cadaverous devastation. Perhaps it is even more than this. When the body deteriorates to such an extent, in life, what conceivable prospect is there in an afterlife? And this magnifies the conflict of whether to do everything possible to haul the poor wretch back from the clawing appetite of death or whether there is any justification in prolonging his agonies in life. The dreadful silence that seems to be waiting an imminent death is dispelled by the clattering of my partner's instruments and the crisp rustle of sterile packs. Noting my evident disgust, he has a proposition.

'Well, there's loads of patients with bedsores around the hospital and you wouldn't send them off to a general hospital for that, so we treat them ourselves', he says. 'In the end, loads of patients will die here as chronic cases.' The initial surprise is outweighed by the growing conviction that once you're admitted to an asylum, you ain't going nowhere!

'Yeah, I've come to realise that,' I reply, almost musingly.

'For most of these blokes, once they're here, that's it, mate. So, when you're near to flicking "pegging it"' – "flicking" is his euphemistic compromise of "fucking" and "flipping" – 'you've probably had a long spell on a psycho-geri ward. Alzheimer's, you see! And that means we all have a long spell on psycho-geris. That pisses off a lot of nurses, I can tell you but I don't mind. It's all nursing as far as I'm concerned and it saves sitting around a lot of the time,' he adds cheerily. This quite simply characterises his general optimism. Besides this, there is nothing optimistic about this mental hospital becoming filled by patients who are really just debilitated by the indignities of old age and infirmity. It seems some of these include the hospital's home grown residents who have simply aged with their years of hospitalisation, on top of their original mental illness! God, what lives! It is as if the asylums are becoming disembarking stations for battalions of psychologically and age wounded elders demobbed by their communities, families, GPs and local authorities. Is the hospital administration really managing a human waste disposal programme for the elderly? Is this what is really happening to the elderly patient population?

'What happens when he dies, does anyone come, is there a service or something?' The query is made with not a little exasperation and without lowering my voice as if the whole protracted procedure has callously desensitized me to the patient's presence and sensibilities.

'I don't know what happens after the mortuary but, if they were poor and had no family in the past, they used to get buried in the hospital cemetery in paupers' graves,' says Keith.

'Blimey, that's straight out of the history books!' That's the parish taking responsibility for your disposal because you're too poor to afford your own grave!

'Well, you think about it. Most of them don't own a thing, spend years here, kick the bucket without any bugger knowing about it, then get buried on the cheap. What else can be done?' While he makes his point seriously enough it is nestled into his hearty cheerfulness as if he's already come to terms with this unsavoury reality. 'Sometimes it can be different, though. All depends on your religion, I suppose. If you're Jewish, a Rabbi will definitely get involved and they do everything! Now, the most important treatment in between dressings is to make sure he gets all his meals and liquids to build up his body mass, and to turn him regularly so that no one area takes too much pressure. That's where we fall down and make things twice as hard for ourselves,' the cheery Welshman concludes. 'Are you comfortable, Mr. Braxton?' leaning down to the patient's ear but not seriously expecting a reply. 'We'll bring you a drink, shortly, old mate,' but there is not a flicker of response other than what can only pass as a twitching, pain filled grimace. 'Right, I'll just get this poor bugger a flicking drink then. I think we've deserved one, too, don't you?'

The procedure appears to be done. The two of us, both students, help to prop up and fold this woodworm infested frame into a pack of pillows, fresh pillow cases, sheets, cellular blankets and bedspread. We move away into the clinic room where the debris is packed away and the entire trolley is sprayed and wiped down with antiseptic. All soiled dressings and equipment are parcelled up and disposed of into the appropriate bags. The clinic has a reassuring orderliness – medicine cabinet and trolley, oxygen cylinders, instrument cupboard, resuscitation equipment – a clinical ammunition dump in readiness for stricken bodies and minds and the long, long campaign of dying. Science has temporarily intercepted in nature's unprotecting incompetence but it is little more than a sudden scaring off of carrion crows which are guaranteed to return to strip away the flesh of life and death.

* * *

On this all male ward some patients are so grossly debilitated they cannot remonstrate or articulate their outrage though it may register in many ways, not least in a silent but confused agitation. It means that they can be subject to the whims of some staff who may be very carefree with their attention. Those, like Topper, who is dementing, incontinent of urine, unable to walk or stand, and pretty deaf are especially vulnerable. He is acknowledged for his wry sense of humour, too. A young Irish student, who has just come on afternoon duty, bawls in his ear.

'Topper, have you wet yourself?' Topper, who has been snoozing after lunch, offers rasping, barely audible responses which are more akin to sighs.

'N-n-n... no. H-h-h... ave y-y-y...you w-w-w... wet y-y-y... yourself?' and looking aside with indignation.

'Have you shit yourself, then?' returns the amused Irishman, satisfied with Topper's mild show of gall.

'N-n-n... no, I h-h-h... haven't. You h-h-h... have a sh-h-h... shit, y-y-y... yourself.'

'I have, thank you, Topper. You don't have to be rude, now,' grinning broadly. Topper folds his face in a toothless show of mild indignation.

'Well, we can't take you anywhere if you've dirtied yourself, now can we?' his glistening blue eyes scanning the room for the approval of his colleagues.

'Th... th... then d-d-d-d...don't t... t-t-t...take me th... th... then. Go aw-w...away,' and Topper nods his head emphatically and stares ahead with comical chagrin.

'Well, where shall I go, Topper?'

'Go where the b-b-b... b-b-b... bloody hell you l-l-l... like!'

'Now, that's not very nice, is it?'

'Y-y-y…yes, it is.'

'I need to change you. I can smell you from here.'

'N-n-n… no y-y-y… you c-c-c… can't.'

'I can, too.'

'N-n-n… no y-y-y… you c-c-c… can't.'

'No, no, I must do my duty to you, Topper. It's my duty to take you out and clean you up. I'll go and fetch a wheelchair. Don't you get buggering off, now.'

'S-s-s-s… stick it u-u-u… up y-y-y… your a-a-a-a… arse… a-a-a…arse 'ole,' to the raucous satisfaction of the staff as the young Irishman, helped by another member of staff, levers Topper into a wheelchair ready for the bathroom. Topper's even temperament suggests he's heard all this banter before. He manages to mix a quiet indignation with a satisfied glint in the eye, as if he does have a considerable appreciation of the derision he sustains and his own participation in it. Maybe he has no choice. But he seems only to speak at all when staff directly attend to him and, maybe, he's just grateful for that.

In the day's routine, patient trips to the bathroom for "toileting" are cut to an absolute minimum in the assurance that any involuntary breaches are soaked up by the incontinent pads which will line their private parts for the rest of their lives. So, after mealtimes, they will be walked or taken in a wheelchair to the bathroom, where trousers will be dropped, the sodden, piss stenched pad removed, and a fresh one rapidly slid in beneath the underpants, and the trousers reassembled, before the old boys' legs – sometimes, their protestations – give out. But the more concerted efforts to wash off the caustic urine from the ageing clusters of genitals, groins, haemorrhoids and buttocks, may be deliberately avoided, like the shunning of a disgraced family. Even when the evening preparation for bed comes, after supper, and Topper's nurse considers that toileting him is futile – the night-time, draw-sheet can always be changed, after all – Topper is stripped of his day clothes but not given the bath that will rinse him of the day's travails. Neither is the barrier cream applied that will protect his leathery skin from the enuretic showers. As with all elderly incontinent males, Topper threads his once ample arms through the shrunken pyjama top, and is hoisted to his feet. In his tremulous uncertainty, for he is barely able to stand, he pinches hold of the nurse's arms.

'Oouuch, Topper, you're pinching my bloody arms.'

'G-g-g... good. S-s-s-s... ser... s-s-s... serves y-y-y... you b-b-b... bloody well right.' The long limbed, towering nurse bucks to left and right to free himself from Topper's pinching, grasping, anxious hold until Topper is unceremoniously spun with a resounding crash onto his mattress, where he begins to scratch and scrape at the stinging streams for the duration of the irritating night. The bedclothes, pinned at the foot of the bed, are yanked across Topper's final confusion.

'Right, who's for a cup of tea?'

* * *

The ward contains a Scots patient who is physically mobile, emotionally accessible, but intellectually inaccessible. In the main, he is easily managed and, when frustrated or hurried, has the capacity to draw our attention to the fact without undue irritation. He is a perfectly charming gentleman with a soft and cultured accent. He tries hard to make conversation with whoever is dealing with him but rarely makes much sense. His intonation suggests he knows perfectly well what he's trying to convey but his mind can do no more than allot him random words from a verbal tombola. We answer him as best we can. He has kind eyes which draw his features into spontaneous smiles and I realise that he is hanging onto the vestiges of his personality before the rampaging dementia tramples his brain to dust. The regular visits from his loving wife must make all the difference for he quite obviously recognises her when she approaches. It is as if she'd just returned from an outing and he's welcoming her and offering to make the tea. She tells us that he's run his own business until sustaining this illness, that he's missed by everyone who knows him, and that this is all so unjust. She pampers him but is not overly sentimental. How can she bear the loss of her husband? Here is an individual who had a place in the world and still lies at the heart of his family. The dementia is not the person; neither can it completely subsume the individual personality however hard it raves! This dear old man has been an excellent teacher.

* * *

215

In time, for each of us, our curiosity and speculations were worn smooth with the rub of daily habit, routine and acclimatisation. We could not then avoid the institutional euphemisms which lay like verbal camouflage over the psychiatric precinct. They were, doubtless, beacons of optimistic, policy strategists which were meant to light a path for government, the institutional staff, and the developing public opinion and prevent the rotting, creeping rise of professional and political despondency and the accusation of moral lassitude. But could the mere use of descriptive words, and their symbolism, convert into effective ideas and then influence practice? Or did they provide some useful, cynical cover under which the real activity took place? For instance, the notion of "long stay", which denoted the discrete care of the chronically debilitated. "Long" more accurately described an assumption that every one of these relatively youthful, or late middle-aged, men would live out the remainder of their irretrievable existence here, until inevitable infirmity demanded their removal to physical care or geriatric wards. The term "stay", while impressing an image of a brief, recuperative sojourn, was an enforced detention in what could even be a locked area. This was irrespective of actual legal status since many would have been originally admitted as voluntary patients, under their own volition, and others having had their involuntary, "certified" status lapse years ago.

Then a qualitative shift was required for what was termed a "rehabilitation ward" where patients were, ostensibly, being skilled up and prepared for a return to either their social and familial roots or to some sort of community home or hostel. Unfortunately, the ideological intentions didn't quite trickle down to the practice for "rehabilitation wards" were, in the institutional vernacular, recast as "back wards". Back wards, long stay wards, all synonymous, in practice, were out of sight and mind in the nether regions of the hospital and, in providing the lowest level of supervision, stimulation and practice, exemplified the notion of being "backward". On such wards one nurse could be in charge of around 40 patients, at that time, and there was precious little they could have achieved in the way of rehabilitation. There was not a solitary area of rehabilitative practice that even entered the professional imagination on such wards. The patients more or less ran the wards themselves, which required a seamless routine and no scope for community re-entry.

At this time, a key feature of the chronic institutionalisation of patients was the inadvertent undermining, and eventual loss, of social skills which exhibited itself in the impoverished communication with fellow patients, and between staff and patients, in addition to the severed family and wider community links. Patients didn't have the opportunity to comment on how their wards were run or how they should spend their days, so was there much left to talk about? And what was it that had been drummed into us students by the Training School, the medical staff, and the ward staff, that helped to limit the communication and social skills? Don't get emotionally involved! This was one of the many informal mores which had illuminated the paths of professionals in the psychiatric field over generations. And newcomers were hard-pressed not to acknowledge the astuteness of experience and of avoiding putting themselves in psychological or physical danger. The diagnosis, the illness, the day-to-day eccentricity and dislocation, were the patients' allotment as if decided by a fateful, not to say deserving, wheel of fortune. Though some staff were undoubtedly fond of some of their patients, social and professional distance was an indispensable talisman characterising their personal integrity, or protecting against being contaminated, or being pulled down by another's misfortune. So, patient involvement would be tolerated until the expectation of either fearful self-interest or careless ignorance, like a background drumbeat, reminded the nurse to step back. It was at such a point that the staff appeared to reify the institution and its routines to such a degree that responsibility for its management wasn't really required; that it was self-perpetuating and indomitable. Indeed, the hospital routine was so fixed and dependable it was as if it had a tangible existence, in its own right, of a life-force that had been built into the very foundations of the estate. It ran like the constantly operative conveyor belts, indispensable to the workings of a mine, permeating every tunnel, running beneath every supporting structure, maintaining the coal face effort, connecting every worker, every piece of equipment, and foretelling the infinitely foreseeable future. Irrespective of the individual staff that were on duty on any ward on any particular day, each shift descended into the shafts of the hospital whose viability was assured via an industry of well honed tasks, procedures and intentions, and economies of scale which, in turn, demanded the barest economy of thinking.

* * *

217

Ambition serves as a generous inflator of a person's potential until the deeper cries of self-awareness draw sensible attention to the harsh scarcity of personal abilities that each believes they possess. Now at the end of my formal training, I had acquired but a sparse theoretical knowledge of a range of care models, each having their very different strategies for working with various patient groups, but little practical experience of the vast majority of them. Initially, I had been impressed by the dynamic, democratic radicalism of therapeutic models such as the socio-therapeutic communities, and the inter-personal psychodynamic models. Unfortunately, I had begun to doubt whether I had the necessary emotional stamina for working in such environments: the protracted demands of patients, the need for personal insight, the expectation of personal therapy, the demands for communal integrity, the emotional furnace in which it was embroiled, the therapeutic confrontation, and the conflict resolution; these were beyond my stores of resilience and adherence. I concluded, at that time, that I was far from equipped to tolerate such environments where patients' anger, outrage, challenges and discontent were permitted to be voiced, explored and painstakingly resolved, even though they were only permitted within rigidly identified limits. Such centres often flourished around a type of patient whose problem was essentially one of "personality", often, but not exclusively, diagnosed as "psychopath" – a highly variable condition of needy, testing, stretching, manipulating, undermining, destroying, damaging, and damaged personalities. I sufficiently doubted my stress tolerance, personal resources, and resilience to question my effectiveness within such a system. For the immediate present I would resign myself to working with the schizophrenics, the depressed, the manic and their many derivatives in the secure and comfortable shade of an institutional bower. Of course, there were the more fractious classes of antisocial and borderline personalities, alcoholics and drug addicts, and the cunning resistance of those with eating disorders, all of whose uncompromising challenges exacted an equally uncompromising reaction from most, but not all, of the health professionals. It led to a curious dichotomy. It was possible to appreciate the predicament of patients with the challenging diagnoses, for whom there might be some empathy, but little sympathy, whereas the same was not to be said of the psychotic population for whom sympathy was highly probable, but empathy for their bizarre realities improbable.

Having survived three conflicting years of alternating stimulation, motivational lapses and, sometimes, the belief that I was completely wasting my time, I struggled through the training and emerged as a *Registered Mental Nurse*. But once the transformation from protected apprentice to exposed, responsible nursing graduate had been negotiated there emerged opportunities for taking control of events, for making your mark, for distinguishing yourself. And I knew all about competition and leadership! Leadership was a vehicle for exhibiting potential, for self-aggrandisement, having waited so long in the subordinate wings, so to speak. Paradoxically, this exciting transformation would have to try to flourish while I continued in one of the most environmentally barren wards in the hospital – the male, disturbed ward.

'Congratulations on your result,' says Ted, the Charge Nurse, on the morning of my final results. Ted's formal contributions to my training had been precious few but, with the exception of sharing his considerable sardonic humour, he also acquainted me with some truly indispensable survival tips that would hold anyone in good stead for many a future predicament. Little could it have been realised how extensively these principles would be used in the future.

Ted had, for some reason, waited on my return from the senior nursing office before sharing a belated breakfast. We stood scoffing the smoked kippers extracted from the patients' breakfast quota. Unlike the leathery, dry skinned samples distributed to the patients directly from the food trolley, Ted had removed the ones for the staff and lovingly softened them in a pan of simmering milk from the ward supply. He suddenly broke off to ask his exuberant companion what I would do if Kilbride, the Director of Nursing, his very self, was to walk into the kitchen at that very moment.

'Go on, what would you do? He walks in, right now, and you've got that fucking kipper half way down your gullet with its tail kissing your lips. What would you do?'

'I've no bloody idea. Finish my mouthful, out of good manners, and swallow hard?'

'You'd swallow hard, all right. Well, you ain't exactly going to spit it out, are you? That's tantamount – that's a fucking good word at this time of the morning – that's *tantamount* to admitting you're doing something wrong, silly bollocks!' I am now seriously choking on a laugh which actually does

219

have a kipper's arse lodged in it.

'What you do is... you say... "Good morning, Mr. Kilbride, and have you had any breakfast this morning because we have a kipper that was left over from breakfast, if you would like it?"' Spitting and spluttering fish flesh over the remains of my breakfast plate, I can only snigger and cough at the audacity of it. 'Course, he's not going to accept but you've got a better fucking chance of getting away with it than if you act all guilty as *you* would have done, you pillock!'

'Have you ever tried to bring that off? I mean, are you talking from experience?' But Ted is enjoying this, ignores the interruption, and continues.

'And while we're at it, what would you do if you were escorting a bunch of lunatics along the corridor and the Director of Nursing, his very self, stops you and asks how many lunatics you're escorting? Only, the thing is, you've either forgotten, or didn't know in the first place. What you going to say?'

'Umm, pass! I haven't a clue!'

'That's no fucking answer. Think of the consequences, you dumb shit!'

'Still pass.'

'Well, before you get yourself sacked, you say the first fucking number that comes into your head, see, because he's not going to have any idea and he sure as hell ain't going to stop and count them, is he? Then you just get on your way because you're supposed to be looking out for your lunatics.'

'Thanks for that, then.' These are pearls of humour as much as pragmatically indispensable tips. I'm preparing to leave the kitchen, still relishing the new status of now being qualified and equally assured that I'm grasping more and more of the hospital's street culture that will help see me through any coming crises. Ted's appraising chorus is like a short bladed thrust in the back.

'As I was saying, congratulations on passing your exams. Now you're a fully certified, fucking lunatic attendant!'

* * *

Everyone had learned of Ted's very personal battle with graduation during his training years, which was spread over several attempts to pass the Final examination, and how it had created a singular, if understandable, lack of ambition for advancement and not a little notoriety within the hospital community.

And these facts were, simply, part of his abiding charm! In keeping with my somewhat masculinist orientation, I suppose, and the unpredictability of the patient group, the one field that had come to interest me was that of the "violent and disturbed" category of patient. Hence, my extended contact with Ted.

'What's your opinion of forensic work to make a future career of, Ted? That's what's appealing to me, right now,' expecting a reasonable chat with him on such a subject.

'Really, well, you'll need to do the two Broadmoor courses, then,' urges the sage. 'They've got a couple of courses: Management of Violence, and Working in Secure Environments; they're the only courses worth doing in mental nursing. None of this General Nursing crap that so many blokes go for. Do you know how many of these blokes here will start the General Nursing course and give it up in no time?'

'I've learned there are quite a number,' I confirm. There was a long established trend of graduating male mental nurses who had gone onto General Nurse training, then given up, prematurely, and rationalised it away as being superfluous to the psychiatric field and their personal ambitions. Not many of them carried the stamp of professional interest about them, while just one or two, who were more dedicated, had had the misfortune to have attempted it, and failed.

'Well, I know where they're coming from, myself. It's a different world altogether. I wouldn't want to have to bleeding well work with all those women. Having to watch your Ps and Qs with the ruddy Sisters. A right bloody carry-on!' I allow myself a little sneer at Ted's stance on the issue.

'Don't you bleeding sneer in my direction, Burrows, you supercilious prick!' snaps Ted, good-naturedly.

'I reckon it's more because the general hospitals are a culture shock and our guys can't handle the intensity of it all after languishing in this place,' I add, presumptuously. 'Women bossing them about! They're having to get their fingers out for a change! It's too disciplined and formal; they have to be on their toes, and there's a lot of bowing and scraping to the doctors, none of which they're able to tolerate. I don't doubt that it's a far cry from sitting about on a psychiatric ward, reading the paper, and not being hounded by a doctor, or anyone, from one week to another,' I pontificate.

'Yeah, the females let the doctors walk all over them, apparently! It's far easier just to bail out and return to the easy life and what they were used to. Well, it ain't surprising really, is it?'

'D'yer reckon? I mean, it has to damage their chances of promotion if they haven't got their *General* ticket, surely.' Being doubly qualified was, indeed, an assurance of future promotion.

'Well, I haven't got the bleeding ticket and I'm running a ward!'

'Yes, but will you go any further?'

'Might consider going for a Nursing Officer's post. Anyway, do you have to go further? I'm happy as I am and you couldn't say that about many of them, that's for sure! Any roads, most of us can get promotion if we really want it. Don't normally take long, either.' The Charge Nurse hoists his feet up onto the office table and slides into his nicotine stained fingers another cigarette from a crushed packet he takes from his trouser pockets. 'Anyway, as I was saying, Burrows, just shut your mouth for a fucking minute, will you? The Broadmoor courses are the best bloody ticket you can get. It shows you can deal with difficult patients and that's what counts in these places. Gets you out of this bloody place for a while, an' all. You have a bloody good time in the bargain because that Broadmoor's got some fantastic facilities, I'm telling you! Their club house has got to be the best in the business. Proper dance hall, ruddy good beer and lager, loads of crumpet and the best hospital dining hall and scoff I've ever experienced. Do you know what they call their ward areas where the staff eat? They call them a mess, 'cos they're part of the prison service.' Ted is always at his most contented, it seems, when he's reminiscing.

'Mess?' I quiz.

'That's what the Prison Service calls the dining room. Special Hospitals are part of the Prison Service *and* they're part of the NHS. I thought of working there myself. Probably the only place I'd try to move to, actually. No fucking pissing about with patients there. Everyone knows where they stand. Guess what happens when the panic bell goes off? Well, say some bastard patient kicks off and a member of staff hits the button? The staff come from all over the hospital and stream onto the ward where there's trouble, just like here, but if there's anyone in their way who's not wearing a white coat they just flatten 'em. Ha, ha, ha! No pissing about.' The skin either side of his nose curdles into a surly grin and a stream of satisfied smoke is pumped from the nostrils.

'Bloody hell, that's a bit strong, isn't it? How do you know that's true, anyway?' I query, incredulously.

'Ask the patients, the ones who've been transferred from there. You'll find them around the hospital.'

'But even then, these things are easy to make up. Makes them feel more important and builds up their reputation that they've had to handle the hard man regime.'

'You know, I wonder about you sometimes, Mr. Burrows. You're quite a sceptical bastard, on the quiet, aren't you?'

* * *

I acknowledged that within this institutional bower I had enjoyed a redemptive fate. But as my self-confidence billowed with responsibility, the longer term effect was to acknowledge that the place was not sufficiently stimulating to sustain my continued loyalty for any foreseeable future. Perhaps I had grown independent of the old place, or believed it could offer little that could satiate my rekindled quest for achievement? Ambition would lead elsewhere. Within a few months of qualifying, bereft of any other immediate goals within the hospital, and craving reparation of the interruption to my education, I left the old asylum, the estate, and its culture, in search of prestige and intellectual sustenance elsewhere. I applied for University, basked in the elevation that an undergraduate status at an exceptional university bestows, and gained a creditable qualification. Following immediately on, I returned to nursing via a General Nurse Training in a London Teaching Hospital – more elitism – now keener to mix the academic with the practical. Then, surprisingly, after having been stoked with the recent campaign of six years of achievement, I found myself ascending the long, umbilical thoroughfare to the old asylum, once more, for a second stint.

It wasn't exactly a vocation that returned me to the psychiatric field. It was a combined motivation of earning more money as a Mental Nurse, and of the assurance of faster promotion prospects after the rigours of my recent development, and of removing myself from six years in the London metropolis. There were still the same elements that had first attracted me to that old institution, and its paternalistic resonance. More than just a physical return to a known place it was a homecoming to the consummate peacefulness of the rural, Surrey idyll and the institution that had stabilised and set me on a career path. By the time I returned in that period of the mid-1980s, it was like gaining a posting in a colonial outpost in the last throws of the psychiatric empire just before its dissolution.

Meantime, the hospital authorities had done their best to keep abreast of some of the major demands for change. For example, on an early sortie along the hospital corridors, I happened on one of the former, long stay patients casually mooching alongside of me, who, I thought, must have escaped and was in danger of being lost! Unhesitatingly, I cajoled the patient, Malcolm, to accompany me back to the long stay ward and, with my door key at the ready, found it to be open. By now, telegraphing that either a catalogue of errors was afoot, or I was making a serious mistake, we approached the staff languishing outside the office on the ward gallery, only to discover that the ward's status as a locked unit had been terminated. It was now a rehabilitation facility, and the patients were no longer considered to be vulnerable or a nuisance and were now free to wander about the estate! Astounding! How had the patients adjusted? How had the staff? What must those first few days have been like?

'And has it worked?' I ask of the staff, no one now recognisable from the time that I had been there, and Stan, the old Charge Nurse, having retired.

'Well, you win some, you lose some,' is the ironic contribution of an older nursing assistant who lifts the front legs of his chair to slouch back against the radiator.

'Now, now, less of your cynicism,' interjects the Mauritian Charge Nurse, who always had a reputation for diligence and playing with a very straight bat, as well as an obsequious reverence for superiors, and who comments in characteristically upbeat fashion, 'You've got to admit it works most of the time.'

'I don't know if that's what Whitey would have to say about it,' continues the faintly mocking nursing assistant. 'I can't help effusing at the memory of the old boy.'

'Old Whitey, is the old blighter still about? What I wouldn't give to see him again!'

'You wouldn't want to wish that on yourself, now. He's dead!'

224

'Oh, what a shame. What a character he was. How come, anyway?'

'Well, it's as I say, you win some, you lose some,' the Nursing Assistant says, casting a wary glance toward the Mauritian, but gathering confidence that his sardonic view might be appreciated. 'He took himself off on his wanders, one day, and never came back. His decomposing body was found weeks later – wait for it, now – *under the office of the Director of Nursing*!' he intones in an exaggerated emphasis at which even the Charge Nurse smiles broadly.

'Never!'

'Never say never! Honest, as true as I'm standing here. Wandered into the cellar area and got himself locked in – must have starved to death, poor bugger. Can you imagine him, down there, cussing and hallucinating for all he was worth, minus his medication, until his dying breath? Tragic, tragic.' The woeful tale does not prevent the teller from ending with a sigh of quiet satisfaction that is a repudiation of the folly of the hospital management for allowing such a liberal plan to go ahead. I muse on whether there had come a moment when Whitey, after crapping, and starving, and emotionally desperate with terror, had a stark realisation that he was not about to be rescued and that he was going to die.

'That is so eerie,' is my ridiculous understatement. 'To die right beneath them! As if to send the clearest possible message to the management – tragic! It's bloody comical! Certainly ironic!'

'Well, thank God, those incidents don't happen too often,' says the Mauritian. 'Now, tell us, Steve, how are you? Haven't seen you for years, it seems. You've come back to join us, eh? I hear you've been a busy boy since last we met,' rubbing his long, manicured hands vigorously in a show of appreciation.

'Well, I had some catching up to do. Had to get one or two things out of the system, as they say. But, yep, couldn't keep away, as they say. I've come back for a quieter life.'

'Good for you, my boy. Now, you will have to turn your attention to the opportunities that are opening up.' There is no doubting the pleasure from receiving the encouragement of a mature and steady soul.

'All in good time, thanks. Anyway, how about you, Al?'

'Well, I married, I bought my house, now I'm a Charge Nurse; the next thing is children, maybe.' It's wholly in keeping that he should so methodically organise his life into successively premeditated steps, the one requiring to be accomplished prior to the next. His brother is an altogether different fish – lackadaisical, unambitious, humorous, sociable and lusty!

'And when you arrived in England just a few years ago you had nothing, I'm guessing!'

'Correct. But that's what we do, we Mauritians. We work hard for what we have and we're proud of it.' That cannot be denied and not only the Mauritians. Most of the foreign staff have this diligent work ethic, working every hour possible. Many of us are to be found in the educational sector, rather than staying on the wards, ducking the flying shit and bullets!

'Well, it's been a pleasure catching up with you, Al,' and, glancing toward all three of them on his exit, 'this has been a most fruitful visit, gentlemen. I wouldn't have missed it for anything,' I tail off, ironically. As I exit the gallery it doesn't escape my attention that there's not much of a trace of environmental renovation to accompany the patients' freedoms. Another residual thought is that Malcolm, presumably against his inclination, had not offered one syllable of protest, not one sign of objection, when he had been challenged on the corridor and been returned to his ward. More than that, Malcolm had remained on the ward when he could have walked off again.

*   *   *

Unlocking virtually all the wards of the large institutions was momentum enough but there were other tidal changes gathering in the offing that should have culminated in an irrepressible surge against the harboured waters of the old asylums. During the late 1970s the burgeoning vortex of political and professional initiatives that tore across the psychiatric terrain had, as one of its major targets, the dismantling of these Victorian institutions, but they, and all that sailed in them, were not quite finished.

The year 1979 was a cumulatively significant one for British mental health care, psychiatric nursing, and nursing in general. Chief among the recommendations of a Department of Health and Social Security consultative paper was the indubitable claim that the National Health Service existed to serve its patients and that the needs of its patients must be paramount. The paper was called 'Patients First'. This was news to the psychiatric nurse of the asylum who had thrived on an alliance of beneficence, utilitarianism and, ultimately, power, the sum total of which could not honestly claim to have put the patient before their own interests, ever. Psychiatric nursing's unquestioned authority, with the potential to resort to physical force, if absolutely necessary, was a calculated, intentional use of power in the face of any disrespectful or miscreant patient who fancied their chances challenging it. Not that the use of power was seen as an ultimate act of institutional repression that compromised the ethical care of the patient body. It was more of an indispensable contingency to deal with patient opposition and pugnacity. But there was a contemporary controversy around the use of power, and control, and repression. A spate of published Inquiries into allegations relating to the physical and psychological abuses in hospitals for psychiatric and mentally subnormal patients encroached into the public forum in the very same year of 1979. It was the usual practice of ward staff in mental hospitals to take little heed of these published maelstroms from elsewhere – other than for the purpose of professional voyeurism – since they believed their relevance was confined to the faulty, distant establishments within which they occurred, and should not be generalised to other organisations. During 1979, the most powerful of these Inquiries, a television documentary entitled *The Secret Hospital*, exposed the regime of an institution which had become marooned in time, place and practice, while parallel police investigations resulted in the criminal convictions of nurses for physical assaults and abuse of patients, after several others had been discharged in the court room. Rampton Hospital – formerly Rampton Criminal Lunatic Asylum – had operated a perverse, militaristic discipline upon its male patients who were expected to change from their day to night clothes in the ward corridors; to wear collar ties at all times; to refrain from talking during mealtimes; and to ask permission to re-enter the ward day room after having lit their cigarettes. This regime echoed not only the prison system, but the "silent" prison system which limited the personal communication between individual inmates. Even to the traditional nurses, apprenticed in the forges of the county asylums, this concerted oppression was a qualitatively perverse regime way beyond their comprehension. If Rampton had acquired a reputation that would have sat comfortably in the Hammer House of Horrors, it was the power of a television documentary to influence public opinion, along with national newspaper headlines and, finally, an official Inquiry into the hospital's entire organisational structure during the following year, that accelerated all the issues of asylum institutionalisation and brought them to the foreground of healthcare debate.

In turn, this maelstrom was hooked up to the escalating expectations of public bodies, and the social policy of politicians and health professions, that were highlighting the rights, liberties and health of the mentally ill and handicapped in what was yet another wave of reform. Another, not insignificant current, was the emerging professionalisation of nursing – a necessary transition for the challenges ahead, and to effect some credibility, parity of purpose, and equality in relation to other paramedical groups. The nursing establishment attempted to modernise its members to measure up to the technological, interpersonal, and academic innovations of a rapidly changing healthcare. In law, the *1979 Nurses, Midwives and Health Visitors Act* established a new governing body to take over from the former General Nursing Council and initiated a slow revolution for the occupation of nursing. The aim was to show that the nursing fraternity had the capacity to monitor and maintain itself as a professional body that was equal to any other. Developmentally, nursing was no longer to be characterised by a once and for all qualification that could, conceivably, see its members through the rest of their career without it ever being updated. For their part, individual nurses were obliged to become personally responsible for their occupational updating of skills and training, in keeping with any other professional body. Such a transformation could not have proceeded without an overhaul of all the training programmes leading to nurse registration. Each discrete field – the nursing of adults, the nursing of children, the mental nursing, and mental handicap nursing – had a revised training syllabus by 1982. For the mental nursing field this was, potentially, the most strategic tsunami to breach the established nursing defences. For traditionalist "attendants" in the field, the very first mouthful of the new syllabus would have been enough to choke on, placing, as it did, a hitherto unacknowledged emphasis on the students' need for *self-awareness* in the way they conducted themselves as nurses; that the psychiatric recruit should have more than a working self-knowledge of their assumptions, prejudices, motives, and body language, and how these affected others. The implications went far beyond the training remit. How would the prevailing, qualified nursing contingent survive the heat of such an appraisal? To the reactionary attendants it must have read like a psychotherapeutic infiltration, possibly with Communist leanings! Up until now, it could be confidently assumed that most psychiatric nurses were endemically predisposed to the traditional view that their patients' mental illness was a fixed, generally deteriorating entity that drifted, inexorably, toward chronic debilitation and death. There was little expectation of improvement or cure, not out of disrespect or perversity, but because their hospital experience exposed them to very little sign of therapeutic innovation or success. Most of their patients had come to stay, indefinitely it appeared, so that the occupational aim of actively cultivating patient health for the hospital in-patient hardly occurred to the staff. The idea of mental health belonged outside of the hospital, in the community. In a word, mental wellness and mental illness were almost mutually exclusive. However, the wider cultural and social policy momentum was fast pressurising the average psychiatric and mental handicap nurse into an occupational conundrum. The traditional containment of illness and the dampening of difficult and deviant conduct within the precincts of the hospital, that had amounted to nothing less than a social control agency, was now required to be transformed into a mental health service. The challenge now was how to negotiate, with the clients' cooperation, a therapeutic path through their emotional, social and behavioural difficulties to effect their mental health and their integration back into the wider community! Psychiatric nursing, or mental nursing, was now old money. The new currency was *mental health* nursing. As such, it was supposed to be moving from the concentrated enclosure of mental illness to the liberated open fields of mental health. They would no longer have to be sentinels who guarded the imperial might of medical diagnoses and medical treatment but were, like a newly constituted peasant army commencing with humble beginnings, to take responsibility for their own nurse-determined diagnoses and nursing care to match these. Even among those mental nurses with the will to follow this through they soon realised that they did not have the knowledge and skills to facilitate mental health.

* * *

When any nurse gained their first major promotion to Ward Sister or Charge Nurse and took charge of their first ward they landed themselves at the very centre of a human and organisational vortex. The sense of achievement, increased status, responsibility and salary, no more than justly reflecting their incremental experience and personal confidence, soon did battle with managerial expectations from above, staff demands from below, and client needs to the left and right. And pressing from within were the nagging self-doubts about their competence and confidence to keep these pressures in some sort of balance. Everyone soon learned that they would cope a good deal better than they could have imagined. Shortly after returning to the old hospital in the mid-1980s, for my second career stint there, I was promoted to a Charge Nurse position in the "disturbed" facility. For me, there had always been an attraction for the uncertain and unpredictable nature of "disturbed" behaviour, whether it be the long-term, intermittently volatile patient, or the acutely psychotic episode. Perhaps I just responded to the stimulation, but I was also not deterred by the demands of patient aggression and violence. This was no accident, in retrospect. Whereas the whole of my psychiatric nursing experience had thrown up all manner of debates about the advantages, as well as the limitations, of psychiatry there was something immediate, unequivocal, and challenging about the nursing management of behaviour which was unpredictable and risky. This was magnified in the rush of adrenaline that was provoked by the emergency incident. When the emergency alarm was activated in any ward it was relayed through every area of the hospital complex, alerting all available staff – male staff was the expectation – that they were required to come to the assistance of their colleagues. For good reason, it was assumed that the trouble was emanating from one of the disturbed wards and the lads would belt off, pell-mell, to either area, or wait for a telephone call to confirm the requisite destination before leaping out of their wards, bolting unceremoniously through the corridors and flights of stairs, and finally pouring into the offending incident like a molten surge. However popular, or disliked, were the staff under threat the rescue – as it was perceived – was an unquestioned obligation. Some rescuers would need to show off their strength and courage and indispensability. There was some merit to the suggestion that such incidents were almost welcomed as a timely means of promoting the reassuring illusion of staff solidarity, and that they acted as a deliberate reminder to the more disruptive, violent patients of who, exactly, was in control of the hospital. And, for those individuals who could control the relatively uncontrollable, a certain reputation and kudos could be gleaned. I think it true to say that I never quite abandoned these illusions myself.

During my absence from the old asylum the formerly "disturbed" facilities had been subjected to an organisational and semantic facelift. The two previous single sexed wards had been revamped into a single, mixed gender "intensive care unit", and had been operational for a couple of undistinguished years. In terms of clinical purism, the revised purpose of "intensive care" was to focus resources on the actively disturbed patient, for the minimum period of residence, so that the patient could resume their treatment back in the original facility as soon as the disturbed phase was over. In this way, the intensive care ward would become a self-consciously therapeutic unit, not just a dumping ground for the hospital cast offs as was its traditional function. Done effectively, this would preclude the patient from acquiring the master label of a "disturbed patient". In reality, the current care was no more "intensive" than it was "extensive"! The change in title was not accompanied by any change in regime or objectives. Effectively, nothing had altered. And the reason was because the single intensive care ward was immediately filled with the long stay disturbed contingent from the previous two single sex units. Long-term patients remained under stimulated, deteriorating month after month, with intermittent episodes when they would "blow". This militated against fulfilling a philosophy of short-term, intensive throughput but, in fairness to the hospital authorities, they were trying to respond to evolving policies while, at the same time, having to locate their chronic clients in residence.

The succession of former Charge Nurses, not to mention people in superior managerial positions, who could have taken responsibility for ensuring some forward momentum, had seemingly lacked the personal energy for change or to alter the hospital's customary ways. The overall ward regime could not have had a more poignant representation than the condition of the ward office. The office was a waste-paper den, so completely stashed with paperwork, official documentation, memos, circulars and the like, it seemed that the staff had been informally contracted to save every scrap and to paper every wall in incoming mental health administration. As each fresh, printed communication landed on the office desk I had an image of the staff avidly skewering it with a drawing pin and stabbing it onto the surrounding walls to create their own casual street hoarding. Outside the office, both staff and patients listlessly littered the ward space. The former displayed no overall goals and scorned and spirited away the current professional development influencing their profession and that should have demanded their attention. Unsurprisingly, the patients dragged their institutionalised imaginations through the long, seamless days. This languor ensured that, like other wards in the hospital, staff could assume a relaxed pose and appraise world events in their scrupulous reading of the ward delivered tabloids. The ward regime was so languorous that one of the side rooms, which had been given over to an ex Broadmoor patient in order to quieten his remonstrations that this was what he had been accustomed to in that institution, had gradually been converted, through accumulation and an entrenched encampment, into something betwixt an Aladdin's Cave and a defensive military pillbox. This smacked of doing anything for a quiet time.

There's little doubt that my time away from the old hospital had afforded me one or two fortuitous advantages over my colleagues who had remained behind. I could not help but be just a tad more predisposed toward accepting the benefits of change from my General Nurse Training at a London Teaching Hospital, and the intellectual niceties of a delayed university education. I must have hit the ground running when I came into post because the first transitional hurdle was the new mental health legislation that had been introduced during the previous year, namely, the ***Mental Health Act (1983)***. Such legislation, like that which it was replacing, legitimated everything that could be done to manage and treat people with a mental disorder, including its very definition. The Act was not something you could take up and peruse like a text book garnished, as it was, in legalistic jargon. Political concern was reflected in reshaping mental health services and improving the lot of the mental patient. The Act was such a comprehensive re-evaluation of the services to the mentally ill and mentally handicapped, with far-reaching implications for the mental health professionals, that it required to have a supplementary Code of Practice published to fully explicate the obfuscating legal language of the Act. You tried to confine yourself only to that which was pertinent to your own occupational needs. Nevertheless, patients' rights were being celebrated and protecting their citizenship as they became a mental patient, the length of time for which they could be held against their will, and the various paths which would remove them from those restrictions.

In 1984, the first year of my return, General Management was introduced into the National Health Service via the ***Griffith's Report***. Although mental health care, indeed all healthcare, is built on political legitimization, it also requires a localised, managerial structure that can bring the law into operation. The Griffith's Report concluded that the NHS had no coherent management system at local level and recommended the introduction of private sector organisation into the Health Service. General Management, the General Manager, and Line Management were introduced to rationalise the use of resources and provide a continuous evaluation of its performance. Decrying the former management model of management by consensus, it made identifiable individuals responsible and accountable for the control and rationalisation of the service, along the lines of subsidiarity. This localised authority was considered more liberating and empowering of local resources and decision making than having these determined by a detached government department. The launch of this radical restructuring coincided, in the same year, with the publication of a book enumerating a series of damning inquires about the unprofessional conduct of staff, scandalous conditions, and the ill-treatment, even patient deaths, pertaining to life in a large number of psychiatric hospitals, since the 1960s. The book, ***Hospitals in Trouble***, by J. Martin, presented the adverse Inquiry findings on a number of hospitals for the mentally disordered. Whether we were familiar with this text, at the time, I'm not so sure but we certainly picked up anecdotal information about its revelations from various sources. The general conclusion among we nursing staff was that any hospital for the mentally ill and mentally handicapped, not excluding ourselves, could have become victims to such scrutiny and that it was only a matter of good fortune that the remainder had not been so identified!

* * *

Consequently, I became promoted to a position of relative authority at a time when new mental health legislation, a new managerial structure, a new training syllabus, a sobering exposé, and a new framework for organising nursing care (yet to be outlined), were radicalising mental health currency. But at ward level there were the most basic matters to be altered, for starters. As an early focus, it was none too difficult to set to, excavating the legacy of these office relics, and the stash contained in the Broadmoor pillbox, and I positively relished the order that this state of affairs brought about. Essentially, the former Broadmoor patient had to be conned into the necessary restructuring of the ward whereby we claimed to require his side-room as an additional seclusion area. It was some feat convincing him to return to a dormitory life as this would lower his status in the eyes of both patients and staff. But the keener focus was to move onto nurse generated therapeutic work that was not reliant on the instigation of either a psychiatrist or any other professional. I found myself in familiar territory, trying to gain control over an uncertain situation through well honed strategies of endeavour that would yield achievement and recognition. A necessary corollary to personal endeavour is that you tend to baulk at others' more desultory efforts. Not much would move on if other staff were to continue with their habitual mores, to be indolent and carefree or, God help them, show active resistance! It was an interesting position. Does change actually require individuals with such character traits who were prepared to set a counter-current in motion and risk the chagrin of others?

For the many staff who didn't realise the full implications of these changes they were, none the less, outraged by what minute implications they did understand and the affront they posed to the ancien régime. For this very substantial minority, they were so confident that they could ignore the gathering and swirling currents of change that there wasn't even an effort to build up their defences, and they simply ignored the whole process of change. It wasn't going to be given the chance to upset the tried and tested routine that had been eked out over the decades. For some others, understandably, they just did not have the personal resources to respond to all this. After all, many of them had been originally employed when they had not been expected to think along these lines and now they were being expected to respond to this educational and professional inflation. Many staff cynically entrusted their fate to a collective, reactionary backlash against this presumptuous and superfluous assault on their rôle. Owing to established practice, nursing activity still constituted either a carrying out of medical instructions or its own catalogue of customary routines. Regarding the latter, for example, a patient's weekly bath was noted in the ward bath book; their weekly or monthly injections of anti-psychotic medication registered in the injection book; their monthly weight in the weight book, etc. In other words, the patient care was aligned to the ward machinations as the institution turned the patients within its rotating wheels. There had to be a pretty unexpected or untoward event such as an outside visit, an accident, a violent confrontation, or an investigative procedure, for it to deserve being logged in the nurses' notes. Their observations, such as they were, were written onto a collection of small cards, each representing a single patient, which actually dissuaded staff from making extensive entries. Their diminutive size, alone, symbolised the lack of authority and significance of their professional contribution, and discouraged any official recording beyond that which was exceptional. Nurses didn't write in the patients' individual case files which were the preserve of the doctors. This, together with an absence of any formal patient review, other than in the presence of a psychiatrist at ward rounds, meant that weeks could pass without nurses needing to register any significant notes. They had been institutionalised into waiting on the initiatives of their medical superiors, something to which many were not, exactly, opposed. To a very large extent, nursing communication resembled the oral tradition of a localised tribe which, because of their shared physical terrain, needed only to pass on their knowledge through word of mouth and hand it on to future generations. Among the ramifications were that when an official visitor, or another health discipline, or relative, requested a contemporary update on a patient's independent progress, they would often have to rely on the word of mouth of the very staff on duty on the day. Feast or famine! Such communication fell lamentably short of professionalism! But for the more adaptable staff, they saw the opportunity for both service and personal development, and how they could enhance ambition and career and therapeutic experimentation.

But a professionalisation of the staff demanded a represented, protected status for their patients who were now to become individuals receiving a service. Patients were to be reframed as "clients". The notion of a client was also not so easily accommodated by others in the professional hierarchy, such as medical, psychology and psychotherapy staff who managed their *clients* in their private practices – and whose notion of a *client* rested on a financially contractual, voluntary relationship – while the *patients* of their NHS contracts were an altogether different animal! In most respects, though, it projected positive inferences which cast the clients as fellow actors with leading rôles in the health production, not merely stage hands who participated from the wings while all major roles were ascribed to the staff. Client it was, then. The client was to be seen as a person, a whole person, and nothing but a person, who deserved to have their holistic needs addressed, schematically and comprehensively. That was the theory!

* * *

I had a determination not to be associated with a relative backwater of a ward. Not so difficult for someone who was achievement orientated, and seeking recognition at the best of times! Our Intensive Care Ward had been forewarned that we were on the itinerary of the League of Friends – hearty representatives of Middle England, no doubt, who would cross the day room boards with the easy carriage of self-importance – who would be completing a tour of the hospital estate. This threat helped me to justify a review of our unit and I conjured a formal staff meeting, after a speedy handover, outside of the office – something unheard of at ward level! All grades of staff were present. I begin by putting a question to the assembly.

'As you know, the League of Friends are about to descend on us soon. In case they ask us to justify our responsibilities on this ward I thought we might benefit from putting our heads together. It would certainly help me, I don't mind saying! Perhaps I could kick off by asking how our *intensive care ward* earns its reputation, as such? Would anyone have any suggestions?'

'Well, we have a different type of patient from the rest of the hospital, in the first place. They can be unpredictable and difficult quite a lot of the time. Only a locked ward can control them, really. Then, nobody else would really want them!' says Alex, a Mauritian Staff Nurse of some years.

'Agreed, but explain the *intensive care* bit. Do we do that? What do we do, exactly?' I retort.

'I'm sure you Charge Nurses will explain that better than I can,' Alex prevaricates with an evasive smile. But we Charge Nurses – Mick is my opposite number – don't want to explain anything right now.

'Look, sometimes Mick and I are stuck in the office, attending patient reviews, or attending off ward sessions, so you're the people who hold the fort every hour of the day. We'd appreciate *your* opinion.'

'Basically, we know our patients pretty well, keep a very close eye on them, have higher staffing levels, can intervene immediately, and defuse their behaviour. I mean, that's it really,' Alex rejoins.

Ling, a male Chinese Malaysian, who has also been a Staff Nurse for a number of years and has an exceptionally relaxed persona, pipes up. 'Yeah, I mean there's nothing to make a song and dance about, is there?' Broad smile, slumps back in his chair. 'Our unit has one job and that's to contain the problem patients so's the rest of the hospital can get on with *their* job.'

'Yes, okay, I'm just wondering about the intensive side of things, though!' I reiterate. Ling continues: 'Well, if they're hallucinating, I give them reassurance and try to distract them, get them to talk about it, or occupy them, maybe. Half the time they're happy with their voices and aren't particularly upset, anyway. If they're deluded, I try and talk them out of it, try to bring them back down to reality, if I think it's necessary. Depending on the patient's mood, it may be all right to have a joke about it. All depends. If there's any sign of suspiciousness, or risk of aggression, or risk of hurting themselves, or wanting to cause damage, then I start to think about keeping them clear of other patients and whether they should have extra medication. Then I'll probably discuss it with someone else. All the usual stuff. I understand the illness, I know my patient, and I only discuss what they want to talk about. I don't go prying; it's just asking for trouble. Let sleeping dogs lie,' he states, with a wry grin. 'I just do what I've been trained to do – what we've all been trained for, really.' He looks at me as if to say there's nothing to be gained by pursuing this. Alex's attitude also conveys a stance that everyone's time is being wasted, and concludes.

'That's it. We nurse them all the same. We observe the behaviour, the speech, any hallucinations or delusions, any bizarre actions, give medication, restrain if we have to, and report unusual behaviour to the person in charge, then the doctor.'

'So, basically, we leave them alone until they start to worry us,' wryly interjects Mick, the Charge Nurse who heads the opposite team of staff – and another Irishman.

'Well, there's no point in sitting them down and reminding them of their difficulties, is there? They'd rather forget them, frankly,' Ling continues. As I'm listening to this I realise the juxtaposition of justifying your work, with whether this is all that reveals our ignorance, with whether it is all a rationalisation for inaction, or whether we've been given an unrealistic task to fulfil.

'Do you think you have to have particular qualities to work with this kind of patient, then?' I prompt.

'Not really,' rejoins Ling. 'Everyone's different, aren't they? All the staff have different personalities. If we were all the same we'd probably not pick up on all the patients' problems. What one person misses, another takes note of. More to the point, not everyone can deal with every patient. That's why we're a team of different characters. As long as the team are all keeping on their toes, the job gets done. There's nothing fancy about it. Anyway, we all want a quiet life at the end of the day.'

'So, if it's down to our individual characters, what's the point of the training?' I ask.

'Well, I'm not qualified and I don't have none of your fancy ideas but I can work with any patient as well as anyone, in my opinion,' says Lou, an African-Caribbean female, Nursing Assistant, with her customary cheery smile. 'You're trained to take responsibility, deal with all the paper work, keep everything legal, like. That's what you're good at. But the patients, that's our job and sometimes you can actually interfere with how we handle situations, if you don't mind me saying. Nothing against you, like.' I scurry for an angle on this to retrieve some justification for my existence! Mick has an angle.

'They're not disturbed, or difficult, or anti-social, or destructive, all the time. So what are we doing with them, otherwise? What about the patients' basic problems, the mental state that causes the challenging behaviours? Do you think we get to grips with these at all? Is it our job to do that? Or should we be handing them over to another ward once the disturbance has settled? Shouldn't our job be done, then? In other words, we could, in theory, be closed if we do our work well,' he poses. He's got a good head on his shoulders when he chooses to use it. Everyone discounts this and is absolutely assured that this ward has been set up for these current patients because no one else will have them, and that it should cater for the occasional new disturbance from others. Essentially, this ward has been created for a hard core of patients. Calling it an intensive care ward is just a managerial sleight of hand. It's difficult to disagree.

'Well, you probably know that we're supposed to be using the Nursing Process, whatever kind of patient, or service, we're managing. Do you think that could help?'

'Oh that! It's just a paper exercise!' Alex decries.

'Well, your lords and masters, in their infinite wisdom, obviously don't think so,' says Mick, with a curling smirk.

'Okay, so you don't think it really helps, but have you given it a go?' I remonstrate.

'We started it recently, but it would be true to say that we don't really know what we're doing,' Mick answers candidly.

'Well then, let's give it a go and learn as we go along. It can't do anyone any harm,' I say, jauntily, but with some conviction. And before we retired from the meeting, the ward's total complement of qualified staff had divided the 24 patients of the mixed gender Intensive Care Ward between them – resulting in an allocation of two to three clients each. Each of these "primary nurses" would be supported by another member of staff who took up the role of "associate nurse" – bloody silly titles, but there it was! Each primary nurse would become the major resource and take responsibility for *organising* the programme of care around that individual. This was in stark contrast to the previous regime where nobody in the team, other than the person in charge, took any special responsibility for a client except as a matter of personal, and arbitrary, indulgence. Patients were selected on the basis of personal preference, affinities, and aptitudes. This self selecting allocation ensured that those who wished to make an impact and prove their credentials generally selected the most recalcitrant clients while those investing little enthusiasm selected the easiest patients to handle.

Yet another fortuitous ingredient was added to the mix in the form of a recently appointed female Senior Registrar, of South African origin, who was an indispensable, enthusiastic component and imbued the team with a refreshingly democratic style and genuine interest. I took quite a shine to her – a lady with refinement and charm.

* * *

239

The Nursing Process was an American import that had come to bed itself into the professional consciousness of policy makers for Britain's nurses. My lower resistance to it was owed to my period of General Nurse Training at a London Teaching Hospital, where I had benefited from being sprinkled with its early showers before the heavier fronts, that thundered on behind, attempted to saturate the entire nursing terrain. The Nursing Process exposed just how much nursing had, up until now, virtually ignored the active achievement of the mental health of individual patients. On the contrary, patients and their problems were all thrown into the collective pile and crushed beneath the grinding slabs of the hospital mill. From now on, the collectivising hold which institutional practice had preserved would be detonated into history. The new position now demanded that the more or less arbitrary behaviour of individual nurses be substituted with the more rationally organised planning of care in response to individual patient needs. Every individual patient! The Nursing Process was no gimmick. It invoked a whole new nursing ideology and language which attempted to keep apace of the wider health care initiatives taking place. It did not constitute the care in itself. It was an administrative vehicle, a procedural framework, for reorganising nursing care in a more systematic way, for approaching patients as individuals, for structuring the care with dedicated planning. It offered the potential for individual bespoke care. On an almost daily basis the staff of the intensive care unit, as with those in the wider hospital, spewed their scepticism over the intrusion into their practice, and, while I had some sympathy for their reticence, I harboured a stronger resolve not to allow this to jeopardise the implementation of an initiative that could open up so much versatility. Furthermore, there was a real potential for exciting the team and changing the fortunes of the unit. All that could be lost was the past!

It was a revolution of sorts. But, like most revolutions, while it enjoyed the most notable success in some areas, it hardly trickled into the silted backwaters of many nursing constituencies. But, though it was an initiative for nurses, by nurses, its implementation depended on the commitment of its practitioners for, like so many professional objectives, it had neither mandatory nor legislative legs.

* * *

The most intriguing of the clients on the ward, mainly because of the sheer unpredictability and wide-ranging deviant behaviours he displayed, was Nial, diagnosed with both mental handicap and autism. For vast tracts of each day he inhabited his own lonely world, staring into the distance, frequently laughing to himself in a hallucinatory haze, showing precious little social initiative, pursuing his solitary interest of listening to music on the radio and television – to which he would rock backwards and forwards in a stereotypical rhythm. Sunday evenings were a particular pleasure for him owing to a radio programme which played the latest music charts and he never failed to remind the staff on duty when that programme would start. But he could erupt into violence against his environment or himself. Seemingly without apparent provocation, he used to smash the ward windows with his bare hands or break up some item of furniture such as his own dormitory wardrobe, but he was renowned for a quite distinctive, spectacular display of disturbance. When upset, he grasped his nose in one hand and pulled on it in a highly agitated frenzy before progressing on to leap high into the air and bounce around the ward like an agitated pogo stick, feet together, flapping both arms at his side, with an expression of indignant alarm. Despite this singular repertoire of disturbance and despite a history of never having actually assaulted any member of staff, we always retained a healthy respect for his potential to do so, not least because his extravagant outbursts required of him a not insubstantial strength. His nose was permanently scarred and scabbed with his self injury. Nial was unable to tolerate the slightest restriction to his person from his clothing and, in due course, every item would sustain damage with the ripping off of buttons and zips, and sleeves which were also rent asunder! Shoes never retained their laces so that he flopped and clumped a noisy passage round the ward areas. At a point after his lunch he habitually and casually absented himself from company and took himself off to the seclusion room, where he would sleep on the floor-mattress until he chose to reappear. If this facility was not available to him he unleashed his fury until it was. The custom, therefore, was to leave the seclusion room door unlocked for his personal use but the laziness of the practice irritated me no end.

When settled, Nial revealed other characteristics. Firstly, he had a propensity for learning but within two limited spheres, alone. Without access to reading material, or record sleeves, or tapes, he memorised the names of music bands and singers. The other sphere was to never forget the names of the staff who worked on his ward. When the mood took him, he could repeat a name, over and over – revolving it in his self conversation as if it was on a slowly turning spit – even though that individual was not in the vicinity at the time, or no longer worked on that ward. Then the routine would culminate in a burst of comfortable and convivial laughter to himself. Conversely, the wind-up merchant could have a field day with this trait. Consider him approaching one of these in an earnest mode of enquiry.

'Hey, what's the name of that new doctor? Her name? What's her name?'

'How about saying please, Nial?' as if put out by the earnest request which lacks the appropriate social skills. 'Say please, please,' I rejoin, with an amused intonation.

'Say please, say please, please,' Nial would reply in a stereotypical imitation of his adversary.

'Go on, say please and I'll tell you.'

'I want to know her name, the doctor's name. Tell me, tell me!' his agitation revealing itself in a steady lowering of his head as if to make a charge. If it was felt the issue had been taken far enough, the staff member might desist and offer up the answer but, equally likely, the matter might be continued.

'Did I hear you say please? I don't think so!'

'The lady, the new lady. Why won't you tell me her name? Why, why?'

'Why don't you ask her yourself next time she comes on the ward?' I prompt encouragingly.

'Why don't you ask her yourself?' he repeats, now a little agitated and turning about to slope away. But he returns, unable to rescind his infatuation.

'Where does she come from? Where does she come from?'

'Again, you could ask her yourself, Nial!'

'Ask her yourself! Ask her yourself!' he repeats.

Any social initiative of his was generally confined to this order of agitated demand and any undue delay might well end in some destructive violence. Nial was always highly disturbed by the presence of strangers or a disruption to his daily routine – despite it never seeming to amount to anything very much, objectively speaking. For these reasons, he was never taken off the ward. He never asked to be taken, and staff were happy not to risk any adverse outcomes for so doing. He had no family that visited him, and no friends. The ward was his life, the staff were his life, and there persisted an uneasy truce on account of what was perceived as his unfathomable cantankerousness and destructiveness.

Into the breach stepped the young Miles, a State Enrolled Nurse on my team, to work as Nial's primary nurse. Miles, somewhat overweight and scruffy, had not exactly acquired a favourable reputation during his short hospital career. He had been marked for a far too casual attitude toward his work, a cumulative sickness record, and a habit of late attendance for duty. He just didn't seem too bothered and people reciprocated by not taking him too seriously. Considering the marks against him, I found him a likeable and decent lad, and was determined to help turn about his sullied reputation. For his part, Miles, the Enrolled Nurse, of whom little was expected, flourished and redeemed himself way beyond others' considerations. It was never quite clear how he managed to get so close to Nial, but he accomplished some not inconsiderable feats in relation to Nial's care and altered the staff perceptions of both of them. Firstly, on most days that he was on duty, and provided Nial was receptive, he tried to sit Nial down and simply talk to him by way of being a companionable presence. He drew up his own plan of care to improve Nial's behaviour and this had to be followed by all the staff that had dealings with him during a shift. It brought to people's awareness the fact that Nial was hardly ever to be found seated before this time, being far more able to control inter personal space if he was on his feet. The first principle of the plan was that it was presumed that Nial resorted to aggression because he was largely ignored and not taken seriously until he committed a disruptive act. It was determined that Nial was to be engaged early each morning to make him feel noticed and to encourage some sort of activity. The first of these was to help him make his own bed, followed by selecting his own clothes for the day! The second principle was that whenever Nial felt like smashing a window, or knocking over furniture, or tearing his clothes, he was to approach the nurse who was allocated to him on that shift to tell him about his intentions. Thirdly, if he enacted an incident without first approaching the staff he was also expected to sit down with that staff member, afterward, to explain what had precipitated the incident. Inconceivable though it might seem, and though not foolproof, this did actually lead to a notable diminution of his disturbed behaviour, if for quite contradictory reasons. The personal contact was so well enforced that staff realised Nial often preferred not to give vent to his aggression in preference to having to sit down and explain himself to the staff. After all, the major issue was that of autism, a large component of which is difficulty in tolerating the attention of others, or establishing relationships. In this context, the strategy became aversive in that Nial preferred to avoid what he perceived as the unpleasant consequences of his behaviour rather than address the causes leading up to it. The initial ideas were not clinically sophisticated but they were a beginning of something positive to work with rather than passively sitting back, waiting and reacting to Nial's outbursts. Thirdly, staff were encouraged to reconsider their own actions, both before and after Nial's disturbances, and how they might offer a more constructive range of responses to help him reconsider his own. And, because Miles started to take Nial seriously, and to demonstrate some engagement with successful planning, all the team commenced treating both of them with more respect. Instead of the previous pattern of derisory, rash, and aggressive responses to Nial's disturbances, the staff started to follow the instructions for engagement. I, for one, was shamed into a recognition of my own aggrieved intolerance of Nial's seemingly unfathomable destructiveness and had cause to revise my own behaviour and attitudes toward him. Incredibly, I became immensely fond of Nial and managed to resist my former frustrations with him, in a very short while.

In an initiative of my own, I became determined to remove Nial's predilection for taking his afternoon rest in the seclusion room which seemed to be maladaptive, on his part, and institutionally lazy on the part of the staff. It transpired that the staff had set up the habit by placing him in the room, unlocked, following his past ritual outbursts of aggression. From his autistic stance, presumably, he acquired an undisturbed, peaceful niche that became a useful way for him to extract himself from the ward tensions and the confounding presence of others. Though intending to defuse his volatility, the staff had unwittingly reinforced his aggressive behaviour by rewarding any outburst with the refuge of seclusion, reaching a point where he only had to give the slightest indication of an outburst and he would be invited to "go for a lie down". Miles had, tentatively, begun to raise the issue with Nial.

Following one lunch, when Nial retired for his siesta unusually early, and I accompanied him shortly afterward, to the consternation of the team and comments such as 'you're just asking for trouble', I took a chair, followed him into seclusion, and proceeded to sit on it behind the closed door. Nial's head shot out from beneath the mattress blanket, disturbed by the intrusion.

'Why are you in here, why, why?'

'I've come to try to encourage you to use your own bed if you must have your afternoon nap, Nial.'

'I want to sleep here. I always sleep here. Go away.'

'It's not a very nice place to be, is it? It's the last place you want to be, really.'

'I like it here. Go away, Steve Burrow.'

'But this is where we put people who have to be locked away for a while. You don't have to be locked up, do you?'

Nial is particularly assertive. 'I don't care. I don't want you in here. Why are you here? Why?'

'Just talk to me, Nial, and tell me why you come here?'

'I don't want to talk to you. I want to sleep. Leave me alone. Go away, Steve Burrow. Go AWAY!'

'Look, how about if I remain sitting with you and we talk about why you come in here? It doesn't seem right that you should have to seek out this space to have a rest, Nial. It's become a habit, hasn't it?'

'I want to be on my own. FUCK OFF!'

'No need to swear, now.'

'I don't care. Fuck off or I'll bash you. I will, I will, I swear.' And with that, Nial scrambles to his feet from the mattress with unprecedented intention so that I, perceiving an imminent assault upon my person, leap up to take refuge behind the chair, back towards the door, incredulous that Nial should have the gumption to strike out and grab the chair, and scurry back, first, into the dining area to the thorough amusement of the gathered staff, who have responded to the fracas. Nial, meanwhile, is heaving the chair against the seclusion walls until the team and I, together, retrieve it, having been forced to restrain him and, because he is now particularly high, follow this by officially secluding him! The interview, the intervention are over – catastrophic, amusing, informative, character-forming! There will have to be some concerted rethinking of this whole scenario but it is stimulating.

Years later, a colleague would pour into my ear the salutary recollection of the day when Nial had had to be formally secluded for violent behaviour toward a staff member! An almost unprecedented action for him!

* * *

Constitutionally, I aspired to the premise that we could be more self-determining and self-sufficient in our own local speciality. One measure of the ward's efficiency would be the extent to which we did not require external emergency assistance. Effecting both would depend on our capacity to respond more effectively to our patients' needs. The substantive early focus for problem identification was what had come to be termed the *challenging behaviours* of the more chronic patients. Challenging behaviours – terminology imported from the mental handicap field – were conducts and attitudes which resisted conventional norms and expectations to such an amplification that they demanded staff intervention to contain them within prescribed limits. Such regular examples on the ward were: recurrent window breaking, incidental or intentional self-injurious behaviour, clothes tearing, furniture destruction, pushing over tables and chairs, food throwing, extended screaming and swearing episodes, urinating on the floor, spitting, inadvertent bodily exposure, refusal to wear clothing, and occasional assaults on staff and patients. General resistance to maintaining general hygiene or to pursuing any productive activity might be included in this category, depending on the individual, otherwise he should be placed within an area of social skills development or activity development, for example. If all patients on an intensive care unit manifested challenging behaviours, in principle, it was the more chronic patients whose lives were dominated by the phenomena and who attracted much of the concerted early attention. Having first registered each challenge, an attempt was made to elucidate the factors which maintained and stabilised it, or what influenced any changes, and gauging how effective they were. This might amount to having things taken away or earning some rewards but the aim came to be more about modifying the patient's original behaviour, to improve it. The very language of *challenging behaviours* put a far more positive, explanatory spin on conduct that was previously conceptualised as deliberately awkward, resistant and destructive. In order to magnify the importance of focusing on the problems, they were translated onto visible charts. One area of the staff office was now taken over with patients' charts and this ensured that the patients' issues could not be obscured within case notes or other administration! The use of charts had the added benefit that the behaviour could be visually monitored over time. This very explicit visualisation spurred the most enthusiastic into achieving successful results as the downward trend of challenging incidents was clearly registered. What emerged was a form of primitive behaviourism, even though the staff did not possess the training or theoretical tools to adequately complete such a programme. How the patients really felt about this would probably never be known, but it was to be hoped that they perceived a difference in the way that they were not, now, merely viewed as hopeless, chronic patients who had slithered into the institutional bowels, but that they were being accorded due consideration. I also trusted that the same applied to the staff.

After being exercised by the challenging behaviours, the task was for the primary nurses to be explicit about identifying all the other areas of deficit, or excess, which their patients manifested, and to set a programme of nurse generated interventions that would supplement the medical prescription. Physical issues were the next most obvious, whether it be incontinence, a skin ailment, hypertension, or diabetes, for example. Take the straightforward issue of applying a steroid ointment to a patient's psoriasis. Previously, under the team system, whether this was actually applied often depended on the integrity of the nurses giving out the medication on the day. But now, the primary nurse, with a vested interest in promoting their patient's improvement, would be actively checking up on whether the treatment had been carried out. Those primary nurses who acclimatised the most effectively followed through their patients' treatment plans in a way that the team system would rarely have ensured without the most punctilious of leaders.

In principle, there was no life issue that nursing could not now diagnose and work with. Difficulties purporting to domestic issues, or life difficulties, might identify problems in managing money or accessing social benefits, using public transport, purchasing food or consumer articles. Social issues, and the related area of social skills and maintaining relationships, came very much onto the health agenda as well as being viewed as a requisite skills area in the professional armoury of the modern psychiatric nurse. Discrete, post qualification courses were instituted to assist nurses to routinely operationalise patient/staff interaction, to try to maintain family connections, and to enhance the interpersonal qualities of patients whose mental illnesses had so damaged these life skills. Another broad range of deficit lay in the area of general motivation, whether it was rising from bed in the morning, dressing appropriately, attending occupational or industrial therapy units, staying out of bed, or defining some personal goals to give a sense of purpose and future to patients' lives.

In time, the team were both amazed and amused to have awakened the attention of the Head of Psychology from the esoteric obscurity of his daily battery tests and who, one fine day, requested that he attend the Clinical Team Meeting. He wished to make observations on the nursing programmes that his department had come to hear of! This was some challenge, potentially, as the nursing staff would not have claimed to have achieved anything more than a therapeutic exploration, which was acknowledged to be short on solid theoretical principles and expertise. The staff opinion was that there may have been a growing concern that the programmes may be wandering too far off-piste, and that the Psychology Department had a professional obligation to monitor such initiatives. But, hey, who cared, the Psychology Department? There was no one else to turn to, certainly no one in their own fraternity, and their very own trainers and tutors were all in the same boat as themselves!

But in the formulation of a patient's problems and their necessary interventions, a revelation presented itself. There was little known or understood that addressed the mental illness itself other than the broadest of principles. What programme could a primary nurse implement for *schizophrenia,* having identified it as a patient's major problem? It was this incapacity which most acutely exposed the training shortfall, and the professional experience that they had all acquired. It certainly went some way to explain the compensatory ritualistic practices endemic within the institution and why the long trail of authority of the psychiatrist had reached down from the diagnoses, to the descriptive itemisation of symptoms, to the range of prescribed medications, to other physical interventions such as electroconvulsive therapy or cerebral surgery, to gathering responses on the effect of the treatment, and recording the whole deal in the case files. The nursing care would simply attend to dispensing the range of medications, so that it would dampen down the psychotic symptoms, and then to manage any residual symptoms of disturbance. In effect, psychiatric nurses would be able to define and describe the condition of schizophrenia, and state the appropriate medication, but not much else. Your job was to attend to the disturbed behaviour – the disruptive, damaging behavioural manifestations of the illness. General domestic management was their forte! Theirs was always a secondary input.

* * *

It would be disingenuous to infer that a huge effort was given over to involve the patients in their own decision making about the ward issues but a shallow beginning was attempted. One such medium – never before imagined in an attendant's worst nightmare – was the introduction of a weekly community meeting involving all the staff on duty as well as the patients. It was deliberately scheduled at one o'clock in order to maximise the attendance of both daytime nursing shifts, and led by we two Charge Nurses. Well, no one knew quite what would happen. But the first week rolled into the next, and the next, without incident, and the staff started to develop a range of facilitative skills of necessity. Often dominated by a patient minority, and the remainder in mute attendance – though how attentive, was never clear – the staff soon learned the benefits of allowing patients to contribute their thoughts on ward matters. But it would be disingenuous not to admit that it might not be used to try and convince the patients of certain strategic benefits that nursing staff wished to invoke, so it could also be used as a powerful forum of persuasion. One of my first suggestions was that the staff wanted to experiment by not setting off the alarm bells, from now on, if there was an incident.

'It must be very unsettling for you to have loads of strangers pouring into the ward when there's an incident,' I propose. 'We want to try and contain any incidents ourselves, and would prefer to avoid any of them happening in the first place. Everyone has their own primary nurse and we want you to talk to them if something's bothering you rather than you kicking off. It isn't very nice for anyone to have the cavalry charging in. Can we try and do that, do you think?'

'What you saying, exactly, Steve? I don't understand yer,' is the contribution of Will, the ex Broadmoor patient who will take any opportunity to regale the assembly with his Broadmoor persona.

'When those alarm bells go off they are very irritating for everyone. I can't bear to hear them myself. We want you to come and talk to us if you feel you're getting upset about something, so that we can all avoid any aggro. Simple as that.' Eddie, a black male patient, a seasoned campaigner in terms of the intensive care environments, laughs loudly.

'What if you can't handle us, Steve? Ha, ha, ha!'

'Oh, well, you'll have to help us handle it, then.'

'You must be joking, man. You fight your own battles, mate.'

'I'm joking, Eddie.'

'Blimey, that'd go down well in Broadmoor, fuck me, they'd go mental if you tried this out there!' says the redoubtable Will. 'No messing, they use any incidents as an excuse to let the patients know who's the fucking boss, and the more, the merrier.'

'How about trying not to swear, Will?'

'Sorry, mate. But you know what I mean, don't yer? A patient only needed to blow his nose in the wrong direction and the bells would be set off and his nose would be readjusted for him. It's like they was looking for bother, them geezers.'

'Well, we're not looking for bother, Will. We're trying to improve things, know what I mean, son?' this last in an exaggerated mimicking of Will's broad Cockney accent. Will takes it well with a smiling retort.

'Now you're taking the piss, ain't yer?'

'No, I ain't,' continuing the mimicking.

'Not much, you f... ing ain't! That was a joke, by the way.'

'I know, Will. Now, f... ng well belt up!'

'Cor, you don't half get away with some things, don't yer?' The good humour is by no means diminished by Eddie whose contribution exposes the crux of the matter. As he speaks, he shifts his bulk beneath the huge shoulders and leans forward, unstably, on the far from adequate chair.

'What if I don't want to talk to the staff? If I'm not happy about something. I don't want to be hassled by staff if I'm not in the mood, do I? I want to be left alone.' From past knowledge of him, all the staff know that keeping himself to himself is an indication of his declining mental state. In this very hospital he has acquired a notorious track record. He is a young man of notable contradictions. Very overweight, but concealing a powerful potential, his mobility is never accomplished with anything more than a lumbering, slumberous minimum of energy. Epitomised at the table tennis table, his shots and returns crack like an unleashed hail of accumulated energy from the bunker of a very convincing slothfulness. It is this veiled potential which makes Eddie the most dangerous patient on the ward and his contribution may be portentous.

'If being left alone means that you're going to work yourself up into a froth, that might not be such a great idea.'

'No. If the staff keep away, then things'll be cool, man. Like, if we want to lie in bed in the mornings, if we're not feeling great, we should be allowed to be left alone, man. Don't need to talk to no one.' This is an archetypal dilemma for staff – the thin end of the wedge in terms of the balance of power. How far can liberalism be allowed to progress – that wants to give up some control, to share it, but not to lose it altogether – before it descends into a laissez-faire regime which hands all responsibility over to individual patients for their own ends? At present, there is a strict enforcement of expecting every patient to be dressed and washed before they partake of breakfast. This is rationalised on a number of grounds. To lock off the male and female dormitories reduces the need to observe these areas, prevents patients from returning to bed, keeps the dormitories tidy once the beds have been made up and the dormitory cleaned, and reduces the likelihood of risk behaviours such as patient assault and fire setting. None of these would be insurmountable if the dormitories were to be unlocked but the risks are minimised and the inconveniences removed altogether. The pre-eminent rationale for getting everyone up and locking off the dormitories is to prevent patients from lying in bed whenever they choose. This is not a hotel, after all! The staff peremptorily go through the explanatory motions.

'Anyone could use the excuse of not feeling too great just to lie in bed for a few hours, couldn't they? How can we tell the difference?'

'Well, those sort of things have been a lot more strict since you've been on the ward, Steve.'

'And you're not happy with it?'

'Course not. You're too fussy, man. Why shouldn't we be left alone in the morning? I can't see no problem with that. Or any other time of the day for that matter. Guy, the other Charge Nurse before you, allowed it. Why not you, man?' Why not indeed! In fact, a lot rested on this single, seemingly innocuous issue. If such a concession was made, a reasonable threshold would still be required to prevent patients from lying in bed the whole day, in principle. I was rescued by Mick, my equivalent colleague.

'You know that if we don't get you all up at the same time the daily routine will go to pot. And you'll be the first to complain if you miss your meals! Then there's the medication, which we can't miss, and getting you to occupational or industrial therapy on time. None of it's going to happen!' It was just one of those issues of ward routine that could not accommodate much slippage especially when the ward regime was in need of such comprehensive revision and discipline.

'Everybody is always looked at on an individual basis, in any case,' is the continuing supportive intervention of Mick, the other Charge Nurse. 'Nobody would be forced to get out of bed who was considered to be unwell and who needed to be examined by a doctor,' is his cunning suggestion. This has the advantage of reinforcing the idea that to remain in bed, indefinitely, was neither normal nor advisable whilst allowing the concession of someone being acknowledged as ill, and being made the subject of a formalised referral. If the patient is likely to be found out if feigning an illness then it is hoped that the whole business will be altogether too bothersome, and sooner avoided. Eddie is used to the wiles of the institution, though.

'No, we don't have to need to see a doctor. You see, you're making it difficult for us.'

'Well, then, there's no reason to stay in bed. You get your lie in at the weekends,' Tim continues.

'It's not enough, man. I mean, what's the big deal about not getting up at the same time every morning? I don't want to get up early. It's against my religion.'

'What religion's that? You're not Rastafarian or anything, are you?'

'How do you know? Don't matter what religion I am.'

'What about missing your breakfast? You like your food too much!'

'You can save it, that wouldn't be too much bother.' All the staff remonstrate with guffaws of derision.

'Well, you can forget about that for a start!'

'On your bike.'

'What are we, servants?'

'Okay, okay, I get the message,' and although he is smiling at the weight of response, Eddie slumps into a disgruntled withdrawal. It is not a satisfactory outcome because it hasn't been negotiated but it will avoid the inevitable conflict of having to navigate a course through encouragement and compromise. In any case, another message has been given out, to the staff mainly, that the strategy to be more consciously therapeutic will not amount to an uncontrolled anarchy.

* * *

Then one Monday, the day of the week on which the meeting was regularly held, and without any prior mention of the event, no less a person than Nial approached me on my immediate arrival on the ward for an afternoon shift.

'Steve Burrow?'

'Yes, Nial?'

'Is it the community meeting today?'

'Yes, it is.'

'What time?'

One o'clock, as usual, Nial'

'One o'clock, as usual,' he repeats, characteristically.

'Yep.'

'One o'clock, as usual. One o'clock, as usual,' Nial reiterates, ambling away. 'One o'clock as usual. One o'clock, as usual.' He returns to me. 'Will everyone be there?'

'All the patients and everyone who's on duty.'

'Everyone who's on duty,' he repeats. 'Who'll be on duty, Steve Burrow?'

'Oh, you'll have to wait, Nial, I can't remember everyone just now.' Nial giggles and looks down to the floor. After lunch, when the chairs are set up in preparation for the meeting, Nial is the first to be seated.

Shared with the staff at subsequent handovers, the scenario was met with frank exclamation until it was noted that Nial had, in fact, attended every one of the past meetings on time, had appeared to listen, although he had never uttered a word and was often observed to be smiling broadly, but had never been moved to indulge any of his uniquely challenging rituals.

* * *

Against the odds, the alarm bells were not rung again to call for assistance to deal with an internal act of aggression or disturbance from there onwards. What incidents there were, were controlled in-house without recall to other wards' assistance. Not even on the day when Eddie showed his mettle, indeed. Retrospectively, it became an exercise in the limitations of the care around Eddie's psychotic illness and the lack of proactive contingencies which might intercede before it ran out of control. But this had to be compared with the traditional style of reactive intervention where a patient exhibiting deteriorating behaviour was ordered to desist, then medicated with the patient's acquiescence, and forcefully restrained and medicated without it!

For some days, Eddie's mental state had been deteriorating, talking to no one, keeping to himself, ignoring staff enquiries, mumbling to himself, avoiding others' company, refusing to participate in any activity or recreation, sleeping poorly, and wearing a pair of sunglasses that concealed his eyes throughout the entire day, every day. The most worrying sign was his air of consuming suspicion and brooding mood. Occasionally, he would only let slip that "the Digger" was looking for him again, and it confirmed the staff fears that he was delusional. One of the lazy interventions used to manage patients' delusions was to go along with them in a pragmatic attempt to defuse, and reassure, the patient.

'Surely, you'd be safer inside the hospital than if you were outside where you'd be less protected from him?' thereby conferring a degree of validation to the delusion.

'You can't be sure of that. Anyway, I didn't ask your opinion.'

'Well, just look at it. He hasn't been able to reach you so far.'

'I said, leave me alone!' He was left alone. He refused offers of extra medication as staff anxieties kept pace with his psychotic withdrawal. His mood darkened until, one late afternoon, he boldly positioned his substantial frame in the doorway of the office while I was seated at the desk. 'You're imprisoning me here, and I want to be allowed out. I'm not mad and it's dangerous for me, man. I'm sure "the Digger" knows where I am and he'll be coming to get me. You people can't defend me, I need to get out, find some safety, that's all.' This was all the confirmation required that Eddie's behaviour was now cause for concern. His notes included the well documented history of this fixed, paranoid delusion which would see him slide into a dangerously psychotic deterioration where he would be suspicious of everyone's intentions. No one had a clear idea of where it stemmed from, whether the named person existed or was a fantasy, but it seemed to erupt very occasionally in history.

'I don't know that you're well enough to be able to listen to someone else's point of view right now, Eddie, but I couldn't possibly let you go out.'

'Oh, don't talk shit to me. What you're saying to me is I'm mad and that upsets me, man. What do you know about it?'

'No, I'm not saying you're mad but it's my job to know when you're not up to scratch and to look out for you when you can't manage yourself. I don't think you can hear this at the moment...'

'Oh, leave it out.'

'... but I really think you're unwell and its impeding your judgement.'

'Impeding my judgement! What do you know about my judgement? Let me go, man, there's some serious business I've got to take care of.'

'Would you trust me if I said I think you need some extra medication?' The point had, indeed, been reached where he was in need of an extra dose of anti-psychotic, or a tranquiliser, and it would have to be administered one way or another. Most of the staff were sympathetically disposed toward Eddie but this was not the Eddie they knew and liked, with the laconic exchanges, easy-going humour, and minimalist approach to making any kind of physical effort in life.

'There's nothing wrong with me, man. Don't try that on me. It ain't going to work, right? You're trying to slow me down. I have to be in peak condition in case he comes for me. That's why I'm building myself up, eating as much as I can to give me power.' Through his assertiveness, Eddie's mood is focused, flat and threatening, sufficient to have me very worried for this is one of those few occasions where I would rather have back-up, than chance a physical encounter alone. I ask Eddie to move away from the door, which he refuses. Convinced, now, that I need to act I call out with just sufficient a note of apprehension to attract attention.

'MILES, MILES! WILL YOU COME TO THE OFFICE, PLEASE?' was my call for a trusty colleague. Miles duly presented himself and, before he reaches the office door with his usual 'yes boss?', I manage to convey a veiled signal of alarm.

'Just hang around, there, would you? Eddie is not too happy.'

'Got you,' Miles replies, catching the indicative tone in the voice. Turning aside to telephone the unit nursing officer, keeping Eddie within peripheral vision, I note the *sod's law* that I've only been allocated this one other male member of staff for this shift.

'I'm going to have a word with Sean Collins, all right, Eddie?' A cryptic few words is conveyed to this fairly recent arrived Nursing Officer while the tense Eddie hovers at the door. 'Um, hi, Sean. I'd appreciate your attendance on the ward, say, immediately!' A mystified enquiry ensues which I interrupt. 'Can't really speak, right now, um, it's concerning Eddie. How about coming to the ward like now! I just need an extra pair of hands,' replacing the receiver.

'What, you going to call all the staff up to get me, eh?'

'No, you just heard me, didn't you? I've just asked for Sean to come, that's all. We can handle this amongst ourselves.'

'Him and all the rest, you mean. Well, I don't care how many come, I'll take you all on, got that?' now raising his voice as if to prepare himself for an assault, while his legs twitch with unmistakable agitation. This is a bad sign. It is one thing for a paranoid delusion to remain fixed with the risk focused on the main subject, quite another when it becomes so generalised that the risk can be free-ranging and settle on anyone. To his consummate credit Sean, the Nursing Officer – guess what, another Irishman! – arrives within three minutes and appears at the door. He is a diminutive, frail looking, exceptionally youthful looking man, with a freckled, pallid complexion, all of which bely the macho qualities which are normally anticipated for this kind of predicament. Though the other female staff have not been corralled they will be nearby if their help is called for. Showing his experience, Sean knows immediately that Eddie is about to "blow", and stands close to him but prepared to defuse matters if he can.

'Hello, Eddie, anything the matter, me old mate?' Eddie turns toward him as Sean faces him, sideways on.

'Plenty. Get me the fuck out of here or someone's sure to get hurt. And I'm not messing, man. You're crowding me, now, so don't fuck with me, all right!' Eddie has positioned himself with his back against the wall outside of the office, his voice rising, resolute, brave, apprehensive, and beyond pacifying. Meanwhile, I can now glide away from my confinement to take my place beside his two colleagues in a show of camaraderie. Eddie is now being faced with the three of us.

'It's obvious you're upset about something, Eddie, and you don't seem about to talk about it. Would you accept some extra medication, please?'

'Now, don't fuck with me, man, you can stick your fucking medication and let me out. Just unlock the door and I'm out of here. I'm staying for no one, see!'

'You know we can't let you out of the ward while you're in this frame of mind, Eddie. You're just going to get more and more unwell and, let's face it, the police will only have to bring you back. Why don't you go and lie down on your bed, at least?' If he refuses this compromise the point will have been reached where an injection of anti-psychotic medication is needed and he is unlikely to accept it voluntarily. 'Has anyone drawn up his PRN?' asks Sean. "Pro re nata" is an extra dose of medication which is administered as an additional measure when the routine regime is not adequate to deal with a patient's symptoms.

'Yes. It's ready now,' says Miles, who has obviously taken the initiative and instructed one of the females.

'You ain't giving me no PRN, you white boys. No way. You just try, and see what you get.' The three of them do not look at one another, as if they have an instinctive awareness that further reasoning will not defuse Eddie's hostility and that, in order to reach some resolution, this will end in an imminent contact, instigated by one side or the other. Miles always wears his tie loosely, while I am forced into slipping off mine as surreptitiously as possible, so that, if there is to be a fracas, I can avoid the inconvenience of being strangled. 'Eddie, come on now, old mate. Will you accept some PRN to help settle you because, otherwise, we are going to have to force you to have some? You don't want that, do you?'

'Come on then, come and get me, you bastards. I'm waiting.' His hands are still clenched at his sides but there is an animated vigilance about his whole bearing that indicates there will be no retreat now. Like any deteriorating situation where there is a perceived clinical need to forcefully medicate a patient, the three of them prepare to move the confrontation onto the inevitable restraining sequence.

'This is your last chance, Eddie. Come on, what do you want to do?' Before any further initiative is taken Eddie has let fly with a lightning punch to Sean's face who, reflexively, throws himself at Eddie, sustaining another bruising clip en route. Like one anatomical being, Sean's companions, like attached tendons to his calf, leap in beside him as he lunges forward and, as they move in one body, both receive consecutive blows directly to the face too. Undaunted, this slightly-built Irishman, who has sustained the worst of the blows, dips his head and digs in, thrusting his head at Eddie's torso, while Miles and myself grope for his arms in a frenzy of determination. Like lions with their nails tearing into him they struggle to pull down Eddie's frame which, like some virile but overwhelmed wildebeest, comes crashing to the floor with the hungry zeal of impassioned youth clawing on top of him.

'Shall I hit the alarm bells?' calls the female staff nurse who has arrived with the PRN injection.

'No, we've got it, thanks.' I reply while venting my exasperation by grabbing Eddie's hair and pulling his head up off the ground.

'Steady Steve, steady now!' is the urgent interception from Sean who is nursing a streaming, bloody mouth but holding on with tenacity. While recovering some composure, Sean turns breathlessly to the female Staff Nurse.

'No, you're fine, we've got it, thanks. Are we agreed, Eddie? We don't need assistance, do we?' searching for some sign of accent from Eddie. Strangely, Eddie appears almost relaxed as if we've temporarily taken charge of the psychosis for him.

'Sure, now?' she checks.

'Sure. You got that injection ready?'

'All ready. You all right down there, boys?' she enquires, somewhat sardonically. 'You will get yourselves into these difficulties!' and approaches with amusement. 'Shall we give it here or in the seclusion room?' she asks.

'Better here, to be on the safe side.' With Eddie lying with his back on the floor it is necessary to turn him over and he obliges without further struggle. The trousers are undone and dragged down to expose the buttocks and the female nurse leans across the huddle to administer the jab with a flourish.

'All done, boys.'

'Sorry, Sean,' I offer, contritely, referring back. I suddenly realise that despite the nature of this incident and the muscular control of it Sean's response, as a new Senior Nurse to the hospital, cannot be properly anticipated. There's no point in trying to rationalise my frustration. I merely stare at Eddie.

'I'm sick, man, I'm sick.'

'Not too sick that you couldn't slug all three of us,' is Miles' dig at him.

'You understand we can't just allow you to wander around the ward for the time being, Eddie?' says Sean in a mollifying manner.

'Right, next stop seclusion,' is Mike's emphatic interruption. 'Are we ready, gents?' Each of them has a firm hold of Eddie and he is lifted and frog-marched to the seclusion room where, but for his underpants, his clothes are removed and he is left behind a locked door for the foreseeable hours to come. It is the most serious incident the ward has sustained since I have joined it but I'm not concerned that it will undercut the veracity of the new initiatives. The incident is a timely reminder that any patient's deteriorating mental state may continue to require physical interventions once the staff lose the patient's cooperation. A little more disconcertingly, there is always the suspicion that, though they chose to resolve the crisis by physical means, there may have been other alternatives to the actual restraint which we selected. But the general practice is to take the shortest route to a resolution and not to tarry. We have, assuredly, done that without rousing the entire hospital.

The three of us are licking our minor wounds but showing tremendous respect for Eddie's ability to hit all three of us with his neatly fashioned punches, despite his obesity. Sean also has my respect for leading the restraint when he could, so easily, have stepped back and let others get on with it, which is what I might have expected from many Nursing Officers. But maybe that's unfair considering that most of them are not quite in their prime and have probably proved their mettle in their younger years. Sean, in turn, is thankful that his staff backed him up and, though he could not have guaranteed such support, could more or less rely on the unspoken code of staff loyalty. Everyone is grateful that the manner of dealing with Eddie is not under scrutiny. Eddie's potential dangerousness has been dealt that critical first step which can now be built on to keep it contained. His progress will be acutely monitored until a new equilibrium in his medication and treatment has been found that will prevent another mental state relapse and a threat to staff safety. The whole episode will have a perverse impact on Eddie's reha-bilitation progress. There will be an unspoken respect for his audacity and pugnacity but it will also mark him for having violated the ultimate taboo. For, irrespective of the respect that staff will have shown for Eddie's illness, he has contravened the rules of engagement – he has assaulted the staff. For the foreseeable future his every move, preoccupation, and whisper will come under intense scrutiny and any privileges granted will be hard won indeed.

In plain terms, in institutional terms, the concerted staff conduct had been efficient. A faltering situation had progressed so far and then been isolated and contained. That was the immediate goal and other concerns, such as the possible damage to relationships, would follow. In trying to recon-cile the incident to the current therapeutic endeavours, it was not entirely unreasonable to invoke the original nomenclature for this type of unit – a Refractory Ward. It was derived from the Latin 'Refractarius', meaning stub-born. Eddie had indeed exhibited stubbornness, and resistance. His relapsing psychosis had not yielded to his regular medical/pharmaceutical treatment, or the prescribed increments. Nor was it responsive to interpersonal interven-tions. In these respects, Eddie's condition conformed to all these elements and this characterised the realistic nature of such a service, that notions of being a disturbed ward or intensive care facility were yet further examples of euphemism. On the other hand, the refractory connotation could also have been applied to the staff, that it was their own stubbornness that continued to fail to adapt and that, however well intentioned, it was they that had failed to respond to alternative stimulation. Irrespective of the arguments, irrespective of the validity of the regimes, there would always be a clinical requirement for the containment of aggression and potential dangerousness, along with the inevitable point of physical contact for defusing that predicament, and the consequent, continuing control until the crisis abated. Restraint was not merely an uncomfortable truth but the ultimate irony for the veracity of psychiatric *asylum*. For asylum was a Greek composite of two parts: '*sulos*', meaning the right of seizure; and '*a*', meaning without. *Asylum* literally meant *without the right of seizure*!

And so a low-key, nursing informed, therapeutic climate – with dollops of manipulation and persuasion whisked in – began to re-orientate the ward regime. For those staff that were bothered, their knowledge of patients and conditions was extended, trial programmes or other initiatives would be introduced to modify patients' behaviour, the patient adaptations and reactions were gauged, the repercussions and successes noted, and everything collected together to encourage further staff motivation and treatment ideas.

But however enthusiastic the leadership might be, however much it tries to participate, to encourage, to listen, to negotiate, things will never run entirely smoothly. Some staff will be captivated and you take them along with you; others will resist each and every innovation, and some just a few! What you soon learn in an institutional setting is the effectiveness of passive resistance and how effective doing as little as possible is in frustrating any change. For those that ran with the ideas, they would claim that closer working relationships developed and the rewards were plain to see in reducing patient deficits and excesses, and their own improving strengths. This was not all. Naturally, staff members enjoyed the personal aggrandisement that came with this. In fact, it didn't much matter if first efforts failed on the basis that the very effort to find a solution became worthwhile in itself, and was an effective motivator. As the ideas of partnership, and empowerment, gained ground so, too, did the further ramifications of the new care regime. In order to reduce patient apathy, alienation, disempowerment and subservience, other strategies should be explored. The nursing process, to the limited extent that it did succeed, did so because it individualised the patient as a separate human being, and because of the ownership which the primary nurses had of the specified patients in their charge. In many instances, this became an over possessiveness, saying more about the staff's own needs than it did about their charges. But it was the degree of liberation for the individual nurse that really gave momentum to individual patient care.

By the mid-1980s, then, it was nigh impossible for the individual practitioner to fail to appreciate the several impressions being made by these centralising forces and the professional metamorphosis that was in vogue. The nurse's relationship with patients had the remit of a contract, of the morally responsible practitioner acting on behalf of another's interests. Rhetorically, it was worth asking the question whether a professional rôle – together with all professional rôles – was an alternative form of conforming citizenship which, when internalised, spread across the whole personality and every aspect of a person's life into an adaptive citizenship? Could professionalism contain the potential to engineer people to be better disposed toward, or better equipped to interact with, their fellow man and construct a broader intellectual integrity that was good for social and political stability?

County asylum nursing practice, within a general mantle of institutional unity, ranged at the individual level from a deliberate vocation to a cavalier anarchy. To the degree that they occurred, the flagrant derelictions of duty caricatured the benevolent intentions of early reformers as the staff used them as a personal leisure resource for as long as they could get away with it. The derelictions of care intimated the bad faith endemic in any other occupation and what we often associate with the commercial travesties inflicted by the notorious "rogue traders" or other professional groups. Bad faith and failing to offer a consistently high standard had been found to be endemic among the police service (corruption, false evidence, miscarriages of justice), the Catholic priesthood (abuse of celibacy, sexual abuse cases), and politicians (sexual peccadilloes, gerrymandering, illegal fund raising, privileges in return for party loans). There were endless examples! For the mental health nurse, it was this bad faith – or was it idleness, or inability, or incompetence, or plain lack of intelligence? – that had brought such critical defamation down on our heads. After all, weren't our contractual obligations to be fulfilled in return for the salary, the subsidised accommodation, the free uniforms and clothing, the many other perquisites such as free social club and sports facilities, the convenience of working away from congested towns, the privilege of working in one of the most extraordinary fields of human activity, and alongside the most individualistic of characters? These derelictions revealed, in one sense, the real strength of institutional care, for despite the variable inclinations, aptitudes and propensities of individual members of staff, the hospital routines largely ensured that patients received their daily care. In their defence, the staff tried to make sense of a psychiatric world that, virtually by definition, was non-sense, and in conditions of geographical, social and professional isolation. It should not be forgotten, furthermore, that staff institutionalisation, where it existed, should not be alluded to in glib, ironic terms. It was perfectly possible that, in terms of traits, they exhibited the central tenets of the phenomena – apathy, lack of initiative and motivation, and a generalised lack of activity.

According to the latent rules of the institution, patients were little more than their illness. Everything a patient said, thought, and did characterised and reinforced their status as someone with mental disorder, someone who was incomplete, someone who required to be regarded with a degree of wariness. They had to be exceptional characters for the staff to allow them to rise above this fairly high bar of acceptability. Since this was an ordinary county asylum there was not even a hint of wealth or celebrity that might confer sophisticated treatment options, or social privileges, or mitigate the lower social status of mental patients. Any pre morbid attributes and achievements were incidental history, nullified by the emerging reality of later development, the present psychological impasse, and a future that promised little change. Mental illness marked the decisive *rite de passage* in their lives and to hark back to what they were, or presume to look forward to what they could have become, was mere sentimentality. A patient's madness served to excuse a short-circuiting of the complexities of normal social conduct between patients and staff so that it was limited to the barest possible contact in many cases. Mental illness meant social distance however sympathetically the patient group was viewed. Such assignations were built into the bricks and mortar of institutions like an ideational damp course, protecting the jealously conceived judgements of the inside from being adversely encroached upon by the inclement political correctness on the outside. Even among the least therapeutically active staff the perception was that their patients' eccentricities were illuminating, spangled garlands that compensated for, but did not wholly dissipate, the overriding illnesses and diagnoses which were heavily and darkly draped around their stooped identities. It was truly remarkable that these independent eccentricities persisted; had managed to defy being trapped in the ritual practices like a series of neat stitches sewn around the edges of an unflattering institutional garment. Timmy, for example, was accepted by everybody and living as full a life as could be imagined within the environs of a secure estate. He never used a watch and never asked anyone the time but he knew when meals were prepared, when to be back on the ward, when the church services commenced, when the staff football and cricket matches were taking place, as if he had been synchronised to the institutional clock. But that was the point. The mind and body adapted to the institution and the latter regulated every activity. Who knew what he could manage on the outside? And he would never know.

* * *

The eventual demise of the asylums turned into a veritable dissolution in the 1990s as, one by one, each was closed after decanting their resident patients into the general populace. Large scale, institutional mental health care was disbanded and the entire staffing population of the mental hospitals migrated with their charges like itinerant Laplanders tracking the reindeer on which their livelihood depended. But the institutional decline and the emergent care in the community, though a laudable inevitability, was no therapeutic Diaspora. The staff took their institutional personas and culture with them and had to acclimatise under much the same circumstances as the dispersed and resettled patients.

Of the asylums themselves, some were razed to the ground to be buried in history while their bones were tarmacked by ungracious developers. Others survived under the "listing" process whereby the original architectural integrity was retained and restored with a suitable makeover but converted into privately owned, self-contained flats and housing. Others survived destruction because they were listed buildings but, owing to their particular layout, were uneconomical to developers. In these latter cases, the existing shells could not be converted into profitable units so they remained precisely that – dilapidated, abandoned shells. But they were also monuments and it is an oversight that some of these have not been maintained for posterity. The old asylum with which I had been acquainted over a few short years was one of this latter genre.

CHAPTER FOUR
STAMPED BY HISTORY

THE BIRTH OF THE PUBLIC ASYLUM WAS a planned arrival but there was no single, mechanistic explanation for its creation or spreading influence. It was an institutional fertility programme that had gestated in the womb of the State from the beginning of the eighteenth, through the nineteenth, and into the twentieth, century. The politically instigated pregnancies reached full term among the confluence of social, economic and political change, and the plethora of development and dislocation of the period. The independent causes were sourced in the high hill springs of the agricultural revolution; merged with the fast waters of the industrial and manufacturing revolutions; flowed on into the social displacements, the demographic explosion, the urbanisation, the social afflictions and diseases that festered among the emerging townships; and conflated into a cascading torrent of political unrest and political reform onto the plains of a reconstituted society. And as these unstoppable forces swept through the landscape, redistributing the economic wealth, they also dragged along the splintered debris of unproductive human casualties.

Before then, the Parish Poor Relief operating from as far back as the **Poor Law Act (1601)** had provided for the native community within each Parish boundary and funded the perfectly respectable Parish Workhouse where the long-term unemployed labourer might find work and financial relief to keep his family intact. It was a forerunner of social service with an emphasis, it would seem, on support. Subsequent Capitalist development saw a sea change in perspective. Poor Relief was perceived as having softened up and cushioned the able-bodied from more productive solutions because

265

they had come to view the relief as their entitlement. Families were being encouraged to be improvident and what was really needed were discipline, hard work, order, organisation, monitoring and control to redeem them. The workhouses were now deemed necessary to dam back the seeping spillage of able workers who would rather choose the drift and swirl of idle waters than the brisk current of work discipline. Consequently, the concerted control of idleness and economic impotence demanded the rationing of poor relief and the **Poor Law Act of 1834** was enacted as a deterrent to encouraging dependency (over half a million were receiving relief beyond these institutions). Hence, the increasing willingness to institutionalise the able homeless within the reorganised Union Workhouses which, abetted by an increasing body of orders, regulations, discipline and punishments, were authorised to grind the productivity out of them. The workhouses did more than rein in every potential worker from the non viable pauperised classes and train them for the working habits of industrial routine within the mills and factories. Symbolically, they became administrative outposts that gauged the economic periphery and guarded the frontiers of social unrest and rebellion. The workhouse glare illuminated the idle paupers in its midst and subjected them to a working enslavement of hard work, poor food, poor hygiene, poor ventilation, overcrowding, loss of liberty, disease and a pauper's grave! It was said that by 1839, around 100,000 paupers laboured in workhouses and they continued in an official capacity until 1930.

This was more than a straightforward condemnation of idleness. The prosperous entrepreneurialism was alarmed by the crippled undergrowth of humanity who dragged around their limping trails of deformities and abnormalities, destitution and poverty, immorality and lawlessness, insanity and disease. There was fear that these broken sticks of humanity might, some day, knit their splintered bones into a heavy limbed rebellion that would require the sending of troops into the streets, as they had already been sent across the seas, and into the cities, and onto the plains and deserts of the Empire's foreign lands. The signs of civil disorder were already evident by the early 1800s with rioting, factory sabotage and striking in the towns, and insurrection that blazed across the rural haystacks in the countryside. Authorities were forced into earnest surveys of the apparent social disintegration, and deteriorating health, of the period and an acknowledgement that the developing industrial technologies, new working conditions, and the sprawling, disorganised, overcrowded towns were an inclement cauldron that perpetuated many of the emerging problems and that individuals, alone, were powerless to implement solutions. The unavoidable conclusions were that a town's unplanned development would inevitably nurture the disfiguring goitre of social deviance. The condition was so dysfunctional to the whole of society that the goitre was deemed to require eradication through systemic treatment. The State took on the social and moral hygiene of society, to match what was being accomplished in the public health overhaul of drainage, cleansing and sanitation, overcrowding, ventilation and the provision of open space. For this to be effected the law had to be transformed from an instrument of sheer bloody terror that had laid a good deal of the blame for all social ills on pathological individuals who deserved punishment to keep them in line. It had to recognise the need for government administration of interventions for both individual maladies and the pathological conditions in society.

It was as if the nation's own peoples, like the heathen abroad, needed to be colonised and governed with the same vigorous organisation as the rest of the Empire. But what was also being incubated and radicalised was a humanistic re-evaluation by a more optimistic and disparate throng of political reformers. The general drift of political reform was toward the extension of the political franchise which had been accelerated by the recent social movements and rapid urbanisation of the population. Urbanisation mobilised political consciousness in a manner that had never been possible within the dependent, isolated, rural communities of the pre industrial past. The criminals, though justly punished, would have moral guidance and contemplate their social rehabilitation in as conscientious a manner as the metropolitan refuse, drainage and water supplies would be sanitised; the physically sick would be medically treated or hospitalised, or exiled to the sanatoria; the young would receive education; and both the established church and revivalist denominations would recharge the spiritual temperature of the nation. A new species of architecture and social administration would be the major vehicle of this reorganisation – the Victorian institution. A political invention of union workhouses, schools, prisons, general hospitals, smallpox and scarlet fever hospitals, tuberculosis sanatoria, idiot colonies, imbecile colonies. epileptic colonies, pauper lunatic asylums, and criminal lunatic asylums. And the institution would be informed by every civilising tool in the box to etch their orthodox interpretations into the consciousness of the people: punishment and control; humanitarianism, philanthropy and reform; education; religion; medicine and science; and, not least, sheer political pragmatism.

The government instituted a host of targeted appraisals, and published reports of all the major social problems which led, over time, to a comprehensively systematic programme of social intervention. These solutions were an unprecedented State intervention for public services. To tackle working conditions and public health, particularly during the 1830s and 40s, a wave of legislation for improving Factories, Municipal Corporations, Poor Law, Towns Improvements, Public Health, and Public Improvements was produced. But, if only for sheer pragmatism, the gross goitre of human casualties that was evident would be cosmetically excised and systematically dispersed across a national network of administered colonies. Thus, set in motion an institutional revolution for the various groups of need whether they be criminal, poor, uneducated, physically ill or mentally infirm. Whether such reforms as separation, incarceration, and treatment would make crooked men straight and justify the economic outlay of a building programme, was yet to be proven but doing nothing was not an option. Such a vast project, at such financial and organisational cost, would never have been countenanced unless the State had no other choice but to resort to institutional action and for want of any other viable solution.

This institutional colonisation especially identified discrete sections of the criminal population, types of punishment, and forms of disposal. From the end of the eighteenth, and throughout the whole of the nineteenth centuries, the law enacted distinct Acts to cater for gaols, penitentiaries, prisons, juvenile offenders, youthful offenders, habitual criminals, transportation, penal servitude, whipping, garroting, prevention of crimes, and Offences against the Person.

* * *

As another, increasingly identifiable sector, the lunatics filtered down through the other provisional nets. The workhouse tide of destitution brought in more and more of the less able-bodied, unruly insane who inadvertently impeded its operations. The insane, who were burdensome to their families and quite beyond abiding by the rules of the workhouse or jails, floated to the surface of these institutions as incorrigible, sometimes harmful, flotsam. The problem of the country's insane was adopted as one part of this centralised, State managed project which campaigned, organised, bureaucratised, and specialised with the assistance of professional expertise.

As government projects, the public asylums came to supplement what had gone before – the private madhouses that housed the men, women and youths who had had their reputations inscribed with allegations of mental illness or impairment. With some notable exceptions such as the Quakers, whose régimes were run through with the religious commitment, these were grand lodgings out of the reach of respectable humanity, far from the world's rigours, far from real time, far from stimulating other peoples' fears. The public nuisances and the sturdy beggars jangled their chains, rattled their iron bracelets, and paced and padded about as privatised exhibits for pleasuring the gentry on their leisure outings. Nothing better captured the atrocious divide between elevated respectability and the despised outsider than these entre-preneurial theme parks of madness. But enquiries into the private madhouses unveiled an accumulating catalogue of abuses that fuelled a reforming, humanitarian outrage and an *Act for Regulating Private Madhouses (1774)* was instituted.

The start of the public asylum building programme for pauper luna-tics was stimulated by the enactment of the *County Asylums Act (1808),* in what was termed as a *permissive* legislation. It was permissive in that it merely recommended that each county assess its own needs and institutional provision for its local lunatics and pay for them from the county rates. Not surprisingly, very few counties abided by the directive and the mentally ill continued to be channelled into private madhouses, armed with a magistrate's warrant, or to the workhouse. But the few asylums that had been erected since the *1808 County Asylums Act* were subjected to accumulating pres-sures that compounded their ability to manage within their current resources: the general increase in population size; the disproportionately expanding numbers of insane; the unsuccessful treatment by hospital psychiatrists; the non-return of the earlier inmates to society; and the very existence of the asylums that encouraged community physicians to refer their patients to them. Additionally, the workhouses, which had done the job for long enough, could not manage the incontinent disability of their insane lodgers and their Boards of Guardians did their best to rid themselves of the extra trouble they caused.

By 1815, the asylums that were in operation came in for comprehensive condemnation by a Select Committee Report of that year which demanded improvements in supervision, inspection, living conditions, treatment methods, reduced restraints, and better informed "keepers". The *Madhouse Act (1828)* did exactly this but its area of jurisdiction was limited to the London Metropolitan area. No doubt these recommendations proved too punctilious for many a prospective county authority who were already vacillating over the basic fiscal outlay of asylum provision. Lord Shaftesbury's 1845 Commons' speech advocated that the country's poor lunatics should be maintained from the public charge. Therefore, along with the increasing pressure for asylum places, there was left no option but to supplement the permissive *1808 Act* with the *compulsory* provisions of the *County Asylums Act (1845)* which compelled every county to build its own localised institutions. Thus was set in motion a structural archipelago that would alter the psycho-political landscape.

Despite the concerted criticism of the workhouse, private madhouse, and public asylums, such large institutions still persisted as the established models for the physical confinement, and administrative concentration, of deviant strains of the populus. The political wisdom advocated improvement but not replacement so that the continuing containment of the insane did not reject the use of the large establishment. Instead, it revised its management with medical reform and promulgated a climate of "asylum". So, what exactly was the asylum from?

The insane and mentally retarded would have a temporary reserve, a retreat, a refuge, from which they would be invigorated back to health. They would be protected from exposure to ridicule or from being exhibited to paying visitors who goaded them into violent reactions. The appropriate physical facilities would be forthcoming where there would be safety, fresh air, rural landscapes, productive work and recreation. Even this access to healthy, open countryside was no accident but, arguably, rationalised on the same grounds as the identified need for open spaces in the industrialised and urbanised centres. The recognition of unhealthy, overcrowded confinement, with less and less space being available for public recreation in heavily populated areas, had necessitated a *Select Committee on Public Works (1833)*. This body identified a need for such open spaces and public parks to promote public health, and as a political necessity to ensure public safety. Presumably, this was taken into consideration with the inclusion of the spacious grounds into the asylum configuration.

Being concentrated within the specialised asylum compound would alleviate the severity of the inmates' conditions and potentiate their cure. All asylum provision would now be monitored by commissioners, who would give written accounts of their visits and investigations. And, anxious to assuage themselves of future political harassment, particularly from charges of immorality and abuse, the local authorities passed on the baton of responsibility to an evolving medical expertise. This expertise was a professional hybrid that fertilised its ideas within the abundant nurseries of medicine and duly obliged with a plethora of publications about the therapeutic management of lunacy. Physicians and surgeons were now put in charge of asylums and patients were to be treated with humanity, to be cured, and this would more than justify the economic and political investment! There was a zealous optimism among the reformers that the mad-doctors and alienists – later called psychiatrists – would find a scientific and sympathetic path through the ideological contentions of insanity. New methods of treatment were being instituted, further validating the expertise of the psychiatric profession. There was some confidence that the very asylum structure, in its own right, would be efficacious and fit for purpose. The laudable conviction of the reformist plan surely buoyed up the political will and helped to resist the pessimism of the apparent social calamity of the period. And with the best will in the world, it was intended that a generally sceptical public would be won over by the prospect that both private and public interests were being served through the collaboration of philanthropy, political reform and medical science.

After the asylum foundations were laid, the incineration and water towers rose beyond the tree line as prominently as cathedral spires and accumulated a final count of approximately 127 establishments throughout England and Wales alone! A segregated constituency whose only common theme was said to be insanity. Though precise figures vary somewhat, the asylum spires tolled for a congregation of between 150,000 and 155,000 during the mid-1950s! A comparison with the prison population of today – around 80,000 – revealed the extent of in-patient confinement during the asylum heyday!

* * *

The institutional provision of asylums has always had its vociferous detractors. It would be inconceivable that this institutional provision of asylums did not have its vociferous detractors, despite the reformist optimism and ideals of beneficence, protection, treatment and medical purposes for an ungovernable wildness in humanity. In the first instance, placing lunatics in asylums was a deliberate and unprecedented annexation, a conscripted exile of its sufferers from society. It could usefully be argued that a psychological sanitisation had swept the families and communities clean of insanity, that in caring for their patients the asylums had, none too discreetly, removed part of its sickly humanity, and that what remained was a healthy, deserving majority. In tidying up the social landscape, politicians and conventional citizens were able to displace a good deal of the blame for society's threatened breakdown and failings onto their many imperfect outsiders. It was the criminal, the unemployed, the sick, and the insane who were the signs and carriers of the flaws in mankind when not adequately controlled. It was they who should be held to account for that breakdown while sanitary measures would be both a preventative and punitive management policy. Shifting responsibility for the accumulating social breakdowns onto all its most visible, deviant exponents was a rationalising projection of the political mind. But there was a cost to this rationalisation of society and its aberrations. With such numbers of mental inmates, for example, there could hardly have been a family in the country that was not affected by a relative's "commitment" or "certification". Small wonder parents could impress upon their children a sanction which had the power and threat of a State sponsored bogeyman – "If you don't behave yourselves the men in white coats will come and take you away!"

It could be argued that the very asylums, themselves, reinforced the impression of mental diseases as they spread like a rash of sickly freckles around the perimeters of major towns throughout the entire country; that they were a variant of the concentration camp where the mentally ill were, in very

272

great numbers, corralled into a confined demarcation from normality. It was difficult to argue too strongly against this in the case of London asylums when they were often erected far out into the surrounding Green Belt while their constituency came from Inner London Boroughs, miles away from family and associations. To the critics this was a calculated policy where human beings were willingly cajoled, or forcefully removed, from everything to which they had been attached on the pretext of a short stay that was conducive to recovery. They, and the political and medical powers that controlled them, prosecuted a pernicious assault upon the individual destiny and freedom of the disadvantaged mentally distressed, depriving them of their citizenship and personal potency. While personal demons clawed at the deranged reason of its inmates, psychiatric power clawed the deranged minds from out of the public domain into an institutional destiny. An institutional destiny meant treading the charted path of the "inmate" in a remote dwelling set aside from town, population and thoroughfare. In the case of the mentally ill and mentally defective a destiny that, despite the benign rhetoric, guaranteed no cure, no dimension in time or space, and equally relieved them of culture, gainful employment, ambition and any responsibility. They were "put away" to become a historical record in a mad archive.

* * *

As psychiatric care evolved it became a conflated alliance of medicine, politics and the law. For example, at the time that I had commenced psychiatric nurse training in the early 1970s the legal framework for organising psychiatric care for *mentally* ill people had evolved into the **Mental Health Act** *(1959)*. At its inauguration, it was intended that it instigate another significant turning point in the management of mental disorder. As with any statute, it did not come to fruition in isolation but as part of the general harvest of thought that was reappraising the pejorative assignations of previously deviant and unhealthy elements in society. The effects of the Second World War laid down a base of fertile loam out of which arose the liberal shoots that would lean toward de-stigmatising, decriminalising and, at the same time, nurturing and medicalising a good deal of previously conventional behaviour and beliefs. The phenomenon of child illegitimacy emerged as far less than

273

the shame of a morally incontinent minority when one third of all child births in Britain, during World War Two, were delivered out of wedlock, resulting in unprecedented increases in both abortions and Children's Homes (the latter also fuelled by the deaths of combatant fathers and impoverished mothers). Furthermore, in the region of 10% of all discharged casualties from the War were suffering from bona fide mental illnesses which needed to be managed with some delicacy. But it was the years from 1957, through the ensuing decade, that saw a surge of legislative and social change all of which, argu-ably, would have had an associated impact on the field of psychiatry to some degree.

In 1957, the government commissioned *Percy Report* – which evolved into the aforementioned *1959 Mental Health Act* – presented its findings on the state of mental illness and mental deficiency in Britain. It recommended, where possible, that patients were to be informally admitted (minimising compulsory detention), their rights were to be better promoted and secured, institutional care should be re-sited to small units attached to general hospi-tals, and a policy of active discharge should return patients to their homes or to local authority care. In total, it was seen to be a huge departure from previous legislation and psychiatric organisation, and had begun the notion of treating the mentally ill in a more inclusive way. It also provided solid grounds for anticipating that the age of the psychiatric asylums was over. When instituted, the *Mental Health Act, 1959*, also incorporated alcoholism, drug use and sexual deviancy as grounds for admission for psychiatric treat-ment so that the law, while trying to decriminalise these activities, effectively transferred State power from a punitive authority to a medical authority.

In the same year, the *Wolfenden Report* published its considerations on homosexuality and prostitution. It concluded that homosexual acts between consenting adults, in private, should no longer be criminalised and that prostitution and pornography should be legally reworked because it believed that, of the many vital functions that the law performed, it should not be the duty of the law to judge sexual immorality. Two years afterwards, the *Sexual Offences Act (1959)* instituted most of the earlier recommendations of Wolfenden. Though continuing to criminalise loitering or soliciting for the purpose of prostitution, essentially it decriminalised prostitution as an offence in itself.

By 1967, the **Sexual Offences Act** provided that it was no longer an offence for consenting men, attaining the age of 21, to commit the practices of buggery or gross indecency in private.

Similarly, the **Abortion Act (1967)**, while not wholly decriminalising abortion, legalised abortion under prescribed medical circumstances such as to preserve the life of the pregnant mother.

The introduction of the **Homicide Act (1957)** transformed the catch all verdict of murder – intentional killing with malice aforethought – with an additional range of more discriminating verdicts. Unintentional "manslaughter", "unsound mind", and "diminished responsibility" entered the frame. And it was not stretching things too far to relate this to a specific provision within the **1959 Mental Health Act** which would differentiate and accommodate a notoriously problematic group in society, namely, psychopaths. Psychopaths had acquired an unenviable reputation for failing to conform to social conventions, abnormal aggression, irresponsible behaviour, and egotistically motivated criminality. The challenges of this category were exemplified by the indeterminacy of their categorisation – were they mad, or bad, or both? But the **1959 Mental Health Act** produced a precise, legal definition of what was called Psychopathic Disorder. In the Act, they were to be reframed as a disorder, the basis of which was psychological and, therefore, a potentially treatable condition which might interrupt their decline toward criminality.

Perceptions of the act of suicide had been a standard bearer of religious and political intolerance. It had been regarded as nothing less than self-murder and if, in attempting to kill themselves a person survived, then they were guilty of the misdemeanour of attempted suicide for which they could receive a prison sentence. The **Suicide Act (1961)** abolished the guilt attached to a person's suicide, or attempted suicide, so that these could no longer be viewed as criminal acts.

It is worth arguing that all this constituted a liberalising legal era which had direct, and indirect, implications for psychiatric practice and the medicalisation of social and psychological difficulties. This surge of relatively political liberalism did not happen in isolation but flourished among a plethora of revelations by social scientists, social commentators, and disaffected psychiatrists, whose analysis of British and American asylums, of psychiatric diagnoses, and of organisational systems, produced a battery of infamously critical publications. Barton, a British psychiatrist, even defined the phenomenon of "institutional neurosis" whereby the very way in which the mental hospitals were run, and exacerbated by the unsavoury character-istics of some staff, of themselves, promoted a disease entity. Institutional neurosis was marked by patient apathy, lethargy and submissiveness, so that such stricken patients were unable to generate any interest in themselves, or their present or future circumstances. One body of radical psychiatrists took up the new intellectual position of "anti psychiatry" which generated a good deal of intellectual attention. They argued for a more empathic reappraisal and interpretation of patients' psychotic symptoms as meaningful experi-ences which the medical profession had no right to attempt to subdue with their non empathic, conventional methodologies. Another emergence was the social psychiatric movement within the field of psychiatry which established small communities of patients and staff to utilise group and milieu therapy. The group, itself, was viewed as a far more propitious therapeutic agent and worked to develop a democratic sharing of responsibility for organising the units. And so was born the idea of the "therapeutic community".

In the psycho philosophical background the World Health Organisation and American Psychiatric Association – the two masters in diagnostic deter-mination – competed for supremacy, researching, revising, refining, and trying to beat out the unreliable and invalid dents in their conceptual body-work. And every few years, a new manual would play down past diagnoses, and would sex up the need to acknowledge and identify the new psychiatric phenomenology, the new diagnostic creations.

The effect of all these intellectual and legal ruminations was for previ-ously criminal conduct to be couched in an illness, treatment and health framework rather than in a crime, punishment and criminal justice frame-work. The implication was that the various behaviours were social problems and that State (or private, or voluntary) intervention was indispensable. Whether or not this enabled a degree of de-stigmatisation to follow is more debatable, but some positive movement in this regard was likely to have occurred. Arguably, another crucial implication was the liberalisation of thinking around the causal factors related to deviant behaviours/problems and the degree, therefore, to which a subject was personally blameworthy for their actions. The *Homicide Act (1957)* was the most blatant example, in acknowledging the many legal caveats that prevented a subject from being held fully responsible for deeds actually committed. Judgements upon the criminal act of murder or attempted murder were supplemented by considerations of a defendant's many possible legitimate defences, including mental illness, and these altered the nature of his criminal *intent*. Linked to this was the intent of the ***Criminal Procedure Act (1964)***, which acknowledged a defendant's "unfitness to plead" in a court of law owing to his/her mental incapacity to understand the court proceedings, or to advise his/her counsel, or comprehend the nature of his/her predicament. The following year, legislation in the form of the ***Murder (Abolition of the Death Penalty) Act (1965)*** determined that hanging for murder should be suspended – pun intended – for five years before becoming permanently abolished in 1969.

* * *

There was an accompanying groundswell of alternative opinion which proposed that mental illness was not, necessarily, a one-dimensional, biological disease process located in the individual person. Rather, the illness was a dynamic consequence of interrelated constitutional, social, economic, and political ingredients and health care was just one mode of intervention. The psychiatrist and psychoanalyst, R.D. Laing, for example, suggested that a schizophrenic was driven insane by the machinations of their own family and the patient was the scape-goated product of the family disorder.

Who knows how much of all these varying debates that eventually led to so many pieces of humanitarian legislation would have informed the Health Minister, Enoch Powell, and his 1961 figurative speech about the water towers that represented the nation's asylums, and of his intended policy to close the greater part of the asylum capacity? He followed it up, the next year, with the publication of the ***Hospital Plan for England and Wales*** explicitly advocating the closure of psychiatric asylums and the transfer of these services into the community.

For us, the nursing staff in the mental hospitals almost a decade and a half later, the ideological tremors and critical mass arising from these radical objections, and the relatively political humanitarianism, seemed not to have leapt across the chasm that had separated off the asylum estate. All that concerned us or, indeed, all we were aware of, was that there was an intended dissolution of our institutions. What cracks of awareness did span the gap and improve patient care remained ringed about by the self-serving, occupational protectionism of the staff. And, within anyone's judgement, the asylums resolutely remained intact, continuing to perpetuate a system not quite invalidated, and which looked as if it would continue in perpetuity. At the internal level, with the exception of the social psychiatry movement, and the bare bones of the *Mental Health Act,* how was it that so little of the foregoing critiques came to percolate down through the strata of central political responsibility for patient care, local hospital administrative responsibility, and into nurse training strategies? Somehow, the new ideas were never quite articulated with policy and practice. What would it take to initiate change? Who would initiate change? What changes, exactly? Why change, exactly? Accordingly, whatever other motives held back the impetus toward the radical deployment of psychiatric services, there must have been some deep-seated reluctance to dispense with the asylum structure, as well as a lingering presumption that patients were, in fact, being delivered into a moral refuge – a place of sanctuary away from a sceptical public, where disabilities were respected, where their rights were promoted and defended, over and above basic health objectives.

The debate about the tardy service renewal for the mentally ill became even more poignant when compared with the accelerated developments in services to the mentally handicapped who, themselves, had been institutionalised to the tune of 55,000-60,000? It was said that there was an additional, eugenic factor in their institutional separation which was to minimise the potential for passing on their genetic handicap to future generations through sexual intercourse. The *1971 Report on Better Services* to this group wrought unprecedented changes which not only soundly undermined the validity of institutional provision, but also transferred responsibility for care and treatment, residence, education, recreation, and access to every community resource, to the local authorities in a wholesale package of community relocation! Hospitals for the mentally handicapped – asylums by any other name – emptied faster than their counterparts for the mentally disordered, proving that the process could be implemented if the will was there. The field of mental handicap enjoyed an ideational inflation in social objectives: the notion of normalising life opportunities so that every aspect of their competencies would be capitalised on; and of valorising the social rôles that this group should be entitled to take up in society so that they were not discriminated against, or prevented from any level of participation within the limit of their abilities. Whether it could be said that there has ever been a corresponding social acceptance of these individuals as equal citizens remains open to conjecture but it could be confidently asserted that a significant integration had, in principle, taken place for the mentally handicapped. And what this assimilation hinged on was a reconfiguration of mental handicaps as a developmental issue rather than that it represented a panorama of illnesses, or psychological pathologies.

By 1975, official recognition that the very converse situation appertained to the mentally ill, as now appertained to the mentally handicapped, prompted a Report reiterating the need for better integrated, alternative services. Some years later, even this failed to galvanise the various sectors into concerted action and the asylum structure remained intact. The mentally ill, after all, were ill, and deviant, and still needed to be closely monitored.

* * *

The uniqueness of mental illness in the public imagination, at least, stems from the tales of roaming, wild, incomprehensible vagabonds. Even the coming of the asylum, with its treatments, did little to assuage the responses of incredulity, comedy and fear. So powerfully has it been stamped into our collective history that its remnants still persist within an oral tradition that reaches into our contemporary life with as much vehemence as ever it did in the past. The linguistic totems that helped define, and explain, the extraordinary phenomena that inhabited the world of mental patients seep into common usage with every successive generation. Even the early legislation stamped into history the social divide between the mentally unwell and normal society. Madhouse Acts! Lunacy Acts! County Lunatic Acts! Criminal Lunatic Act! The emerging, psychiatric language, though manifestly diagnostic, became a euphemism for extraordinary social differentiation and condemnation. Take the earlier diagnoses relating to seriously disruptive people who have the contemporary label of personality disorders: moral insanity, moral imbecility, psychopathy, degenerate constitution, congenital delinquency, constitutional inferiority, moral deficiency, and sociopathy! These and general psychiatric terms such as madness, insanity, lunacy and derangement were but the official surface which has fomented a monumental ideological denunciation of mental illnesses that spawned a plethora of admonishments: psycho, maniac, screwball, screwy, screwed up, zany, loony, loony tune, loopy, dotty, crank, crazy, cracked, crackpot, crackers, nuts, nutty, nutter, nutbag, sick, batty, bonkers, barmy, bananas, mad as a hatter, out of his tree, off his trolley, short of a sandwich, off his rocker, and flipped his lid! When the Prison Service transferred an inmate to a psychiatric facility the vernacular was that he/she had been "nutted off"! These terms were more than matched by the field of learning disability where the formalised, clinical diagnoses such as handicapped, defective, retarded, subnormal, cretin, Mongol, imbecile, moron, idiot and feeble-minded, slipped from diagnoses into common parlance and popular vernacular. Extensive alternative denunciations were also available: daft, silly, dim, witless, thick, thicko, dense, dopey, dozy, nitwit, nincompoop, simple, simpleton, low grades, wops, mess-pots, soft in the head, and not all there!

The staff themselves not only absorbed these descriptive assignations, but were probably responsible for creating some of them. In fact, they were party to other discrete aides-mémoire, in an effort to maintain a notional compartmentalisation of the range of psychiatric diagnoses and symptoms. They included such scant formulations as the association of certain personality types with specific body constitutions. So, the schizophrenic was said to have an *asthenic* build (tall, and narrow), the manic-depressive to have a *pyknic* build (short and plump), while normal people veered more toward an *athletic* build (normally proportioned and muscular). On another theme, current wisdom still chose to teach a 1930s' model of the "psychopath" as if it was the only one in existence. The model, described by the psychiatrist Henderson, took the psychopath's general manifestations of asociality, lack of guilt, and involvement with drugs, alcohol and crime and extended it into three subdivisions. It outlined the incompetent, *inadequate* psychopath; the intelligent, *creative* psychopath; and the amoral, *dangerous* psychopath.

But among the most useful shorthand was the differentiation of the four major mental illnesses into the "mad", "sad", "glad" and the "bad". The mad – those with schizophrenia: the sad – depression: the glad – mania: the bad – psychopathy (specIflcally, psychopaths). It was a brIllIant shorthand! Between them, they displayed the major psychiatric symptoms from which all the more discrete neuroses, and psychoses, and other deviations, were derived.

This terminology rested easily on a fertile bed of long established condemnations of psychological deviance which would not have been remotely associated with health care. Physically descriptive words such as cripple and invalid were notions of social excommunication, physical worthlessness and, ultimately, invalidity. The unpalatable irony of the medical science of psychiatry and mental handicap was that, in attempting to differentiate the syndromes of a social minority, they provided an offensive, linguistic armoury that transformed professional definition into the common vernacular of social exclusion. In so doing, language was a brutalising tool brandished by conventional society that branded, insulted, and condemned a social minority. Besides this, when used in a wider context, it was intended to condemn not only that very minority but anyone else whom society at large wished to insult. Using any of these labels was, other than directly swearing, the next best way of causing common offence against someone. How much was medicine inadvertently accountable for becoming a force for bad, rather than for good, a public disservice, rather than a service?

* * *

A lunatic attendant! A Registered Mental Nurse! If the one title was denigrating, the other was somewhat irksome and trivialising. The lunatic attendants, a disproportionately large proportion of them males, emerged within the hierarchy of the lunatic asylum. They were the legitimate, uniformed ranks of trained men and women who, as certified members of the Medico-Psychological Association, had displayed the necessary "Character, Conduct and Aptitude" that qualified them as having "attained proficiency in nursing and attendance upon Insane Persons". And the designated *lunatic attendant* recalled an era which many of the contemporary male staff would have been content to reinstate because it denoted an image, and position, of considerable power, authority and control. This sat more easily with the self-image of those modern male nurses who were noting their traditional rôles slipping away, compromised and feminised by notions of care, and therapeutic techniques and all the rest of the bullshit, as they perceived it. It was not so very fanciful that masculine control and feminine care usefully divided the sexes into opposing camps, while not precluding the possibility that for each individual a unique combination of both sets of attributes might exist. As progress re-vamped their title, attendants became registered Mental Nurses. "Mental" was almost comical, and certainly, but unintentionally, ironic, whereas the idea of a "psychiatric" nurse had more specificity, some gravitas to it. Yet, strictly speaking "psychiatric" was inaccurate owing to its Greek roots, "iatros" meaning physician, and "psyche" meaning mind, soul, or spirit. Thus, while the psychiatrist was a physician of the mind, the nomenclature of a psychiatric nurse denoted the extent to which nurses operated in the shadow of their medical superiors! Additionally, "nurse" was more comfortably associated with the tending of physical problems, rather than with the mental, and other connotations which centred on conventional femininity! Caring, nurturing, bed baths, serving meals, bed making, uniforms harking back to convents, nuns, religious robes and cowls, religious belief, dedication, sacrifice, vocation, silence, poverty and low pay! Admittedly, there were also heroic and military associations like the First World War's Edith Cavell smuggling wounded allies back to their own lines; and the Crimea's Florence Nightingale and Mary Seymour battling the infectious conditions in which wounded soldiers were cared for. But they still reinforced the image of nursing as a supportive, reparative, non-combatant womanhood. It was one of those much discussed issues that was fuelling the current industrial unrest in the psychiatric hospitals that the poor pay and conditions of service for all nurses, male and female, were attributable to this female history. A history that epitomised the subservient role of women, where they obliged their male counterparts – doctors' handmaidens was the figurative norm – while doctors pursued the superior profession of medicine along with all its associated trappings. It was these combined assignations of subservience, domesticity, low status and womanhood which were ever so slightly humiliating for so many, but not all, male nurses to be identified with. It was now considered an unalienable truth that it was necessary for men, allied with trade unionism, to become the reforming instruments of economic advancement in nursing. The past was fading.

The gender bias among psychiatrists was even more explicit. All the psychiatrists in the hospital, admittedly few, from Consultant to Registrar, were males. There was not much sign of females taking up positions in other hospitals, either. Male or female, psychiatrists were a scarce commodity who were invested with a vast range of powers and authority. In fact, up until the not too distant past, every hospital's senior psychiatrist, carrying the illustrious title of Physician Superintendent, lauded over every clinical and administrative aspect of their hospital domain. Medical hegemony extended so broadly within the *psychiatric* field that it even prescribed the training of nurses, wrote the very text books, taught large parcels of the syllabus, examined their competencies, and finally helped enter the successful candidates onto the Medico-Psychological Register! Social status and power extended to giving dispensations to members of his nursing staff: to those wishing to marry; allocating senior staff to the tied cottages and giving permission for such tenants to own a dog (much as a servant would be required to do of the lord of the manor). In due consideration of his superiority, and a salary 40 times that of a "first class attendant", he was assigned the supreme perquisite of the best individual dwelling on the premises as his very own home. Privileges of office aside, real power lay in granting dispensation to special patients to be allowed access to his, and others', private space to tend and cultivate the garden, clean the house, or wash the automobile. Their inordinate power had included the authority to hire and fire a substantial section of the workforce and where much of an individual's advancement, or other leverage, might well depend on partiality and patronage.

* * *

Human lives bear some resemblance to those of institutions. They are not born just of themselves, free to fulfil their latent potential, unfettered. In the deep, primitive caves of an infant psyche the parents carve and etch their presence, their parenthood, their dispositions, moods, stances, beliefs, language, voices, and most tellingly, familiar ways of relating to their children. Once these are scrawled and daubed onto the walls and ceilings of that mental landscape they will hang there throughout a child's, then an adult's, lifetime as permanent fixtures. They become an indestructible part of their offspring's story, editing

283

reflections, commenting on intentions, forever influencing. Like any child's early development, mine contained the internalised representation of my two parental figures as they encroached into my conscious and unconscious terrains. The forbidding image of a tyrannical mother, glaring with criticism and aggression, dominated a vast space, cast in grim colours. The vaguer picture of an ambivalent father was portrayed as a barely outlined sketching, in a hazy, indecipherable light. Presumably, there must have been space on this internal wall for the repertoire of other experiences, other relationships, and new ideas that would come my way but they would forever be agitated by, and clouded by, these predominating portraits and their voices. Even so, an individual's life chances are never wholly determined and that irrepressible living force that is the distinctive self, aware of itself even in the womb, reaches outward and upward to make its own tenuous, liberating strokes.

Presumably, many people can take for granted that their personal history should include a birthright entitlement of protective nurturing and the nurturing of emotional resources that make them fit for purpose as a social being. It was not how I could have characterised my own. On the contrary, mine was a legacy of unmitigated family conflict and disintegration. When only a young lad, I had been shocked by my paternal grandmother's admission of her lifelong antipathy for her own mother and siblings whom she rarely trusted, communicated with, or acknowledged over the many years up to their deaths. This compounded the revelations from my mother's side which showed an extensive history of relatives plummeting through the frail strands of parental and sibling support and stability. There were short-term psychiatric admissions for some; one uncle's long-term hospitalisation; another uncle's imprisonment and alcoholism; another uncle's rail track suicide, all marching in step with my unseen grandfather who returned from the First World War shell-shocked and epileptic. The family strain was psychologically infected and lay in wait to blight each successive generational crop, condemning them to the shared frailty and destructive dramas of their inheritance. Both extended families – a conceptual rather than a viable network – were riven with disputes, lifelong hostilities and general dysfunction, which were way beyond reconciliation. Discovering that devotion and loyalty were far too exacting the members preferred to ignore each other's company, in large part. And that's how they died, one following on another, bitter and unreconciled.

My own birth had been a "breech". It may well have been a plain, anatomical aberration, or a technical glitch, or have occurred for some other contingent, medical reason. Looked at in personal retrospect, however, it seemed to symbolise and enact, even at delivery, that the unborn child is capable of auguring the coming conflicts with the hosting mother. And a painful, laborious three days, rounded off by a forceps delivery and episiotomy, was the price paid by my mother before I was dredged out. Presumably, the nine months of pregnancy had provided more than enough prescience of the travails to come, of the awaiting tempest of childhood and youth, of a family that would offer little refuge, and the prospect of a world of relative strangers. The staff of the maternity unit presumably called out "Come on, let's get you out of there", and I, presumably, regaled them with "Not bloody likely, I'm staying put!" Caught between being expelled into the world and resisting its invitation it had seemed eminently sensible to turn my back on the intrusion of birth, to face the placenta of that world, and lodge my arse in the exit for as long as I could manage. When delay had been sufficiently protracted the forceps clinched the day and reticent, my limbs and buttocks, closely pursued by the bloody rest of me, were evacuated despite my protesting efforts to remain in situ.

One of my very first memories was of an early morning when a single faecal stool lay like a recumbent pupa in my cot. Until, that is, mother's ire transformed it into an accusing log of shame. My mother threatened to recount the fouling deed to an expected family visitor later that day so I hid under the kitchen table at the sound of the doorbell until she drew me out, stood me up, and did as she had warned. Then, as a four year old, along with my younger sister, our parents cajoled us, via an unprecedented taxi ride into the countryside, only to abandon us in the hallway of a local authority children's home while they drove away to a surgeon's knife that scraped our mother clean of her womb and any further threat of childbearing. This, despite the extended family of a dozen aunts and uncles, plus grandparents, whom my mother probably avoided asking to accommodate us two children, aged two and four. As we sickened our way through that short, inexplicable sojourn the reluctant conclusion was that abandonment was acceptable if it defended someone else's principles. Tellingly, though, there was the small consolation of the starched warmth of the uniformed nurses of the Children's Home.

Not too long afterward, I acquired a stammer and juddered a course through conversations as if my stuttering and tainted diction spoke of a stage fright of life, of hesitating to express my lines, of not daring to utter feelings, of finding them beyond my scope, and finding myself stunned under the uncomprehending lights of the family and my little world.

When our parents decided the family would move from our Council house to our first private home in the Midlands, 200 miles away, my sister and I were not permitted to share it with friends, neighbours or teachers. On the removal day itself we attended school as usual, in the full and secret knowledge of our imminent disappearance, and were later snatched from the classrooms, and classmates, with hardly a word of farewell, only a trail of abandoned, unfinished endings, as if we had no past of our own that was worth speaking of. Overall, I did not care for the junior school life I left behind. It was an affection-free zone headed by the stiffened, ghoulish headmaster whose grey, mean eyes, yellow, slab teeth, and lizard lipped grimaces intimated how much he hated his rôle in life and the kids about him. His presence was repellent, the reptilian head jutting out of a scraggy throat whose skin folds shook copiously over his tight collar, while it croaked out threats of canings and other ignominies. And every blessed God-send of a morning, raised high on the stage, he conducted the school assemblies with vengeance on the agenda. But there was no question that after our move we did acquire a consolation in the warmth of the new school and a different educational climate where children were physically embraced, where the headmaster took a child's weeping head and buried it into his ample stomach and clothed it in his giant hands, and who filled the classroom with his love for people. The school worked wonders. At the age of eleven I swam my first mile, captained the school football team and the local district team, won medals and certificates, and passed the 11-plus exams.

There was a similar warm record during my young adolescence schooling when I was nursed within the graceful, middle class folds of plumed young females at a London Teaching Hospital for an operation on some lymphatic glands that had inflamed my neck. Arguably, the accumulating infection of family contact had been siphoned into the lymphatics, producing an unremitting pain in the neck that deserved the surgeon's sharpened point to bleed me of the malady! The time there was gratifying, with the affections and assurances of the sturdy, cultured nurses cloaked in their proud smiles and capes, and the affection of older fellow patients. By then, I took no chances and fitted in my goodbyes and made good the farewells before they evaporated into the past, and I returned to the place called home.

It was no common feat that my mother managed even the most basic of situations as if she had to complicate, agitate and reproach in order to feel viable. For example, there was not a house at which we resided where we did not have neighbour conflict, mostly instigated by my mother. Even delivery men, and postmen, could be roundly admonished for cutting across the garden grass or stepping over the low wire fence separating our garden from our neighbour's. Oh, that it had only been extra familial conflict! No such luck! My overwhelming childhood memories of the relationship with my mother were of being dominated, undermined, and sworn at. 'I've told, you what to do, now bloody do it, you little bleeder!'; 'Don't you dare talk back to me, you cur!'; and 'I'll ask you when I want your opinion, now shut your mouth you argumentative little sod!', were the orders of the day. My mother also had a penchant for striking out at me and catching me across the head and shoulders whenever I was within arms' reach of her bilious temperament, whilst invoking the phrase 'I'll brain you if you don't do as you're told!' She had to dominate every aspect of the family, every day, and would entertain not a smidgeon of dissension. It was possible to be struck for the minutest of infractions and so, on the occasion of family outings, I pleaded to be left behind in the home. Conversely, when school holidays arrived I was ordered out of bed at an early hour, and out of the house, with instructions not to return before teatime, which necessitated stoking up the confidence to call upon one friend or another in the hope of play, shelter, food and company for the day. When such fortuitous arrangements were not possible, resorting to wandering about was the beginning of a life trait. During these adolescent years I was never allowed to host friends for tea, play or overnight stays. I became accustomed to my own company.

All through my childhood, but particularly early youth, an ill-disposed, irascible, and easily slighted mother unleashed her battering petulance, taming any disagreement, independent thinking and intentions, but not the gathering outrage. Any defiance simply ignited her. When my father eventually left home she took hold of every family photograph, spoiling it with incandescence, literally cutting out my father's presence, slicing through his potency, emasculating him for eternity.

There was no literally no choice but to seek a survival tactic beyond the family, and to adopt the one sure route to achieving a fragile self-affirmation, recognition and self-worth that is open to the youngster – to become assimilated into the relatively impersonal machinations of the school experience. Even so, I did not enjoy any parental support here, either. But in the striving competitiveness of the school there would be some reflected image by which I could gain some purchase on who I was, who I might be, whose self-worth I might come to recognise. At my strict, conventional Grammar School the stiff, stunted Headmaster, with the creamed remnants of a hair quiff, stuffed a hanky into his brilliant white, loudly protruding, double-cuffed sleeves, horned himself into patent leather shoes every morning, extracted himself from his office with a smoking cough, and winged his cloaked flight just a short distance to school assembly. There was no personal relationship with this doyenne of emotional distance throughout seven years but his signature and fatuous comments lolled at the bottom of your school report, pretending some knowledge of your existence. He made promises. He particularly promised, during summer months, that if the Grenadier Guards were ever permitted to lick ice creams while dressed in uniform, then the school contingent of 700 co-ed students would be allowed to do likewise! Until then, such things as lollies, ice creams, bags of chips, and other culinary impedimenta to decent etiquette were forbidden. It was not so surprising, therefore, that I should suffer a reactionary rebuke with my own novel contravention of the school rules when it occurred. Not that I ever intended to contravene any school rule but Mother had to indulge her awkwardness!

In the first instance I was betrayed by my uniform shoes – my only pair of shoes owing to my mother's over scrupulous financial management. The wear and tear on these shoes, accelerated by daily playground football, couldn't be hidden from my mother's inspection and the inevitable cost of my trip to the cobbler's shop. For all the dreadful while that the cobbler held onto them during his hours of toil I became the innocent party to a cruel conspiracy of ill fortune. Since my mother refused to pay for more than one pair of shoes at any one time, when that one pair was being repaired, I had no choice but to wear either my Wellington boots or my white PE plimsolls to school! Thus would commence two or three days of hellish ignominy and of being roundly castigated by teachers and school kids alike for it must have appeared to be some sort of mischievous, anarchic act on my part not to be wearing the regulation black shoes. But there were other aberrations of appearance that I similarly agonised over when my mother forced me into the shearing, pudding basin haircuts which exposed me to the spiteful, raucous ridicule of merciless boys. These two repeated episodes were the abiding dreads of school life and I would never find it within me to forgive my parents, or my fellow pupils, for such humiliations which came about with the regularity of a slowly turning wheel of misfortune. I learned to anticipate the searing flush of embarrassment and the treachery of the family and school and to find them not as inseparable as I had hoped for. Regarding these two issues and many others that were to follow, I could never comprehend mother's disavowal of my expressions of searing torment.

Whether it was unfinished homework, or impending exams to revise for, she forced me to early bed, without flexibility, with no justification, exactly when she determined, lights out and no argument. When I returned home from football matches, she would refuse to entertain the dirty football strip in her washing machine and so I learned the art of post match scrubbing by hand. Compelled to wear but two school shirts throughout the week, my darkening, limp collars were shamed against the crisp glow of my daily laundered schoolmates. As much as I could, I practised the art of necessary deceit to avoid the humiliation of being singled out at school, whether it be for failure to complete homework, exam preparation, and presentation for sport and classroom. I managed by slipping out of bed in the uninterrupted calm of the night when parents had retired to bed, and into my studies, homework, exam revision, and scrubbing my shirt collars. I learned to survive my mother's stormy petulance with my own reciprocating brand of confused emotions. At a younger age I was clearly overwhelmed by an impotent hurtfulness and could only respond with the cowering, mean steps of enforced obedience and suppressed protest. As I grew older there was a contained opposition, contrariness, and contempt. Older still, this was supplemented by an anticipation of vengefulness and hatred toward her incomprehensible ignorance.

* * *

And all the while, a working father looked away to the solace of his long, six and a half day working week away from the home – with long hours of travel thrown in for good measure. On the other hand, though my father showed no animosity, he manifested an emotional hesitancy and unsupportive presence that it was difficult to get the measure of. How could a father not defend their child, manage to shake off such abuse, exhibit such impotence and unreliability? I concluded there would never be a father's protection. I was left feeling unprotected by him and only able to help myself. If anything, I protected my father, encouraging him to escape the marriage even when I was but 14 or 15! But a deep contempt was also flourishing. So, on the receiving end of the earlier years of my mother's battering and fractious bullying, and my father's emotional impotence, I stumbled through a fragile adolescence in the guise of "persona non grata".

As I was soon to learn, the Grammar School I attended would appreciate and reward a competitive, compliant spirit that was motivated to succeed. I soon felt adopted into an environment which acted "in loco parentis", or so I perceived it. Therefore, in return for a senior school that offered conditional acknowledgement, I reciprocated with the requisite, competitive compliance and became the consummate all-rounder, competent in most fields, but never brilliant or exceptional. Academically, I was always toward the head of the class, and the year, in most subjects. In respect of sports: school football captain and district and Under-19 County representative; and first team player in rugby, cricket, basketball and athletics. In respect of extra-curricular orientation; a lead school play rôle in the sixth form; the Sixth Form Society Secretary; the House Captain; the writer and director of the House play; and Deputy Head Boy! But what may have appeared to be self-motivation was, rather, a driven dependence that relied on excelling at everything in order to source the need for self-approval and self-esteem. Ego attached itself to achievements, all lending themselves to aggrandisement and carving out a shape in which I could recognise, and acknowledge, myself. Yet these achievements were earned between periods of insuperable anxiety. While motivated by the need to succeed in the world of school that was so vitalising, and so conferring of recognition, there was also the accompanying prospect of failure that hung above my aspirations like a scorpion's tail. It was not just about the fear of coming last, or even to meet parity with others.

It was the anxiety provoking horror of failing to keep right up there with the front pacemakers – in everything. Nothing could be excluded. The need for success was enjoined to the stinging riposte of failure, stabbing and stabbing in an unavoidable self-punishment. And the most potent, potential instrument for failure was the examination – impersonal, judgemental, capable of destroying reputation and self-esteem! Even the anticipation of examinations became the most incapacitating threat of all. Striving to compete with all school comers was not done with a calm satisfaction but with an excruciating horror of being undone, defeated! I so feared the very prospect of exams that even the preceding revision build-up hailed an extended period of anxiety, occasional petrification and tearfulness. This never changed throughout my life.

* * *

When the sixth form came around my mother's chagrin toward my very attendance at the Grammar School, let alone any achievements, far from abating, was intensified. She argued vehemently that 'you think yourself high and mighty and better than everyone else because you go to that Grammar School', and that I wasted my time with 'all that study'. I had to resist the constant invocation to 'get out and get yourself a job like everyone else'. When I did work during school vacations, my holiday pay was diverted into purchasing the school armoury – leather briefcase, shoes, barathea blazer, soccer boots and other paraphernalia. It couldn't even be said that I could differentiate a dreadful home life from a compensating school because the one leaked into the other, emotionally distracting, and detracting from my capacity to concentrate. All I could do was to feign normality and cheeriness at school. But in the home I was a big lad now. Any blows provoked facetious replies.

'Didn't hurt! Can't hurt me any more!' But the day came when something qualitatively different rent the air between my mother and me.

'I'll murder you one of these days if you keep answering me back!' So, there was murder afoot! And, if she could not bring herself to complete the act, then the message was scrawled into my unconscious. This memory disappeared for decades, only to re-emerge within weeks of my mother's

death, as if it had lain like a murky catfish among the sludge of my unconscious until it had been released to break the conscious surface and draw a
long gasp of air. She was not alone in the death stakes! Many were the times
that I wished my mother dead while I answered back, continued to answer
back, resisting, festering.

It was one day, sometime in my early sixth form, that the years of
battened hatred belched to the surface and changed my conscious landscape
for ever. From a squabble in the living room, when my mother reached across
to fist me once again, I turned on her in an act of reciprocating aggression.
That seed of self-hood that was there in the womb, that had held me back
at birth, eventually demanded some small retribution. It was only a strong
shove that was administered, almost an accident, surprising me as much as
my mother and father, who sat in an armchair. Yet it realised a revolt that not
only sent her rolling onto her back but issued a tremulous warning into the
family future. The wife, stunned to her core, screamed at her husband.

'Did you see what that boy did? Did you see it? Well, go on, what are
you going to do?' she bellowed, in shock and breathless exasperation. It must
have broken against the walls of my father's timidity for, as if given licence
to act himself, his own lethal hopes snarled upon his wife's prostration.

'Nothing. Good for him. It's not surprising, is it? It's about time that
boy stuck up for himself. You ought to think yourself lucky he hasn't stuck a
knife in your belly before now!' The one and only time he had ever spoken
out that I can recall! Then he sat down! That was the last time I was struck
by my mother. But the revelation now showed that at least three of the family
had lethal intentions!

*   *   *

It was hard to define how much of a fresh start this single, spontaneous, act
precipitated. It appeared to give everyone some sort of permission. It gave
me permission to stand up for myself, to shout back, to walk out, to stop
complying with my mother's dogmatism and to oppose any similar manifes-
tation in school teachers and others. It appeared to give my father permission
to act too, as he packed a suitcase and absented himself completely, without a
word, never to return. It was the lack of confiding, or emotional consideration,

which made it difficult for me to look favourably upon such an abandonment. Nor was this ever repaired when, from the safety of a new family and partner, my father later invited me to join them.

The new beginning, that airlifted me from mother's wrath and goading and set me down in a contrasting home terrain where none of the old rules of family engagement now applied, had many unforeseen consequences. All the previous antagonism that had spurred me into a purposeful, reactive motivation was no longer present. All the energising defiance that had sustained me against a father's indifference and a mother's unmitigated domination, that had been compensated by school achievement and applause to ward off frustrations and humiliations, all was missing, believed dead. There were, now, no rules to speak of, no restrictions, unlimited freedom. Indeed, I now resided in a new home where there was neither opposition that would goad me into reaction, nor encouragement, for I was all but surplus to the new family's requirements. It was yet another nuance of "persona non grata".

This family relocation/dislocation and adjustment/maladjustment coincided with the maturing demands of Sixth Form life. Other than learning how to play bridge, I don't believe I managed the acclimatisation from blackboard-copying GCSEs to independent "A" level study. As my fellow pupils engaged with "A" level studies and exams, in a final rite de passage that was preparing them for their school departure to university or working careers, I was rapidly disappearing from school life and their lives altogether. Like a subsiding cliff face that eventually breaks off to cascade into the worrying waves, the increasingly tenuous attachment to the sixth-form experience of academic preparation, exams, and university progression, let alone sporting and social development, eventually sheered off and fell away. In a feat of wilful anticlimax, I was to encroach closer, ever closer, toward the crumbling, unstable edge of my educational experience and topple into the buffeting currents of oblivion. I lost the only security I had known. This premature departure, in spirit and motivation, would never wholly submerge my school past, could not obliterate all of the accumulated pride gleaned from an achievement filled adolescence, nor could it cancel all that had been sustaining.

Thriving alongside all this there emerged an irredeemable loss of mental concentration which decimated any attempt at studying and reading, along with a mounting lethargy and incapacity to enjoy anything. The remainder of sixth form life became an existential vacancy and input gradually diminished and detached itself, culminating in truancy. The school, the teachers, the schoolmates must have watched me slowly recede but made little effort to hold onto me as I sacrificed the conventional route to gainful employment or a university education. After all the seven years of effort and achievement, the whole time dampening down the erupting disturbances within, it had culminated in a very conditional acceptance, after all. If I could not succeed then I was a failure! It was a kind of betrayal!

The decline, at one level, was even exemplified by the relationship I had with football. As a team sport, this had been a source of idealised aspiration and belonging. I had always gained a place in every team I'd ever competed for – club teams, school teams, schoolboy district and county teams – and, moreover, had often been appointed the team captain. More poignantly, the soccer experience permitted me the temporary persona of uncompromising determination fuelled by winning, skill, vitality, potency, and aggression. Then during the sixth form, in one of the most significant woundings of my life, I was dropped from the county first team side and, though I continued in the second team, I was never to recover from this. The sensible balm of pragmatism should have informed me that the best players occupied the team places, that they were of a higher standard or fitter than me, therefore more deserving, and that plenty of fun and honour was still to be had in second place. But this was would be sidestepping the vulnerability to, and strength of, narcissistic pain! Second place meant, at least, a failure, if not rejection – a kind of banishment. It was like being cast into the void! And so I reciprocated by banishing all serious intent toward any future football, beginning with withdrawing from the school team and transferring to the school rugby first fifteen!

* * *

The indefatigable conclusion was that schooling, like family experience, was a functional staging post where personal ties were no more than a succession of temporary alliances. School was a treacherous history. In this existential void, where the topsoil of an achieving, potent, aspiring persona was gradually brushed away, there remained only the barren sediment of equivocation, self-doubt and self rejection. More to the point, as you moved through the challenges and vicissitudes of your life, you had no choice but to live out the essential solitude that had signalled your destiny as early as the conceiving womb. Whatever you did from now, you might never quite belong, may always be at the social margin, would unavoidably be drawn to the verge of dropping out. However, although never expecting an easy transition into the working world, aware that the future would be rootless, uncertain and uncomfortable, this did not preclude a hankering after a very real independence. I fell into a somewhat nomadic lifestyle, moving from one residence to another, and drifting into an alternative, unstructured nihilism which fidgeted between periods of casual labour and hitch-hiking, neither of which facilitated too great an expectation of either work or ambition. The lifestyle accommodated a comprehensive revulsion for the whole unscrupulous pace and intrusion of modernity; the unpalatable inflation in residential growth, traffic congestion, frenetic suburbia, and rampant materialism. Motor vehicles, those choking files of oppressive machinery, capable of a distracting cacophony, capable of killing, were despised. Pedestrian life leaned ever harder against an inconsolable gale of bullying, rabid, motorised convention. Conversely, the most valued pastimes were cycling, and walking, far away from the frenzied and harrowing urban blight into the consolation and respite of the remote, still lanes and paths that slipped between the meadows, woodland and hedgerows of the Surrey hills, or any similar pastoral retreat, as if an inflamed ulceration, infected with urban intoxication, was being healed by the herbal remedies of the countryside.

On balance, it was impossible to decide whether the interests and intellectualisations of this period were either youthful angst, the conscientious objections to conventionality, or were the perverse consequences of a life's predicament. Whichever of these they were, it would have been preferable that they be accompanied by a greater sense of contentment than I actually experienced. The disconnected emotions that flew about in a furious search for meaning and contentment undermined the intelligence to hammer out the arguments for political persuasion, spiritual belief, or philosophical creed. There was no advantage to be had in aspiring to intellectual integrity, of pursuing ideals, when the drive for emotional connection was so exercising that all else was inconsequential. And all in an age resonating with the fulminating European rebellions of the Baader–Meinhoff, the Red Brigade, the Angry Brigade, and the Basques; these self-appointed, self excommunicating, disconnected, social heretics who sought to wreak a Utopian order out of what they perceived as the perversion of civilisation. There was a passing attraction and political romanticism for such movements but, like most people, I presume, I settled for the stronger doubt that such a show of uncompromising destruction was more a symptom of social instability and emotional pathology. I did not believe that indefatigable political principles would satisfy my search for an emotional grounding but, just as likely, I was too ungrounded to be capable of such commitment. Political discussion and opinion was just one thing which the school experience had not attempted to cultivate other than the absurd French Master who, interspersed with his putrid cynicism, instructed us that Communism had been proven to be an evil regime.

*   *   *

Hiding my background was familiar to me. Throughout the earlier years of my schooling I learned to conceal the burden of family disruptions and my personal turmoil beneath the heavy gabardine of school conformity and achievement. But disguise was never more symbolic than that which presented itself during my drama performance in the school play when in the sixth form. The evocation of one of the lead rôles through words, actions and spirit was a welcome flight from the more enforced, daily performance that I had undergone. Those revitalising few months of rehearsals and performances had allowed a temporary respite from the anticipation of school detachment, imminent exam failure, and future uncertainty. How the whole cast had been applauded for inspiring a dramatic vitality, for conjuring a brief episode of pretension, for performing way beyond their years, of replicating a life beyond adolescence. A life apart, intermingling the real with the unreal. It was to experience how the audience settles for the convincing pain and guise of the players without a consideration of the real pain that can stride about the stage. And when the performances ended, the stage emptied, and the cast and audience and applause disappeared, so the dramatic self was deconstructed, slumped and crumpled, as if stunned, onto a cold slab of oblivion that was infinitely worse than not having experienced it at all. But I was learning that I had the ability to be cast into any rôle and now I would be a hospital attendant and become the latest part to which I had assigned myself. In the event, as if there was a ripple from an appreciative audience, some consoling voices must have droned about my reflections during those first few weeks and months at work and I settled into the part as if embarking on the extended run of a repertory company's season.

It could well be argued that achievement that is primed by a compensating compulsion is less virtuous than that derived by those with an altogether more sanguine and relaxed temperament. I sometimes entertained the idea that this early achievement, forged in the conditioning, parental environment into which I was plopped, somehow gave me an unfair advantage. Then, I would counter that with the parent-supported advancement of most children who were nudged before an encouraging breeze while others, like myself, were obliged to lean into an unremitting gale of familial antagonism and apathy. In the main, I believe my efforts should have been framed within a value-added dimension that took account of how I had had to negotiate school competitiveness hampered, as I was, by the disadvantage of my background. It was merely rhetorical to have preferred to have been less striving, less needy of recognition, to have been better able to enjoy things just for themselves, better able to indulge in camaraderie, defeat, and more accepting of being plain ordinary. Even in retrospect, it was difficult to wish away that trait which was such a driving force while also recognising how much less self defeating it would have been without it. For, as much as this was a deeply compensating, conscious predilection, it was almost an inevitable survival strategy also. And as to how much it reached down and swirled around as an unconscious undercurrent, then it probably feathered through my whole being like the fatty marbling in a joint of meat.

* * *

There is no cure to the truth and the truth is always known, and everyone more or less knows it. The past, like inconvenient and unsightly graffiti, can never be covered over and buried but is available to inform us of our concealed roots. Words, voices and images ring around our consciousness. However the future developed, it was my allotment that I should carry an internal history of maternal domination, paternal disinterest, school abandonment, and unfulfilled expectations, all of which belched up from the hot shallows of the unconscious, periodically, to blanch the conscious surface. A history, but for brief episodes of integration and belonging, that would struggle for emotional connection, reconciliation, and self-contentment. None of this was easily spoken of, or shared, and would demand to be secreted for many years. Even then, the slowly informing, slowly relieving, tide of insight would never quite reconcile, certainly never obliterate or cure. Years would pass before I would come to accept that my mother, as the fourteenth of fifteen children in a very poor working class family, must have had a very emotionally deprived and neglected childhood herself. Leaving home to marry, yearning to have some focused attention, to have her own child, something she could call her own, was a potential salvation, whether the husband was ready or not. And he was not. Marrying a man who was the only child of doting parents was probably the least likely place where she would have such profound needs met. Only at her bedside at her death could I forgive her, then slowly loosen the thick rope of vengefulness for what I had condemned as her failure as a mother, and take up the thin thread of forgiveness of one who just could not manage to change what her own background had largely made her. Additionally, if my father could not negotiate the travails of a needy wife, he certainly did not have the resources to handle the cumulative burden of a son, too.

Hiding is only a transient opportunity. As all parents inscribe themselves into the deep reaches of their children's forming minds the children come to see themselves, to a large degree, as their parents treat them and it takes a lot to cover that. As my own internalized, parental figures reaped their insistent demands over my entire future they were the main mirror through which I caught a glimpse of myself. Imposing themselves from the unconscious, they interfered with my meditations and negotiations with the world. Whenever I was later confronted with representations of either of my parents, they served as emotional prompts that jolted and stirred the parental figures and the uncon-scious, coaxing me into using the prepared props and scripts for which I had been trained over the years. It was as if I was trapped in these past dramas that would never let go; that there was no choice but to work with the colours and forms that were inextricably and indelibly daubed onto the foundations of my perceptions so that, when provoked by similar situations or persons, they were acted out as if the parents were present in the room. And so, re-enacting my mother's presence, I would detonate my rage at someone's undermining denigration or criticism of me provided I was not utterly overwhelmed. On the other hand, I was easily slighted by another's cool, distant ignoring of me, enacting my father's presence. More positively, but not without its own complications, I was sustained by a psychological diet of other people's affirmations. In these I became visible to myself, acquired a persona. When there were none of these I could almost disappear. And these were what comprised my personal repertoire – either enraged into resistance by someone's criticism or aggression; or deflated into oblivion when overlooked or ignored; or inflated with self-approbation by others' affirmation.

Chapter Five
Forensic Asylum

I n 1986 I departed from the hospital for a second time to pursue the next stage of my career trajectory – forensic mental health nursing – and spent the next 12 years in medium security mental health organisations, as well as Prison Service Health Care, and two high security "Special Hospitals". The term "forensic" derives from the Latin "forensis", meaning a Roman forum, which was the historic locality, and process, for settling legal disputes and now administered in contemporary society through the appropriate court process. The relevance of the court, in respect of mental disorder, was to determine whether a defendant could be held fully accountable for his/her proven lawbreaking behaviour or whether they could not be held fully responsible on account of their psychiatric impediment, thereby being adjudged to require treatment rather than punishment. In essence, the forensic psychiatrist, as with any forensic specialist in any professional field, contributed to the forensic process by presenting their conclusions to their examinations to the court. It was then the court's task to weigh this evidence along with all other contributors and to determine the defendant's overall "responsibility" for their criminal actions. A successful psychiatric defence, meaning that an accused defendant was not held legally responsible for the criminal transgression, would almost invariably result in the client being delivered into the forensic psychiatrist's jurisdiction for ongoing treatment in a health care environment, rather than the alternative of a conviction, then sentence for punishment, and prison.

No one was more surprised than me when I returned to the old asylum for a third stint in 1998 to take up a position in the medium secure unit which had been constructed but a handful of years prior to the closure of the remainder of the hospital estate. I would own up to the sentiment that, perhaps, the fates had drawn me back to help breathe life into this diminutive embryo, a frail little object relative to its parent. To breathe life, that is, along with all the other staff and residents. In career terms, I was moving on to a further stage which the old place, despite its infirmity and closure, still had the capacity to facilitate. A career begun in those early days with the unrefined and cavalier dampening of refractory insurrection and evolving, incrementally, through the nurturing of intensive care, toward the more sophisticated control of clients with forensic problems.

In contrast to the broader mental health field, the rising star of forensic psychiatry presented novel terminology and contradictory professional objectives. I daresay the anti-social excesses of the clients, together with the defensive management strategies of the staff and hospital sites, created an image far removed from therapeutic care and more akin to social control – hardly worthy of being called a mental health speciality. The very nomenclature for the client group generated professional confusion. Originally called *criminal lunatics*, this only slightly improved with *mentally abnormal offenders* and, ultimately, *mentally disordered offenders*! These patients were a complex, psychiatric conjuncture encapsulating a mental illness, on the one hand, and the criminal behaviour deriving from, or coinciding with it, on the other. For example, the unfounded delusion that someone was persecuting them might be strong enough to act on, resulting in the patient killing the identified individual.

* * *

To take up my post in this medium security unit I returned, then, for my third and last stretch amid the mixed nostalgic memories of my cherished hospital. Pursuing the same route that I had ventured onto about 25 years earlier, and with the reverence of a dedicated post-mortem, I traced the unravelling degradation of the old institution. During the intervening decade everything, every quarter, showed signs of terminal decay. The metalled road was no more than a decrepit byway, the smooth surface of its youth now scraped bare, pitted and scarred. The shabby verges were as untended tufts of whisker and the

301

rhododendron piles hung like monumental shoulders. Debris, like hair falling in liberal handfuls, was strewn from the untended arbours. The flower beds that eventually emerged were barren, indistinguishable scrapes, and the only blooms were fuchsia bushes grown into sprawling, irrepressible hedges. The administration block and every other building was in disuse, and disrepair, and ringed about with offensive metal fencing to keep out the earnest visitor and wanton intruder. Behind the fencing, the smashed portholes of the old galleon sides suggested a dilapidated hulk that had been dumped in a dry dock for the rest of its years. The water and incineration towers, for all that they appeared intact, had such a lack of vitality that they seemed to lean limp and impotent against the ravages of deinstitutionalisation. The social club was but a charred frame, the victim of incendiary youths stealing into the grounds for the immediate gratification of making an instant impact on their surroundings – their destructiveness a statement of their presence, their need to be noticed. From the two former Nurses Homes, flailing curtains sprung fitfully from smashed windows like shrouds signalling the memories of favoured occupants. Machinery lay abandoned in an open barn that I could not admit to having noticed when they were in use in their heyday. I wallowed in a reverie of explicit voices, individual faces, recapturing specific dramas, not just of the exceptional but the absolutely ordinary. I was paying a kind of homage, revisiting with gratitude, willing the place to come to life before my eyes. But though the institution was there in form, it lacked the internal life-force of activity, fraternity and culture. The asylum had been condemned to a living death, its organisational guts and human spirit had fallen away like muscle wastage, and it must needs go on standing for as long as its skeletal remains could hold. It was all part accident, part celebration, part obliteration, part monumental travesty.

Rising from the dereliction were the now towering, resplendent buddleia. Throughout the hospital's decline the buddleia had made exploratory forays into the unguarded terrain, assessing the viability of the land and buildings in readiness for the colonising hordes that were preparing themselves for dispersal. Resilient in all cracks and crevices, the colonisation established itself until the flowering plumes predominated over the blooms of almost any other competitor. The yellow freckled, purple lilac masses, heavy in their abundance, pulled down the branches into long, arching bows, then sprung back and danced in the wind gusts. They managed to embed themselves amongst the domesticated fraternity of bushes and shrubs, only now there were no remaining gardeners so that their overreaching, inelegant limbs were saved a judicious pruning down to the stumps. On my many circuitous ramblings around the perimeter of the sealed off hospital shell, I would come across whole nests of them in the farthest, reclusive corners of the estate. Towers of uniform, blooming colour taking advantage of a desolated waste plot. Rooted from every crevice they leapt, and glanced, and bowed, and stroked the air. And from every aspect of the buildings I caught sight of the dwarf like seedlings high in the guttering, or sprouting from the roof tiles, and hanging from the pitted masonry, as if they were seeding an abundance of funereal wreaths over the grave of the asylum in a living memorial to its former existence.

* * *

Medium secure units had become all the rage and had their own definitive origins from the late 1970s onwards. While generic mental health care was dispersed across the land in a variety of open community arrangements, and some residual in-patient facilities, the highly controlled psychiatric units for patients breaking the law had risen out of the asylum ashes like institutional fledglings. As a whole network established itself it nestled against the old asylum foundations like a reformed psychiatric archipelago. Despite the general impetus toward emptying the old asylums and decanting their residents into the community, there was a corresponding awareness of the shortfall in hospital accommodation for two groups of outstanding patients. The prevalence and needs of the "disturbed" patients, not offering a threat of danger to the public, were identified by the *Glancy Report (1974)*. This was followed by the identification of "mentally abnormal offenders" in the *Butler Report (1975),* a patient category found to be highly represented among the prison population, or bottlenecked in the Special Hospitals waiting to return to their original localities. The Butler Report conceptualised the "yawning gap" in mental health provision for these folk who presented variable levels of danger to the public. The high security Special Hospitals, and Prison Service, at the extreme end of in-patient, mental health care, had to be bridged with the "open-door" policy of the conventional, county psychiatric hospitals. The Butler Report gave patronage, and extraordinary monies, to the commissioning of a nationwide network of what were called "medium secure units". These would now accommodate the urgent, somewhere-in-between patients who presented "severely disruptive behaviour" which would be too problematic for the ordinary hospital yet not presenting too great an immediate risk to the general public if the patients were to be at large. The patients may be convicted offenders or not, and may be rehabilitating patients from the Special Hospitals, but they should be treated as a category requiring only medium secure conditions. In effect, this was the new, downsized asylum, using upgraded technology that ranged in size from 15 to 90 beds, in the first instance.

One of the most significant organisational benefits of the MSU, as with all small, specialist services, was that all the staff were physically allocated to that specific unit alone. The medium secure units supported a comprehensive, multidisciplinary team to include medical, psychology, occupational therapy, social work, and nursing staff – quite unheard of in the traditional asylum wards! This could not do other than focus the therapeutic task, enhance the potential for inter-professional integration and closer staff/patient relationships, and produce a general democratisation throughout. The most notable staff advances were the relatively high tolerance for disturbed behaviour, which could even extend to interpersonal abuse, the reluctance to use extra medication to quieten the patient disturbances, and the minimum use of seclusion. The outdoor areas were used as much as possible to generate recreation and to defuse the patients' frustrations. But all this, and the opportunity for closer contact between staff and patients, was facilitated by the significantly higher levels of staffing with a far smaller number of patients.

But if there was a therapeutic contradiction in forensic psychiatry, the regularity of adverse events involving psychiatric patients at least justified its existence. For, coinciding with, but not necessarily determined by, the loss of in-patient bricks and mortar, and the relocation of psychiatric provision into the community, a concerted publicity was regularly fuelled by serious crimes, particularly homicides, directly linked to psychiatric patients. While the majority of the homicides erupted in community settings there were still residual instances persisting in hospital establishments themselves. With disconcerting regularity these transgressions regularly wounded the integrity of the mental health services and other agencies.

None was more spectacular than the horrifying image, in 1996, of the homicidal rampage on a young family in a pastoral setting that assailed us from the television screen and newspapers when another long-term psychiatric patient, Michael Stone, killed a mother and daughter and the family dog, and attempted to kill another daughter as they walked home along country lanes from school. The attack was accomplished with a hammer and ropes and Stone had a diagnosis of severe personality disorder complicated by severe drug misuse. These spectacular cases have assured the amplified attention of the public, policy makers, and the informed, independent lobbying of voluntary bodies such as the Zito Trust, and generated a continuing commentary on the effectiveness of community psychiatric management. The Zito Trust, particularly, have demanded greater acknowledgement for both public safety and the victimisation of public citizenry consequent upon the failure of community provision. The Trust's independent study in 1998 examined the contributory elements resulting in these fatal outcomes, itemising details such as patient non-compliance with treatment, the poor standard of aftercare and supervision, the patients' lack of insight and substance misuse, poor communications, patients' non-attendance for appointments, and the correlation between mental illness and violence.

* * *

This particular medium secure forensic unit had been erected as a new build prior to the old asylum's closure. It was as if a miraculous infant was spawned from its institutional mother much as the New Testament's Elizabeth, whose child, whom she bore in her belated old age, had been the fruit of her ancient womb. To accommodate the modern venture a charming, residual enclave of the old asylum estate had been sacrificed to its construction. This enclave constituted a separate nurses' home adjacent to a delightfully discrete garden and orchard. The nurses' home had been saved and included in the new development, converted to patients' living quarters, and overseen by staff. The main feature of the forensic development was the accompanying, single storey new-build of utterly non-descript architecture, giving if anything an impression of a compact, elderly care home from the front. Around the back, a continuous perimeter fortification of high, narrow-gauged, metal fencing hugged the undulating contours of the uneven ground. On this it was virtually impossible to gain either a hand or foothold. The limited outside ground was a sorry comparison with the generous proportions of the former asylum, as if the fresh air was not that relevant in the new scheme of things. This, together with the cramped organisation of the building interior, made for a highly claustrophobic environment indeed.

The spread had the benefit of a closed circuit camera system, an intercom and electronically operated entrance, and carbonated windows designed to withstand attempted breakage. Reception staff were dedicated to monitoring the comings and goings in the unit, to giving out staff keys, and generally surveying the internal environment. Physical security continued with a succession of locked doors which made physical progress around the building extremely arduous and cumbersome, requiring staff to draw upon their chain linked keys with monotonous regularity. Alarm points on the walls, some staff carrying two-way radios, physical checks on the building fabric and perimeter, and searches of patients' visitors and relatives to reduce the flow of drugs and other contraband, were all standard fare for such a unit. Anyone who has visited the prison system will have recognised all of these elements and, since much of the operational advice would have derived from that sector, this was no surprise. It was intended that the final therapeutic product be a far less oppressive mimicking of the Prison Service, however, and this included an absence of staff uniforms to reduce the formality and the social division between staff and patients.

The 15–bedded unit funded a high staff/patient ratio, including a daily minimum of five nursing staff per shift, and more if patient disturbance demanded more! Weekly case conferences were a relatively intelligent affair compared with the scant psychiatric analysis of the old institution. It came fully multidisciplinary – medical and paramedical; psychologists, social workers, nurses and occupational therapists – and with an ideological impetus that encouraged the team to embrace a therapeutic agenda. Patients' mental illness and mental health, their offending past, the risk of potential offending, and security requirements, were weighed in equal measure. The operationally explicit therapeutic climate was couched within the constraints of secure conditions, the patients' past history of offending and the potential for harm, the need to safeguard other patients, the staff, and the community, as well as the attempt to keep patients in touch with the outside world. At least, these were the manifest ideals. They did not necessarily match the perceptions of the body of staff who exercised their scepticism by alluding to the unit as the "Wendy House" on account of the excessively high investment in this class of criminal patient, the provision of all modern facilities, and what was considered to be a too relaxed operational policy. In essence, for many staff working in such a unit the perception was that the mentally disordered offender was virtually being rewarded for breaking the law and that their mental illness permitted entitlements that they did not deserve.

Such attitudes had permeated the therapeutic tone of this small establishment since its inauguration due, in large part, to its geographical distance from the London NHS Trust to which it had been organisationally affixed. I counted myself fortunate to have arrived following an organisational overhaul initiated, and tenaciously carried through, by a new Nurse Manager. For those of us who had sound relationships with him he represented personal and professional integrity and a certain avuncular quality. Consequently, his necessarily ruthless attrition toward the outmoded reaction persisting within the unit was a welcome, if astonishing, contrast. It was to his singular credit that individuals representing this virulent reaction were disgorged and replaced with staff of a more adaptable predisposition.

* * *

It is 10 a.m. on a Friday. The Psychologist and I are seated in the unit day room awaiting any stragglers to join the once weekly Community Meeting. When I say stragglers, I mean patients – for the nursing staff, who coordinate an alternative programme of recreational sessions, tend to opt out of this forum – as do the patients themselves. The day room is set out like the old hospital wards. The large armchairs are all ranked around the walls, leaving a billiard table at the centre. For the purposes of this communal gathering we remove the table to the adjoining dining room. The chairs are mottled with cigarette burns which give the appearance of a ravaging disease of the furniture. Large strips of material have been rent from the chairs, exposing the inner organs of sponge. The carpet is so cruelly discoloured and disfigured that you hardly want to look down. You would not tolerate such disgusting materials in your own home. They would end up on a tip. The air is a hanging drift of cigarette smoke, unwashed bodies and meal odours that clog the whole day room space. Metal ash trays are the only other adornment perched on the arms of chairs, spun onto the floor, rested on knees. The three patients have arrived in varying degrees of presentation and dress even though it's now ten o'clock. Current policy does not permit us to have much control over how a patient dresses, whether he shaves or not or even brushes his hair. We can advise someone we think requires some encouragement. If the issue is ongoing, then we may choose to invoke a care plan that tries to address it with the cooperation of the patient.

The Psychologist and I have been pursuing this therapeutic trial for some months now. Ostensibly, we are attempting to draw the patients into a more searching appraisal of themselves and their relationships with fellow patients in the hope that they might be able to generalise these insights into how they function with people generally. Of course, this is not a closed therapeutic group, so we do not have hard and fast rules about its operation. We would prefer that the patients evolve their own group rules and that we help them. Today, there are three from the 15 potential available. The numbers have been going down. The reasons are not difficult to determine and, though we don't beat ourselves up over the lack of attendance, we're now considering if our effort is worthwhile. The forum is a voluntary one and we don't insist on anyone being present. We just aspire to the idea that, precisely because it is voluntary, each member of our small community will recognise the benefit of such a forum. But it's situations like this that say so very much about the whole mental health enterprise. Essentially, mental health care and patients' responses to it are like most other issues – education, employment, and family involvement. Given a choice most people will opt out, seeing no reason why they should participate unless they have immediate, vested interests in doing so, particularly financial remuneration. We are perfectly well aware that payment for attendance would produce a full turnout but the objectives would be lost. On the other hand, it is all very well that we practitioners bang on about the personal benefits the patients will gain from therapeutic work. But we're being paid, paid for work, work we choose to do, work which is our career, and our bread and butter. To the patients, it must seem like another set of authoritative impositions – like schoolwork/ homework, or unpaid employment/overtime – or a whole load of unnecessary confrontation, when all they really want is to be allowed to pass their time in their own way, relaxing, watching TV, or remaining in their rooms. It's bad enough that they should be in this unit at all, forced to take medication, forced to attend the daily activity programme, encouraged to get up and attend the daily morning meeting or missing the chance to procure personal items of shopping. But the unit policy is that if these enforced parameters were not invoked, many of the clients would reverse their days, spending the daytime in bed and the night-time awake, and engaging in nothing essentially therapeutic. From a personal point of view, I'd like to think that this small demand on the users' week – the politically correct term for a patient is now *service user*, by the way – is potentially more stimulating than a lot of the material they are committed to attend. We try and put the matter before the assembled few, and whether we should move to making the Community Meeting a compulsory venue?

'It depends,' says Michael, an African-Caribbean who attends the meeting consistently. 'What's the meeting meant to achieve, like?' In my silence, I lean forward with barely concealed frustration.

'What do you think it tries to achieve from your experience of it, Michael?' I pose. He is a consistently slow speaker and his response is a laboured, pensive drawl.

'Well, we're supposed to bring up points that is bothering us patients but we do that in other groups so I don't really know why we do the same thing here, Steve.' It's a benign response but disappointing coming from such an enthusiastic individual. 'Have I said the wrong thing?' he adds, after scouring my blank stare. He looks to the other two attenders. 'Come on, help me out somebody, what do we say?' He fidgets, amused and affable, before David, a younger, highly intelligent patient, intercedes – much to our relief.

'The idea is that we bring up matters that affect us all so that we can find ways of settling them without the staff needing to make decisions for us.' I relax, glad of his presence.

'Right,' says Jay, the Psychologist, ably concealing a sense of relief. 'Good man!'

'Trouble is, not everyone wants to bother with discussion and they'd prefer to just have an argument or hit someone, or something, or just ignore people,' David adds. The remaining two laugh out loud. 'Not everyone's cut out for a debating society – suits me, like. And what's the point of arguing over something which you know most patients won't abide by, and will probably need to get sorted by the staff, anyway.' Of course, this is a well-founded criticism but it's exactly for this reason that we're encouraging assertiveness, and people arguing their case without having to resort to unpleasantness, aggression or violence. Michael opts in again.

'And, without disrespecting you two, you're not the general staff on the shifts – it's them who should be helping us out. Not that you don't try to help us, like, but it's them that have to agree at the end of the day, don't you think?' Of course, this is the very reason why Community Meetings should be just that – forums for the whole group of staff and patients so that all aspects of a problem can be represented and everyone included in the suggested outcomes. However, most staff prefer to opt out of such a group since, presumably, it demands the same democratic qualities from them that we are attempting to promote in the patients. Obviously, the name of this session is a misnomer and goes to show how these professional terms are named for exacting reasons. And, though we are trying to inculcate some important qualities into the group, we are falling into pitfalls of which it will inevitably fall foul.

'But let's assume we can encourage some nursing staff to attend future meetings,' continues Jay, 'we still have the problem of whether this session should be voluntary or compulsory!'

David pipes up with a mischievous grin. 'You're best putting that to all the patients but they're not here!'

* * *

Jay and I thank the three of them at the close of the meeting and retire to a rest room to review the state of play. Clearly more frustrated than my colleague, I suggest that they realise, by now, that there are no sanctions to non-attendance at these meetings and, in the absence of them wanting to examine their relationships with one another at some depth, they don't have

310

to risk putting themselves in a difficult place. 'We have the choice of making the forum mandatory, of course!'

'Do we want to go down that route? If they can't be bothered, why should it be imposed on them?'

'It just feels like we're about to offer them the chance to repeat a pattern of disengagement that reflects everything else in their lives, really. They're opting out of responsibility. Let's face it, when they get the chance they'll opt out of accepting their medication when back in the community if they possibly could!'

'Only that's not a real choice for them,' replies the psychologist with assured resignation. 'They know there are non-negotiable things such as having to accept that they can be recalled and re-admitted if we think things are getting out of hand for them.'

'It just seems so clear-cut that if you've opportunities to learn about yourself and your characteristic responses to other people, and what might antagonise you into dangerous behaviour, that you'd want to avail yourself of every chance to do so, and to avoid unfavourable consequences,' I add with some exasperation.

'Maybe that's just a professional, dare I say, middle class aspiration which we both share but doesn't much apply to their situation,' he suggests rhetorically. 'Their circumstances more or less encourage them to think in the immediate present with no great regard for the long term!'

'But the consequences of them acting only in the present, and underestimating their illness and circumstances, are potentially catastrophic. You'd think they'd make every effort to avoid the possibility of falling foul of what they know to be their weaknesses, wouldn't you?'

'Well, yes, but maybe that's just us being in a position to be rational, because we can organise our lives. We're asking too much, maybe, of highly damaged people with lifestyles that are so very chaotic. Perhaps we're doing nothing more than imposing our orderliness onto their chaos and it's not always quite appropriate! If you put yourself in their place, with so little family support, few relationships, no jobs, a modest income, no prospects, no home of their own, why should they bother trying to invest in the future when everything is stacked against them? It's motivating them that's the problem. What have they got to be motivated about?'

'Put that way, even having their mental health would be poor compensation for that little lot! Just shows how unrealistic it is to handle mental health in isolation from everything else that's going on in a person's life.'

'Well, exactly. Trying to motivate someone with such a chaotic background and thinking style and no vested interests in the system, that's the real issue. It's no wonder they succumb to unhelpful stuff like drugs and alcohol.'

'Instant gratification, no less. And we do the same – get drunk when the load gets heavy.'

'Maybe they've given up thinking about the morrow and there's only so much we can do!' he adds, none too perplexed, as it happens. A realistic resignation, then. 'Well, back to the issue in hand,' Jay prompts, abruptly. He seems to want to settle this thing. 'They're saying what we've known all along but that things have been brought to a head.'

'For myself, I don't want to give up on this and I'm very keen to take an assertive stance and involve more of the staff. There's not one of them who wouldn't benefit from the professional experience, anyway.'

'I agree but, as we've pointed out before, we want people with some psychological consciousness who can look beneath the surface issues and appreciate the personal dynamics beneath.'

'Of course, it really requires a teaching programme to acquaint the staff with these ideas. I could do that for those who have an interest but you'd like to think that individuals would be self selecting and not too many come to mind, off hand. You agree?'

'Yes, I agree. But the issue for me is whether the patients have voted with their feet.'

'But we know they can only benefit from doing this work,' I add, exasperated.

'Maybe we have to ask ourselves who is benefiting, then. Is it just us? We're feeling frustrated because we are psychologically minded and know that we can expand the therapeutic base beyond the medical model. That is the bugbear, isn't it? Having to accept the dominance of the medical model which is just so limiting! But the unit's just not ready to modify that.' I'm surprised, but delighted, by Jay's admission as he hasn't shown such forthrightness before.

'Look, it's initiatives like this that are going to build up the unit's thera-peutic practice. And it's individuals who will initiate them. I've learned that throughout my career. You don't wait on invitations.'

'Oh, I'm with you, Steve, but perhaps this is not quite the time even so. There's just not enough of a psychological baseline among the staff to work from. And as for the patients? We obviously can't expect them to see the benefits of turning up to these meetings if they feel it doesn't really accom-plish anything for them,' offers Jay. 'Let's face it, we're thinking *process* and long-term *outcomes*, when they're interested in short-term benefits and personal advantages. That's understandable. And we're also trying to make them more psychologically minded when it's a sufficient hassle merely to have to accept medication as treatment.' I nod vigorously, silently incensed by the salience of it all. 'Quite against their expectations of just having to take medication, we're asking them to expose their feelings and motivations toward one another, and handle them in a different way. It's just too much, perhaps,' says Jay, in a conciliatory admission.

'It's utterly depressing. After all, no one wants to actively prevent non medical models from being put to use – certainly not the psychiatrists. They're perfectly happy to let us experiment, of that I'm sure. If we don't show the initiative we can't blame them for allowing the status quo to continue!'

'Absolutely not! Still, as things stand, I'm reluctant to make this another compulsory part of the patients' day, Steve! Happy with that?' I can't help believing that we've let something slip away. 'Thanks for your participation!'

* * *

One psychologically minded member of the nursing staff, who has under-gone training in Social Learning Theory, now operates as a Clinical Nurse Specialist. His specialist practice is Cognitive Behavioural Therapy. He is practising as a CNS; he is at the pinnacle of *clinical* work for mental health nurses, and not such a rarity these days. He has instigated an Anger Management Programme on the unit. He doesn't make it up as he goes along because, as is the mode these days, much patient treatment is delivered via manuals, just as with packages of education for students. This therapeutic

313

initiative comes in prepared, progressive sessions that take 12 weeks to complete. The programme is based on cognitive behavioural principles, which is to say that treatment aims to acquaint patients with their routinised, unhelpful thinking patterns and behaviours, and to modify these into more helpful, adaptive styles that will improve patients' negotiation of conflict situations and minimise the adverse attentions of public agencies. Stan has the authority to set up this programme owing to his credentials as a Clinical Nurse Specialist and it is the most exciting therapeutic venture to have taken place here. He selects those patients who he feels have the psychological and intellectual capacity to undergo the Programme and accompanies them through the various sessions. Assessing the results will take some time but it will be impossible to determine how much the programme itself will have been responsible for any significant change. As with anything, each one of us is bombarded with a host of conscious and unconscious influences all the time. How much more determinate is one influence over another? Pretty difficult to measure the outcomes even if none of the patients are involved in any violent or excessively aggressive incidents during the remainder of their stay with us. But it is a sound initiative, completely relevant, and indispensable considering the purpose of the enterprise.

Stan is one of those rare species in mental nursing. He manages to combine a high expectation of contemporary therapeutic practice along with incisive thinking, intelligence, and outspoken criticism. In short, he's got bright balls! Whether it's the clinical management meetings each morning, or the weekly Clinical Team Meetings, or the Patient Case Conferences, he manages to assert an incisive stance on the care of difficult patients and is usually well worth listening to. It was bloody frustrating, sometimes, that he had the ability to unravel apparently inconsequential issues with such immediate clarity! He, particularly, has a penchant for setting boundaries to patients who exhibit excesses in inappropriate behaviour – gleaned from his Cognitive-Behavioural training. We all find it immensely helpful in creating care plans which inform, shall we say, our management of an aggressive patient who is confined within a seclusion room. He will be informed of what, exactly, is deemed unacceptable behaviour; what behaviours will enable his confinement to be relaxed, and of other appropriate conduct that will further extend his freedom beyond the seclusion room. It enables both the staff and patient to understand, precisely, the boundaries between behaviours which will not be tolerated and those that are to be encouraged. The ideas are not cobbled together orally, but set down in a written care plan that is verbally explained to the patient, and of which he receives a copy. Limit setting is not exclusive to Cognitive-Behavioural Therapy as it very much predominates in most psychological therapies. However, most of the psychodynamic therapies enjoy only limited exposure in the National Health Service, largely because of their inordinate cost. In contrast, CBT has enjoyed an emerging psychotherapeutic hegemony owing to its accessible training schedule, the relatively short period of therapy, and the relatively focused treatment objectives. In consequence, its therapeutic language has filtered down into more basic mental health practice in a way that was never achieved by the more traditional and, dare one say, esoteric therapies.

The opportunity to operationalise boundary setting as a therapeutic goal within the unit was partly expedited by a report which I produced on the management of a specific patient. My position as a Lecturer/Practitioner granted me a specially strategic position for overviewing the general care and therapeutic strategies within the unit. Before I had taken up my position, the unit had accepted an emergency admission via the community forensic team due to the exceptional difficulties that he presented. This was his third admission to this secure unit. His case was an excellent example of the kind of background history and challenges which can be presented by mentally disordered offenders. Railton had a forensic history (i.e. past convictions for lawbreaking), which long preceded his admission for psychiatric treatment. This had included assault against family, neighbours and the public, actual bodily harm, burglary, theft and criminal damage. He also had a psychiatric history extending back into his late childhood as well as disturbed behaviour that had presented itself throughout his schooling. During his subsequent spells in prisons and the psychiatric services he had offered threats against people's personal safety and was considered to be highly dangerous if he should have acted on his delusions, which were wide ranging paranoid delusions involving the State Security Services and the IRA. During three admissions to the MSU he had exhibited continual disruption, verbal threats and racial abuse, and physical violence toward male and female staff members and patients. Threats to kill identifiable members of staff and the general

315

public frequently involved the intention to use firearms and knives, and he had secreted various items in his bedroom which could have subsequently been used as weapons. He also had a history of absconding from the unit premises. On one particular day of this latter admission, I presented myself in the day room area to help manage Railton, who had single-handedly consumed the attention and involvement of most of the nursing team for some hours owing to his display of challenging behaviour. Challenging behaviour was the contemporary therapeutic language for a wide range of behaviours which did not conform to conventional standards. Railton was allowed to move around the day room areas singing loudly and including the oft-spoken words, 'stroking my prick with her fingers'. What became most noticeable was the inability of staff to create a window of opportunity for confronting his challenging behaviour and, in so doing, applying the brakes to his escalating lack of control. It was me who eventually approached him and asked if we could take some time to discuss what was happening, and why nothing appeared to be helping him. I suggested that we retire to his room if it made him more comfortable. When he did return to his room it was not, so I discovered, to avail himself of my services and he rounded on me when I reached the threshold to his room. Swearing at me with some abandon, he left me in no doubt as to the consequences if I was to remain standing in the doorway to his room. Without further ado, he approached me and struck the arm that was leaning against the doorframe. It's hard to explain how rapidly the situation deteriorated but, in an instant, we were embroiled in an interlocking struggle on the floor with the unit alarms blaring in our ears, my arms clasped about his frame, and his teeth sunk firmly into my chest! The struggle culminated in his restraint by my colleagues, the administration of intramuscular medication, and his removal to the seclusion room where he continued to offer unmitigated threats of imminent oblivion to the staff. Obviously the medication had had no effect on his level of arousal whatsoever.

In appraising the current and historical care which this patient, Railton, had received while an in-patient at the unit the issues that presented themselves were, to some degree, symptoms of the modern mental health strategies. In the asylum past, patients were discharged from the hospital and remained where they resided until they gave the authorities cause for further involvement, which might well lead to another hospital admission. Until such time as another relapse, these ex patients were more or less left to their own devices, as the saying goes. As it later became apparent that this policy had significantly contributed to the homicides and other seriously disturbing public incidents involving psychiatric patients, a new policy, the Care Programme Approach, introduced the Key Worker.

However, when I reviewed Railton's care some immediate shortcomings came to light. No one, it seemed, had all the available information on this client. Different disciplines had specific parts of his history. More alarming was that much of the information that did come to light about his dangerous behaviour was repeated verbally to me, essentially anecdotally, since it had not been felt necessary to note down the issues at the time.

The second major issue that became apparent had emerged for the best of reasons as I have previously described. Contemporary mental health nurses were faced with a fairly unpalatable dilemma as a result of the legislative and policy increments. In the old asylum days, the rigidity of the regime, the explicit domination and submission between social categories, the staff uniforms, the divided social space, and the general stigmatisation of mental illness, produced a virtually unquestioned inequality in the status between staff and patients. However, the slow revolution which I have described now promulgated a therapeutic tenor of unmitigated client advocacy which could be disempowering. Now locally devised regimes permitted the wearing of staff civvies, and a relative blurring of social space, while the national mental health policy demanded a greater egalitarianism between staff, patients and the general public. Patients were deserving "service-users", entitled to the staffing and physical resources of the "service-providers". Also reflecting their full citizenship as society members, clients were now actively encouraged, as with any other citizen, to make use of complaints facilities for any aspect of their treatment with which they were dissatisfied. Formal complaints procedures had become *de rigueur* throughout the NHS. This, in itself, had further ramifications.

While all this rightly pressurised mental health staff into ameliorating their interpersonal relations with patients, and acknowledging their human rights, it also effected a general camaraderie, informality and matiness that was inappropriate and self-defeating in the longer run. In this case, it became clear that many of the staff were well acquainted with Railton, having been exposed to him over three admissions; that they treated him respectfully and had a genuinely caring attitude toward him; that they were much taken by his caustic sense of humour; and that they felt their mutually good relations helped to defuse his challenges and hostility. Yet this relational informality and sound intentions were unexamined and, inadvertently, had created therapeutic blind spots and distortions. Of course, this had always been one of the potential stumbling blocks of working closely with individual patients, reaching back to the key workers of the Nursing Process. Many a time, patients have been defended by their key workers whilst other members of the clinical team were bent on taking alternative actions. In the worst scenario, staff would virtually come to view certain patients with whom they had had close relationships as their personal protégés! The issue arose here. Some members of staff had tried to defuse Railton's excesses by *befriending* him so that they could be viewed as non-threatening mates. This was all very well while his behaviour and mental state remained accessible but was fairly impotent when his conduct was racing out of control and required assertive limit setting. Conversely, other members of staff felt strongly that Railton should have been dealt with in a more confrontational approach. Others just stood back in an indeterminate haze. Overall, the management was exactly that, a confused and indeterminate haze.

The cumulative consequence of these related factors – the lack of a full history, the protective qualities of key workers, and the informal socialisation – was that the degree of risk which Railton presented was greatly underestimated by most people in the in-patient setting. This, despite warnings from psychiatrists from other facilities, and the views of other agencies such as the Prison Service, that Railton's mental illness made him a potentially homicidal gentleman.

It is conceivable that some may think a great deal has been made of this one scenario so I must acquaint them with how it related to the subsequent sequel and to a wider professional matter. With reference to the sequel, after being confined against his will in a seclusion room, Railton was not only unable to calm down, but persistently beat at the seclusion window for a couple of hours until, after knocking it out completely, and making good his escape, he was eventually recaptured and taken into police custody. But there were other reasons for labouring the point.

* * *

It was for precisely this sort of client history that such a unit was constructed now that the dissolution of the old hospitals had removed the vast majority of in-patient beds. In the old asylum and subsequent hospital era, unequivocal and unquestioned boundaries determined the behaviour of patients and staff, but these had gradually been dissipated by a raft of enlightened, democratising policy-making relating to all health care. Nevertheless, it was somewhat taken for granted that the skills to deal with, absorb, and safely manage such clients still existed in the mental health system and that, if they did not, they would soon be acquired.

The setting of therapeutic boundaries to tackle patients' symptoms, including dangerousness, was an indispensable strategy in medium security care, and for effecting safety for the client, fellow clients and the staff. Implicitly, we had the authority to do so. This was one of the major thrusts of my report into Railton's previous management. Once these issues were digested and eventually accepted by the body of staff – no mean feat since some staff were highly offended by my criticisms – Stan's cognitive behavioural skills came to the fore and the unit strategies were revolutionised with tightly controlled limits on challenging behaviours which threatened to get out of control. As a team, we evolved a standardised care plan to manage this and similar eventualities. It itemised the client conduct which was giving cause for concern, the requisite staff limitations that would be applied to this, the ensuing client behaviours to be encouraged and displayed in order to relax those limits, and the consequent opportunities for full socialisation that the patient could then expect. The major benefits were that all the staff had access to the clear guidance and parameters so that the management was not undermined by the predilections, and the resulting potential for manipulation by the patients, of individual staff. There was yet another reason for labouring the point of managing this particular client, Railton, adequately.

Whether today's mental health staff have a higher tolerance for disturbed behaviour than was the case previously probably has to remain a mute point. But one of the unspoken aims of anyone managing a ward environment is that their environment should be a safe and therapeutic one. Any challenging and disturbed behaviour, while unavoidable in individual circumstances, should not be permitted to become normalised so that patients believe they can exhibit their frustrations in an uninhibited way, detrimental to a stable climate.

*   *   *

As already intimated, the old hospital system did not demand care planning for individual patients until late in its history. This had a certain irony to it as this became a major pathway to bringing to life the individualism of each patient at the time of the hospital's own death throes. These early, primitive efforts at care planning introduced not only individualization, innovation and personal initiative, but a benign possessiveness around the key worker role toward their named clients. For those that were interested, it was an immensely exciting period of discovery and development. This proved to be a period of sustained professional development for nurses, urged on by their professional bodies. For all this encouragement, the care planning that *was* undertaken among mental health nurses remained studiously bereft of a comprehensively well structured range of interventions. And interventions associated with the actual mental disorder were, inappropriately, the most superficial! Often the mental disorder was actually left out of care planning, presumably because the nurses believed that this was not their area of expertise, but that of psychiatrists and psychologists. Even where the mental disorder was identified as a problem for nurse involvement it was quite usual to note the struggle to describe the objectives and therapeutic interventions to meet the patient's needs. While the medical priorities of physical, somatic treatments such as medication and ECT still predominated, nurses scouted around to "observe for deterioration in patient's mental state", to "provide time to allow patient to ventilate feelings", "to provide reassurance", and "to counsel patient". None of it quite hit the button. But there is another very straightforward reason why it was not so easy for nurses, or any mental health professionals for that matter, to know exactly how to manage a client's mental illness, per se. The very nature and experience of the illness was so removed from their personal lives that it was nigh impossible to empathise with any but the more recognisable manifestations such as minor depression or anxiety. Psychotic episodes, schizophrenia, bipolar disorder and personality disorders are way off the beaten track of most individuals' experience of themselves. This was even more resonant in the field of forensic mental health, where we toiled with the additional components of clients' dangerousness and criminal behaviour.

Regarding care planning, it would have been preferable, in one sense, for staff and patients to have cemented their unique professional contact via individually crafted care plans. But what this yielded, in practice, was an uncomfortably varied compilation of intervention practices among the many practitioners which hardly bore any resemblance to each other. From a professional and personal level I had just become too frustrated over the intervening years with the lack of awareness and sophistication of nurses' care planning to tolerate it any longer. The question had to be asked as to what level of planning actually denoted a reasonable level of care? Should we not be assuring a baseline of care above which talented individuals could always extend their problem-management? It all led me to two conclusions. One involved the necessity to standardise care planning and the second was to take on my own advanced training in order to be more therapeutically capable personally and to give further momentum for others to follow a similar line.

The strength of Medicine as a discipline partly lay in the body of diagnoses which generated its disciplinary activity. Nursing had only recently achieved a limited range of diagnostic credentials. Led by the United States, Nursing produced a body of nursing diagnoses to guide its discrete nursing operations quite independent of medical authority. For myself, I had now reached the conviction that there was no reason why nursing diagnoses, and their attendant nurse led interventions, even therapies, should not apply across the whole range of client problems, including offence related phenomena. These were to run, conterminously, alongside the work of the rest of the multi-disciplinary team, to be viewed as equally valid and not to be consigned to therapeutic leftovers. To ensure this, I was also persuaded that the current lottery of nursing care-planning could not be tolerated. Leaving the quality of care planning in the hands of individual nurses was an organisational indulgence. To take a simple example of a client's diabetic problem, it no longer made sense to leave the care planning of that complaint to the variable knowledge and competence base of individuals when a pre-formulated baseline was a better guarantee of optimum planning and health outcomes. With the benefit of an audit of care plans, the situation was laid bare. There were three major findings. Considering the wide-ranging problems which beset the forensic psychiatric client – physical, psychological, social, challenging behaviours, functional, forensic, and substance misuse – very few care plans were operational to target these problems. Astonishingly, this included both the diagnosed mental illness of the client and the forensic issue which was related to it. That is, the two most significant client problems for which they had been admitted. From my contacts and work in many other establishments I knew that this was not exclusive to our unit but endemic throughout the field. Neither did it necessarily emanate from professional idleness. Just as had pertained in the old asylum, it was more about a lack of professional expectation linked to local institutional routines, and lack of managerial leadership, both of which have a tendency to lag behind innovation. This is much about ambitious nursing staff, of necessity, being steered into a managerial career which generally prioritises organisational efficiency over clinical innovation. Clinical innovation was more of an optional extra. The associated issue, which has not changed since the old asylum days, is that staff retain a "shop floor" mindset which is shift based. Morning shifts, afternoon shifts, and night shifts have their routine duties and it is these that govern the working schedule rather than individualised interventions with service users. I was convinced that Stan's unprecedented innovations should be maintained to draw the nursing activity away from just a sociable facilitation.

I moved to create, along with the input of interested colleagues, a set of standardised care plans that tackled the regular issues on the unit. They were produced on computer to make them reproducible, better presented, more legible, and more accessible for improvement when the necessity arose. On the whole, these were accepted with a good deal of enthusiasm, partly because staff did not have the arduous task of reproducing the same exercises in longhand with each new admission. But they also acquainted everyone with guidance on what was expected. Initially we dealt with the general management of a patient, such as admission routines, acute violence, mental illness, physical problems, and some challenging behaviours. Later, the work slowly extended into the indisputable problems of challenging behaviours, mental illness and its forensic derivatives. The whole exercise also ensured a certain impetus toward professional development and the acquisition of skills which individual staff would require to deliver in the interventions such as symptom management or illness awareness programmes.

At the same time, I have not the least hesitation in admitting that this standardisation was as much a route to dispelling my own deep frustration with my colleagues' difficulties in care planning, having to follow them up and prompting them, then having to decide on how much more time to spend reviewing progress. There were frustrations in other quarters. One of the adverse effects of all this for one or two individuals was that their individuality had been sacrificed for a kind of political correctness which valued only the standard rather than individualisation. I had a good deal of sympathy for this view but never hesitated in assuring such individuals that their efforts to secure therapeutic care beyond the standard would never be frustrated, provided that they had the resources to achieve what they intended to achieve. Of course, acting "out of the box" in the old hospital days was merely a show of initiative which went against the general grain of routinisation, ignorance and indolence. In the contemporary climate could there be any repercussions for a nurse choosing not to use the standardised care plans and acting "out of the box"?

"Out of the box!" Now, there was an issue. In the past, this would have rested on little more than whether a staff member had behaved abusively, or criminally. There was a transition stage whereby nurses were determining whether they should be expected to perform their duties in the public arena – say, resuscitating a member of the public having a cardiac arrest. I can remember quite distinctly being advised that we should not expose ourselves to the possibility of litigation for acting out of duty hours, with no organisational authority to support our actions. With the professionalisation of nursing gathering increasing momentum, this all changed. In the contemporary setting, the case is whether each of us conducts ourselves "professionally" in any setting. This extends to inviting service users, their relatives, members of the general public, and colleagues to report "unprofessional conduct" to the professional body, namely, the United Kingdom Central Council, later to become the Nursing and Midwifery Council.

* * *

Forensic, mentally disordered clients bring a wide repertoire of complicating problems in the wake of frank mental illness. Any of the major diagnoses can be involved – depression, mania, bipolar disorder, psychoses, personality disorders, schizophrenia, and less well known ones such as Munchausen by proxy. Whatever the features of these, the most dangerous single symptoms relate to paranoid ideas which lead the patient to believe that some conspiratorial state of affairs exists which has him or her as its focus. In an effort to ward off such a perceived threat and to protect him or herself the patient may be compelled by their beliefs and hostile thoughts to resort to acts of violence against themselves or others. Hence, the dangerousness which they can present with if left untreated. Occasionally, patients will also present with a further psychiatric diagnosis of learning difficulties owing to a relatively low intelligence quotient. Even in the absence of an explicit learning disability, a relatively low IQ is quite a prevalent feature amongst forensic clients. These baseline psychiatric disorders are complicated by the ready availability of illicit drugs and alcohol in today's society which undermine a patient's capacity to maintain stability, especially when under stress. In the more generic field of psychiatry the combination of mental illness and drug/alcohol misuse has long been described as a Dual Diagnosis. The forensic client, comparatively, often has a triple category of disorder which includes the Dual Diagnosis combination as well as dangerousness, which often amounts to an indictable offence.

An indictable offence is a serious offence committed by an individual that usually requires a judge and court jury to officiate on a tiral. In this respect, forensic clients can exhibit serious criminality that is directly related to their mental disorder. The crime may be assault, grievous bodily harm, attempted murder, murder, arson or sexual assault, often involving the possession or use of offensive weapons. Additionally, there may be a well-established, pre morbid history of criminal behaviour which precedes the dangerousness or indictable offence linked with their mental disorder and resulting in the forensic hospital admissions. Clearly, it is hard to argue with the hypothesis that if the mental disorder can be treated, then the derivative, symptomatic dangerousness can also be ameliorated. The trouble is that any number of life events can compound this attempt to control this volatile potential. Client instability can be caused by everyday stress, a lack of appreciation and insight about their psychiatric vulnerability, illicit drug and alcohol use, the potential for relapses, medication lapses, therapeutic disengagement and residential abscondence. Accordingly, a huge area of forensic work has focused on the evolution of risk assessment and the risk management relating to mentally disordered offenders. This was yet another activity which was introduced by Stan, the CBT specialist, who commenced another prepackaged programme, this time a risk assessment schedule covering 20 separate indices. The programme attempted to measure a client's risk of future violence from a compilation of information drawn from their past personal history, their current clinical progress, and future potentialities. As with everything, the usefulness of this exercise very often depended on the diligence of the assessor to seek out the relevant information, in the first instance, and then to draw specific scenarios and conclusions from the findings in which the patient's risk might be precipitated. As with all such instruments, however rigorously conducted, the assessment could never be anything other than a likely formulation and could never pretend to be a determinate picture of an individual's actual dangerousness. In practice, the individual client might respond in a more dangerous, or less dangerous, manner than predicted in the risk assessment but it represented a necessary and informed prediction. It became one of the strategies to be incorporated into the unit's organisational battery so that it became an operational expectation that every client would be processed through an assessment of their risk of dangerousness and a management plan devised as a consequence of it.

Though this was neither an option devised locally, nor one imposed by government policy, there was an implicit expectation that the forensic mental health units compile risk assessments on their clients as part of the treatment repertoire. There were sound reasons for this. A risk assessment of dangerousness may determine that a client now represents a minimal future risk to society, based on the clinical progress while in treatment, but it also establishes the circumstances in which the risk may be potentiated. As with most work in the forensic mental health field, the risk assessment schedule is a necessary measure which can adversely colour a client's future prospects because it draws attention to, perhaps overemphasises, prospective worst scenarios. In other words, there is always an anticipation of future harm to society, based on the knowledge of a client's past history. In short, the gathering of information on the forensic client serves an explicit detective function, not just a straightforward therapeutic one, and cannot but highlight the negative aspects of a client's character and life circumstances.

* * *

When Stan departed for more illustrious career pastures, I saw the usefulness of taking over some of his invaluable work as both personal advantage and to maintain necessary unit activity. I elected to continue running the Anger Management Programme and, after first acquainting myself with the session materials, co-opted close colleagues who took it in turn to share in its facilitation. Each programme could accept up to 12 patients but because of the limited potential, numbers often had to run on about nine clients, plus we two facilitators. Naturally enough, bearing in mind my personality, all this smacked of a certain competitiveness, an opportunity to strive, to achieve, which I noted and accepted. Very early on we found the clients struggling to keep a focus, to identify the background issues which influenced their anger, or avoidance, or aggression, to complete any of the homework which was set them. At every opportunity their participation would erupt into humour and we realised how necessary this might be to enable them to stick with the project. But it wasn't long before you kind of doubted how much they attached themselves to the programme and how much they actually wanted to understand their behaviour and their responsibility for it. The programme identifies the occasional rôle play scenario to help draw out the feelings and characteristic behaviour of the participants and to provide an observational opportunity for the remaining onlookers. It also detracts from the venture resembling a bookish exercise and helps make it more palatable. These are treated more or less as games with tremendous enjoyment and laughter all round but, as to the level of insight and generalisation that they are capable of making, I have my severe reservations. When seated after one such scenario one forthright character, Darren, who has watched the rôle play with wry smiles throughout, voices his query in his deliberate monotone.

'Course, that's not what they'd say in reality.'

'What do you say to that, people?' I reply, addressing the others.

'Well, I can't say. I just said what come to mind in that situation but every situation's different. I don't always act the same. Depends on my mood,' replies Paul, who has enacted one of the rôles.

'So, when you just said what you did, you were in what mood then?' I ask.

'A good mood!' Everyone laughs heartily as he regards me with an expression that suggests the answer was obvious.

'So, although you seemed to realise that David was goading you and were able to step back, you couldn't always act reasonably and keep out of trouble?'

'Well, some days you can take being wound up, others, you can't. If it goes beyond a wind-up then I might be left with no choice but to do more.' The female staff nurse who is co-facilitating has an amused expression.

'I think you handled that better than I would have done, actually.'

'Cos it was in here, it's not reality, it's not what'd happen on the street, that's why,' sneers Darren, but amicably enough. 'That's the problem with doing this in here, it's not realistic. We wouldn't do all this on the street.'

'You don't think so?' continues my colleague.

'Well, who can tell? Maybe you could,' intercedes Paul.

'No I couldn't 'cos I know who I am.'

'What, you wouldn't try and play things down, if you could?' pursues my colleague.

'Look, you don't waste your time trying to talk the geezer down. You keeps your mouth shut tight and ignores him. If he keeps on at you and he ain't got the hint, you turn around and whack him – good and hard, no messing!'

'And you want to change that or not?' continues the female nurse.

'No, not in that situation. That's his lookout.'

'So why are you doing this course, Darren? What's the point of it?' she adds with unambiguous scepticism. He takes a while.

'So's I can learn how to manage my anger better,' regarding her as if she's stupid. 'But once you've got into a situation, you have your own ways of dealing with things and that ain't going to change now, is it?'

'So, you can only work on keeping out of the situation?'

'Yeah, sort of. Knowing what's going to get my goat and keeping away will help.'

'Avoiding a difficult situation is not really anger management, is it? It's just that, avoidance, backing out if anything.'

'I don't back out of nothing,' continues Darren, as if he's been slighted. 'But I could keep away from things that are bound to rile me. That's why I don't see much of my kids 'cos if I have to go to her place we're going to get into shit. Best thing is to stay away.'

'He's got a point, really.' Paul has a speaking style that is thoughtful but ponderous and can be a little time-consuming when you're wanting to move on and I try to gently interrupt. 'Suppose we do all this work and learn to manage our anger – what about everybody else? What are they doing to help the situation – nothing! And your anger is more about who you're dealing with, half the time, don't you think? Supposing it's the police?'

'That's a completely different matter for a lot of people. Apart from that, it's my mood that gets me angry in the first place and if I'm feeling upset it's best to avoid people, keep out of it altogether.' I'm pleasantly surprised by his awareness. Now Darren is becoming animated. He is unusually diminutive in stature for an African-Caribbean but his muscular frame is granite. His moods can vacillate between an infectious sociability and a reclusive withdrawal.

'You can only act as you feel, man. How else can it be? If you're upset about something or someone then anyone gets in your way – better watch out! It's up to them to cotton on to what your face is speaking. The face speaks. It's not hard to know what a face says. If they can't be bothered to do that then that's their lookout.' He's a little wound up, himself. 'Ain't it time for a smoke now?'

'Okay, in a minute. What you're saying is interesting. What do you all think about what he's said?'

'Except that you can't just expect people to be what you want them to,' replies Carl, a quieter, quite reticent individual who it is difficult to imagine getting disturbed by anything, frankly. 'But I do agree that it's not just down to us to take the blame if there's trouble.'

'So, there's our own moods, and there's how others treat us, then. Doesn't knowing those two things help us to do something different, though?' is my tentative rejoinder.

'No, 'cos just because you know that, don't stop you being in a mood or nutting someone who's treating you like shit, does it? You're still gonna act the same,' says Darren, holding his tack.

'So, are you suggesting that you can't help yourself, that you've got no control over how you act?' I risk tempting Darren's irritation, I realise. You can see him turning this over, realising certain implications. He is regarding me directly, steadily.

'No, man, 'course I got control.' He says this with a hint of disgust and looks down to the floor, brushing it with his feet.

'So, you never lose control?'

'Well, that's a different matter. If it's a copper who's treating me like shit, then I'm not going to take it lying down. Nor some tough guy who thinks he's a big man and thinks he can get away with disrespecting me, man. I'm going to get a gun and seek him out, aren't I?' He delivers this with a sweeping laugh that all join in with. But it punctuates the momentum that has just been building. In fact, for a man living apart from his children, this boyish grin, self-centred thinking, and lack of regard for consequences, all suggest the thinking style of an immature, impulsive adolescent. It is a caveat that is not given consideration in the programme guidance and it is not insignificant.

'Now you're doing the same thing, Darren, talking unrealistic because you're in here,' interjects Carl. This is surprising coming from a participant who rarely commits himself other than to the group humour.

'Am I? You ain't never seen me when I'm upset man. I can get hold of a gun. What, do you think I'm going to sit back when all I have to do is get in touch with my gang? No geezer's going to shit on me. You gotta be hard and show 'em you're not going to put up with their crap. No, I'm telling you, man, geezers have gotta know that you're not taking their shit!' He is shuffling his feet some more and we all anticipate further revelations. 'Apart from that, people have gotta back off if they don't want trouble. When you're upset about something it's for a good reason, man!' We let this settle for a few moments.

'So, the lesson, so far, is that you don't see any reason for changing yourself and how you deal with situations, is that right?' asks my colleague.

'I see what you're saying and maybe you can change just a little bit, but you can't change much or you're going to end up losing your pride, your self-respect. That's not what I want.'

'Can't you change some things which are unhelpful to you and still remain the person you are?' I try, with some equivocation.

'I'm happy to change if it means I don't have to stay in one of these places,' pipes up Benjamin. 'The most important thing is to get out of here and stay out.'

'That's a cop out, man,' replies Darren. 'You don't have pride. You prepared to do anything just so's you can keep out of these places?'

'Yeah. Course.'

'So, why are you coming to this group, Darren?' interjects Paul pointedly.

'Cos I wanna get out of here, too. I can say I've done the Anger Management, can't I? Not many people get to do it, do they? That must count for something!'

'Yeeees,' I admit, hesitantly. 'But you'll have to show that you've benefited from it, given some indication that you've wanted to change, not just attended,' I add, coaxingly.

'Well, anyone can *say* they want to change but how can they prove that?' It's a good question and we know that passing through the programme can give us no real assurances about the longer term. However, we'd like to think that it's possible to gauge a participant's benefit from the nature of their participation.

'Well, I want to get out of here and it's not going to do me any harm coming to this group,' Darren compromises.

'You give me the impression that it's like a subject that you're learning about in school – which you can dip in and out of as you choose. This is about understanding yourself better, understanding your background and the ways in which you get aggressive, learning new ways of handling old situations, taking more control of your emotions, and being more aware of your options. Does that make sense to everyone?' There is a unanimous nodding and grunting of agreement rippling around the assembly. This is something that we reiterate like a mantra so they are accustomed to the message, but as to whether it makes an impression…. 'So, Darren, does that mean that there are situations which are non-negotiable and you don't have to have control?' Darren unravels a very telling line of argument.

'Maybe. But if you take away our aggression you're taking away a part of us, a really important part, of who we are, what makes us tick, man!'

'You seem to be suggesting that your aggression is part of your personality, then, not your mental illness,' interjects my colleague in timely fashion. We've noticed that Kevin has, as usual within the sessions, remained steadfastly removed from the discussion but he's all ears, and grinning none too discreetly! From individual work with him I have learned of his unceasing conflicts with intimate relations, neighbours, the Police, and Prison Services. He has accumulated a criminal record, largely from these infractions. I try to tempt him.

'Any thoughts, Kevin?' He's clearly been distracted but comes to with a detached composure.

'No, not really.'

'You must have a view.' He assumes a relaxed stance, placing his head on one arm that, in turn, rests on the back of his chair.

'I don't have problems with aggression so I'm quite happy to listen to you all talk away,' with more than just a smidgeon of contempt.

'So, what you doing in this group, then?' Paul stabs with the tact of an injection.

'I am here,' glares Kevin, 'because I was asked to come, that's all. Like everybody here I want to leave this damned place. If it's one of the necessary hoops then I'll jump through it, gladly, and whistle "Dixie" while I do it.' Uproarious laughter issues from the group. Kevin has only partially aimed at being humorous, however, being far more intent on advertising his customary superior air, for which he is well known. 'Besides, I've done all this Anger Management lark before in prison. But... if the staff in their infinite wisdom feel I can benefit from another group, to add to all those I've already accomplished, who am I to argue?' he tails off with disdain and a solid battening of eyelids.

* * *

This discussion has deviated from the programme schedule for that week but illuminated fundamental aspects of some of the debate that is to be had around the issue of aggression – its purposes, its justification. These are as significant as to whether its sources are derived from a patient's essential

331

nature, nurtured in their surroundings and upbringing, or are a derivative of the mental illness to which they have been subjected? The debate, curiously, does not seem to preoccupy most of the patients. They only want to know what will prevent them becoming liable to the attentions and hospitality of police custody, imprisonment, or psychiatric detention. And the simpler, the better. From running several of these groups, the overriding belief they share is that they are not aggressive by nature and, while they conceded their backgrounds have some material influence, it is their illness which is the more determinate cause for landing them in trouble with the authorities. Most of them have acquired some sort of assurance that the psychiatric treatment, namely medication, will prevent them from relapsing into illness and, consequently, violent behaviour. Furthermore, that all the rest of the treatment regime – the daily activity schedule, key worker interaction, occupational therapy, individual therapy, psychological assessment, etc – is more or less superfluous. But they know they must play along in order to earn their passage out. It is the Consultant Psychiatrist who holds most of the strings, the power over admission and discharge, prescribing medicine, and who reports to the Home Office on progress. The only other useful personnel are Social Workers who organise all their benefits and allowances and secure their living accommodation. Ultimately, their stance is a passive acceptance that, whether or not they can change their behaviour, the medication surely can, if anything can. Otherwise, they may as well be in prison serving a sentence, knowing when that sentence ends and when they can get back to their normal life! In here, in a medium security unit, your mental health section can run out, but can then be renewed indefinitely in theory! It really appears that a deep-seated belief prevails that self-control of their aggression and violence is of relatively little significance when stacked up against the determination that, since it is more likely to be caused by their mental disorder, they cannot be held wholly responsible for it. Therefore, there is very little they can effect themselves and that's what they are in treatment for.

From a professional standpoint these revelations are confirmation of the worst form of rationalisation which informs our patients' self perceptions and responsibility. They also tell us that aggression is an indispensable attribute for some individuals all of the time, and for others most of the time, irrespective of whether it springs from personality or is grafted on by social origins and associations. For those individuals for whom aggression invigorates, confers status and self-respect, and is the very essence of who they perceive themselves to be, there is little likelihood of stimulating any ownership over the adverse consequences of their behaviour. It is crucial to identify such individuals and follow up later with individual work so that they have an improved chance of detaching and teasing out these characteristic aggression styles from aggression, which is a function of a deteriorating, erupting mental illness. The motivation for Darren's anger management work may well be to discover the background influence and style of his aggression but it takes the form of a curiosity around his personal biography rather than a vehicle for exerting personal change. I suspect that the nearest we'll get to altering his aggression style is to refrain from the actual physical contact with a perceived perpetrator based on the metaphorical application of a road traffic "red light". And his motivation, even here, will be founded on his desire to avoid the inevitable consequences of being convicted, imprisoned, or treated. Anything more, from his viewpoint, is to believe that an intimate part of him will be lost, that he will be depleted in some way, that he will have lost some of his Human Rights, indeed!

As the subsequent programme sessions unfold, other points of contention come to light. Firstly, you have to wonder who the programme developers were targeting when they put together this highly structured presentation of the whole cycle of aggression. My fear is that our clients, most of whom did not perform well in the educational system, will not be able to relate their personal aggression to this theoretical concoction. Clients in the general population who may display anger issues may be more amenable to such an educative approach but our cumulatively disadvantaged forensic clients clearly struggle. Unsurprisingly, the pace is far too fast as no sooner are they introduced to one set of concepts and tasks, than the following session brings yet more. I find myself revisiting and reinforcing the material from the previous session because there seems no point in losing folk in an abyss of accelerating confusion. We conclude that getting through the programme is easy enough but far from guarantees that clients can retain the ideas presented, or any personal awareness emanating from it. For these clients, the enterprise must smack of past educational experiences – sitting in classrooms, having stuff imposed on them, being pretty disengaged, expecting to fail the exams if there are any. And homework is virtually a no-no! And this is important because it can help integrate the sessions with daily life on the unit, as well as link each week's work. So basic educational competence and attitudes seem as relevant as any and this is a significant treatment issue.

Secondly, we completely underestimate the immensity of what we are attempting if we believe that we can bring significant change to highly disadvantaged individuals in a matter of 12 short sessions, with home-work. Personal aggression styles that have been soldered into psychologi-cal armoury to survive personal circumstances are not a matter of choice which individuals can easily replace. We're ultimately asking them to risk letting go of what has served their circumstances, however problematic, and giving themselves over to ideas and skills called *assertiveness* and *compro-mise*. Oh, so very easy to say! All you need is to stand up for your rights while respecting the rights of others to do likewise! These self-explanatory euphemisms that supposedly characterise the well-balanced, stable civilian who can negotiate and harmonise his or her way through any social tempest just come sliding off the tongue with all the falsehood of presumption and condescension. Well for us here, the tempest is trying to enable people to trust the difficult path of assertiveness and compromise. We come to realise how much we have underestimated how powerful these concepts are, so that they virtually become implausible snares. They belong somewhere else – in a psychological Shangri-la where a divining adaptability leaps to a person's rescue, restraining them from the faultlines of hostility and violence, at one extreme, and beckoning them from the cracks of submissiveness and passiv-ity, at the other! It is precisely because assertiveness and compromise are so demanding, so indeterminate, so time-consuming, that people resort to the very converse – a relatively uncomplicated, uncompromising, immediate resolution to conflict. Assertiveness and compromise are highly sophisticated skills and the acquisition of them massively underestimated, in my opinion!

* * *

If, like many, I could borrow the oft quoted lines from T.S. Eliot's "*Little Gidding*".

> "We shall not cease from exploration
> And the end of all our exploring
> Will be to arrive where we started
> And know the place for the first time."

It would usefully mirror the place I had reached in my own professional and personal awareness. I had started out in the asylum two and a half decades earlier working in the direct presence of patients in the clinical area. But each successive advancement in my career seemed to contain an impetus toward a progressive removal from immediate patient contact. I resisted this at every stage but this carried its own consequences, some foreseen, some not. Most nurses are prone to the same dilemma if they elect to seek promotion rather than remain on the "shop floor".

From my personal perspective, these professional endeavours were all part of that established need for unabated striving, for excelling, to be slightly different. That competitiveness had driven me into exploring most nooks and crannies of my profession beyond the basic practitioner – management, research, education and university lecturing, and writing for journals and book chapters. The training of nurses had been removed from our old hospitals and standardised under the aegis of what was termed a "Project 2000" University education. But I didn't need to be a lecturer to understand that, of all the mental health courses on which I had been taught and had, in turn, taught very few mental health trainers among us had acquired advanced therapeutic skills which could be used to inform our students, or be utilised with our patients. As a consequence, nurse training was still not producing nursing practitioners capable of skilled interventions with mental illnesses.

I re-embarked on a route that would veer more directly to working alongside clients, at a higher organisational level and a more profound therapeutic level. In my own efforts to secure a therapeutic skills base I gave up on nursing to source this requirement. I turned to a non nursing discipline – just as Stan had done – and pursued a training in psychotherapy in what became the most productive move of my entire career. Not forgetting that in the more advanced and intimate work which would help to unravel the linkage between a patient's mental illness and their forensic derivatives, there would be a necessary and concomitant appreciation of my own personality and continuing challenges. It was both a beginning and an end. It was very much an end to spending much of my time working alongside staff, of my association with nursing practices, and the beginning of aligning myself to psychotherapeutic work with patients. And if that was what I might have anticipated as being the essence of psychiatric nursing when I had commenced my career, it felt as if I was returning to where I had wanted to start out from.

Psychotherapy is very challenging for any patient, not least a forensic client who has the multiple burden of generally being admitted against their will, and of having their mental state and law-breaking propensities scrutinised ad infinitum. As a result of this and frequently having had some "stir" (prison), they develop a cumulating resistance toward any form of authority, mental health services included. Additionally, their community lifestyle incorporates, as has been indicated, somewhat chaotic organisational and thinking styles complicated, for many, by illicit drug use and/or excessive alcohol use. So, though we might be tempted into believing that patients with psychological difficulties and confined to a secure facility because of their proven propensity to act in highly disturbed ways, would leap at a chance to do individual therapy, it is not too surprising that they might resist this perceived intrusion. Conversely, it might also be expected that any staff with therapeutic training, or insightfulness, would similarly be prepared to work with any service-user. Unfortunately, this potential harmony is shot through with human frailty. To some base degree, the potential compatibility between two parties does play a part, though it can be argued that it should not have done. More important is a therapist's judgement of a client's *psychological mindedness*! In other words, does the client have the capacity of engaging with someone in a relatively intensive introspection, looking beyond the taken-for-granted surface, and of sharing and working through the emerging feelings and ideas, without viewing the process as debasing or intrusive? The task of engaging a client who is not prepared to do so, while not insurmountable, can be an arduous one. One early salutary lesson was learned by me from an inaugural meeting with one particular patient with a very difficult in-patient experience despite our pre therapy exploration of what therapy might entail. Talking *about* something and engaging in it cannot wholly prepare either party for what actually transpires.

'Good morning, Ambrose. Take a seat, won't you,' I say, offering him the chair opposite to mine after he's closed the door and I've re-seated myself. He is a young African-Caribbean who manages all the trappings of modern fashion despite living off benefits. His spanking new white trainers have a distracting brilliance. He also adorns himself in a natty headscarf. During one of our preliminary talks he has informed me that, among today's London male youth, owning a gun is not only standard but considered a fashion accessory. 'Well, thanks for coming. Now, perhaps we could start by you saying something about how you're feeling right now, starting these meetings?'

'I'm fine,' Ambrose replies with a blank facial expression but plenty of expression in his widely spread legs and in leaning well back into his chair. Long pause, me waiting in the hope that he'll be encouraged to continue.

'Could you say any more about that?' Instant response of clicking his tongue and looking away disgustedly.

'I've just told you, man!' he snaps. I'm stunned because this has disturbed what *I* take for granted! There is an expectation that the client will generally run with that opener, expand on it a little, but certainly not rebuke it when they've accepted starting therapy! A few moments sorting my confusion and distaste.

'Well, it's clear you're feeling something,' I pose, cautiously. He surveys me intensely, in disbelief.

'I just told you, didn't I? Why do you have to keep on?' I'm opening my mouth with the intention of continuing but Ambrose kicks himself from his chair, and launches himself toward the door, spitting 'I'm not having any of this shit, man!' I wait. I wait some more; after all, the thing is to take note of this and figure what it means. Hopefully, he'll come back. Or do I really want that, now? He reappears at the open doorway, undecided on whether to re-enter, it seems.

'Come and sit down. Let's try again.'

'No thanks. You asked me a stupid fucking question and I ain't listening to any more, all right?'

'But come and explain it to me. You're angry, come and tell me why.'

'If I say I'm fine, that's it, all right! I don't need to say no more. What you asking me for?'

337

'What would you have liked me to say, then?' He clicks his tongue again and turns away.

'No, no, no, I ain't putting up with none of this. You can stick it up your arse.' And with that, he was gone, never reappears, and tells his primary nurse that he doesn't want any therapy. It's a pity because there could be any number of reasons for his change of heart but he needs to be able to give vent to these, as well as his anger. And maybe he can't manage this because his behaviour and presentation are dominated by any current mood he's experiencing? Whatever is going on in his own mind has been manifested in his disproportionate response to our meeting. For him, I have had my place replaced with someone from his past. He is enacting a past drama. There has been a *transference*. He has attributed to me qualities that actually belong to someone else and responded accordingly. He may even be unconsciously projecting his aggressive impulses that he represses within himself, onto me and, having done so, he becomes fearful of the impulse manifesting itself inside me and then attacking himself. This causes him to want to control me. Hence, the inordinate resistance and anger shown in the room. This is known as "projective identification" and was revealed by Ambrose's accusative reaction which had the quality of an projection (repetition form the past) as it seemed out of proportion to what I had said. The strength of his reaction has taken me by surprise and indicated my lack of experience with these unconscious processes. I write in his notes and offer him the prospect of future work if Ambrose should change his mind.

* * *

Then there was Kevin. Kevin whom we had attempted to engage in the Anger Management Programme but who had separated himself to the vantage of the periphery where he could look down upon the assembly, sometimes with humour, mostly with scowling derision and superiority! Kevin, a middle-aged man who was contemptuous of his fellow patients, the staff, the psychiatric enterprise, the prison system, the police and all forms of authority. To him, the multiple shades of officialdom served only as odious stumbling blocks to the realisation of his personal ambitions. He has resided in the prison system for over 20 years, having been given a life sentence for killing his young son.

His ongoing refusal to accept responsibility for this death, and the nature of it, give the Parole Board grounds for doubting his rehabilitative potential and they continually turn down his parole applications. When he is transferred to our medium security forensic unit he does not take to the majority of staff and these sentiments are mutual. He expects to be taken seriously and to be attended to, pretty promptly, but the staff do not oblige efficiently enough for him. They take umbrage at his "attitude". Other than this contact, he generally wishes to be left alone in his room, outside of the mandatory sessions, and to be returned to the prison system from whence he came. Actually, it was me who assessed him in prison and recommended that he be offered a spell of in-patient treatment with us. At the prison interview I found him an engaging character, with a cultivated accent, articulate, somewhat reluctant to envisage a psychiatric transfer, but giving me some grounds for optimism that he would use the time in our service productively. That's what I learned from that first encounter – that he responded well to those that took him seriously but woe betide anyone who displayed a less than inviting stance toward him. They were treated to an uncompromising banishment. He has made little progress since arriving on the unit and the team, having considered their options, have a pessimistic view of his progress. He can be returned to prison but he'll be faced with the same open-ended sentence he's endured to date.

I have suggested that I try to build on the rapport we already share, gauge how far he is capable of closer contact, and attempt some individual therapy. The level of optimism within the team is not encouraging, especially with the feedback we give about the Anger Management Group, and I only have my good relationship with him to go on. I commence the sessions in the belief that he is relatively emotionally accessible, which is not the case with so many of our users. During the initial session I ask him if it is possible to state what would be helpful for us to look at together. He doesn't want to look at anything together, he replies. What would he like to gain from the therapy, then? He doesn't need any therapy, he replies! Isn't it possible that the fact that he has submitted himself to individual therapy will sit well with the Parole Board, I prompt? He has a ready answer for this, honed from years of failed attempts.

'The bloody Parole Board have ignored everything I've done throughout my time in prison. I might just as well not have done any of it for all that they are interested. It's racism, man, don't you see that? I'm a black man and that's all they see.'

'You really believe that?' He tuts and clicks his tongue, loudly.

'What other reason is there?' he replies as if it is perfectly obvious. 'I've done course after ruddy course, jumped through all their bloody hoops, and still they turn me down. The Police, the screws, the Crown Prosecution Service, they're all the same – racists.' The word is pronounced with a strong Caribbean lilt.

'And you think that therapy will be treated similarly?'

'Course it will,' looking away.

'Or,' I draw out the word in an exaggerated emphasis, 'you're concerned that you might learn something new about yourself, unexpected, you know.'

'What more is there to be learned? I know myself very well. Nobody can tell me nothing I don't already know, let me tell you. I've done all the courses. I've done that anger management thing. I've done group therapy – two lots, in fact. I've done the "lifer's" course. I've taken part in sport. I've done academic subjects – bookkeeping, I completed. I've worked as well. I'm not lazy, man. What you see before you is not an idle person. I've not sat on my arse for 20 years!'

'I'm impressed. I'd be really interested to know what you discovered from the group therapy, Kevin.'

'Oh, for goodness sake, I learned what there is to know, ok? I stuck it out. I saw it through. I don't need to go through the whole exercise again.' He is becoming slightly incensed and agitated. I chance my arm with a little confrontation. 'I'm interested that you can't see the benefit of sharing that information with me. I'm wondering why that might be?' A protracted tongue clicking ensues.

'Why should that be interesting to you? Tell me because I'm blowed if I can see!' I keep silent. 'What do you want me to say, then? You want me to go through every detail of what we did, and what I got out of it? Is that what you want?'

'I think that you believe you have your anger and aggression sorted on the grounds that you've not actually been physically violent toward any individual over the past ten years. It's done and dusted and there's an end to it. That's why you haven't really committed yourself to the Anger Management work this time round.' His few remaining teeth, very prominent between the gaps, flash with indignation.

'Are you saying that all that I've told you is not good enough, then? Doesn't it all speak for itself – that I've not been in a fight for ten years despite all the provocation I've endured from those racist screws? My God, what more proof do you want?' He surely has a point irrespective of alleged provocation.

'Let's put it this way, Kevin, if you can't speak to me about it I'm willing to guess that you haven't convinced the Parole Board about how much you may have benefited from the therapy, and education, and work, and how they've altered your ways of managing conflict over the years of your sentence. Do you see?'

'No, I don't actually. They have made up their minds about me and I might as well accept that I'm not going anywhere.'

'Would you admit to having become angry while you've been with us in hospital?' Naturally, I am aware he's reported to have displayed his anger on a fair number of occasions. I can't miss the fact that his already exophthalmic eyes, probably due to a physical condition, are even more prominently glaring at me.

'Not what *I* would call angry, no! I stay out of people's way most of the time. I don't have any need to get angry. I retire to my room and read, or listen to the radio, or write my letters.' We survey each other, quiet now. Tension is palpable. I toy with the idea that I've had a misplaced optimism about therapeutic progress with Kevin. But, no, I prefer the more comfortable idea that these are signs of resistance and denial, the extent of which varies from one client to another. I'm clear he's taken very little on board from our group since he believes he no longer has anger issues. There again, he was always present, always turned up, and that's a positive statement, in itself! Probably another collectable ticket that he can present to indicate his commitment to change. Of course, there is the possibility that his reluctance to acknowledge any benefits from the past therapeutic work is a result of not having gained any personal insight. From his point of view, he turned up to every session in his prison work and, ipso facto, completed the programmes! Crucially, he's failed to internalise his experiences within these several groups, somehow managed to distance himself from the material, and parcelled off the issues as other people's problems, not his. So his defensiveness is understandable. And if I don't feel he's made much effort in the group context why should I be entertaining his prospects in the more intimate relationship of individual work? He certainly won't tolerate much enquiry into the past or present. So, what will he tolerate? And then it hits me! It is precisely that very individualism, that favoured attention, that sense of being treated as special, that will engage him initially, at least! You are not supposed to be complicit in accepting the client's distorted material that he or she brings to the therapy. There is meant to be an ongoing clarification and confrontation of the material to help the client re-evaluate and integrate it into awareness and personal development. Well, Kevin will simply not tolerate such strategies and I have to find a way of working with him that generates trust and rapport without compromising the aims of therapy. The golden rule is to move at your client's pace and capacity, and I have the benefit of not being compromised by time limitations. To what degree therapeutic outcomes will follow, well, I now have my doubts.

'I think it would be helpful if we began by you just telling me your story, Kevin. Talk about your past life because I'm sure there's much that I don't know about you. How does that sit with you?' The bristling defence recedes almost tangibly. He adjusts his seating, rests his jaw on an arm crooked over the chair back, and relaxes his face. His whole stance reads as 'now you're talking!'

Over the ensuing sessions, which he conscientiously attends, and on time, Kevin relates a disciplined childhood and a trouble-free school performance until he emigrates to join his mother in England as a teenager. As he progresses through his work history, then his extensive list of academic subjects studied, and the accruing certificates and diplomas achieved at work and throughout his prison experiences, there are some emergent themes. It is the inordinate pride he has in his "accomplishments". Not that any indication is given that any of them have been put to any use. Equally obvious is that he is forced to terminate his various employments due to serious disputes with the employers which he blames, squarely, on them. As the sessions pass, and I facilitate this comfortable dissemination of accumulating pride and blamelessness, the most startling finding is that he omits any reference to his past mental illness and offences. It is only a matter of time before I encroach on those areas that he has avoided during the telling of his tale. For I am acquainted with his pugilistic past, having read on his Probation Service Report of a criminal record – including a number of assaults, and some involving Police Officers – where convictions culminated in a number of short prison sentences prior to the conviction for murder. Furthermore, during his tally of prison sentence he attracted a significant number of official adjudications because of his disciplinary infractions. I want to confront his partial tale and the reasons for his heavy editing of the most crucial elements, at least, to any observer or assessor. I have thanked him for all the information he's relayed and it has told me a great deal about his personality. It bears the hallmarks of narcissism.

'You must realise that I am aware of, shall we say, the other interruptions to your life, Kevin, that have caused you to spend time inside?'

'Naturally, I'm sure you've had a good read about all the lies that are said about me.'

'Are they lies?'

'What else can they be? If a man can't stand up for himself, can't stand against the system, and it locks him up when he defends himself, then what it says about him are lies. The truth is, if people hadn't provoked me, if they'd just left me alone to get on with my life, I shouldn't have ended up in prison.'

'Can you give an example?' He's glaring at me with those exophthalmic orbs.

'Okay. Take the time when my kid had to go into hospital because the doctors wanted to carry out some investigations. He'd stayed in there for two weeks, finding out nothing, so I pick him up and take him home with me. And, because it was against medical advice, the Social Worker is sent to my home to persuade me to bring my boy back to the hospital for more tests. I told her I wasn't allowing it. So she goes off and returns with two coppers. What am I to do? They tell me they have the authority to take him back against my wishes, and I resist them. And because I stand up for my rights, they arrest me and accuse me of assaulting *them*! The authorities can do anything they like. Bloody outrageous! Human rights, pah!'

'I can see your point to some extent...'

'Why don't the police go after criminals, or drug addicts, or paedophiles, all the low life? Why do they go for someone like me? I'm not a criminal, I don't cheat people, I don't rob them, don't walk about beating people up. I've never taken drugs, never touched alcohol.' It's this attitudinal set, including an abstemious approach to substance misuse, that makes Kevin somewhat unique here. He has a strong value system which, in its way, contains its own ethical logic. The problem is that it is an encapsulated value system, so exclusively dictated from within his own reclusive self-centredness, that he cannot allow it to be compromised in any way by external influence. The result is that his entrenched stance leads to him breaking the law and bringing him into conflict with all shades of the public and authority. But, from his stance, his beliefs sustain him through his trials – literally, in some instances – so that he almost believes himself to be embarking on a righteous mission. But what is a cognitive distortion for some, is life enhancing for him, and the therapeutic difficulty is envisaging the sequel to him giving up his beliefs and replacing them with a more conventional stance. There is every like-lihood that he could lose his sense of self efficacy and decompensate into apathy, lethargy and suicidal depression. His rigid thinking has enabled him throughout a trial and the subsequent 20 years of imprisonment to continue denying killing his victim. He has vehemently denied any direct involvement in his son's death and, thereby, reveals no remorse even though he is perfectly aware that this lack of confession provokes the Parole Board to keep refusing him his licence. Because it is such a high price to pay for personal principles it gives an indication of how indispensable are those principles to his self image and wellbeing.

'Look, I know you mean well and you're trying to help me, Steve, but I don't require all this therapy nonsense. I don't need to examine anything more about myself. I admit, when I was young I had a bad temper and an aggressive personality. But that's all in the past.'

'What about your run-ins with the prison officers? There were a fair number of occasions on your record and they're more recent.'

'Yes, many run-ins with the screws but that was due to the situation, man! I didn't have those sorts of difficulties before prison!'

'And how much did your bad temper and aggressive personality contribute to those situations, do you think?'

'Look, you have to survive in those places. If you don't stand up for yourself you'll be trodden into the dust. A man can't just cast off his pride and, believe me, that's all you have left in prison, nothing else. Everything else is taken away!'

'You'd say it was situational, then. I understand, but the Parole Board, and ourselves for that matter, can't ignore the record of incidents because it suggests that you haven't learned to keep yourself out of conflicts. In fact, that you go on managing conflict in the same old way without compromising!'

'Look,' he says, with intense conviction, 'I can rise above all the baiting they want to dish out. I can play their game.'

'It must have been hard.' Throughout, I'm trying to keep in balance an observer's view of his conduct and perspective compared with his own inimitable stance. 'But are you suggesting that the Prison Service has attempted nothing on your behalf? What about all those courses, certificates and therapy? What about your illness, for example? You were referred for treatment as soon as you needed it and here you are!' More tutting and tongue clicking.

'What do you mean *ill*? I just had a nervous breakdown, that's all.'

'In your own terms, then, how did you see your nervous breakdown, Kevin?'

'Things got on top of me, that's all. Perfectly understandable when you live in such conditions.'

'Do you think the breakdown required treatment, you know, from doctors, from the mental health service?'

'No, I didn't need the mental health service; I just needed the medication and it did the trick.'

'You're still on the medication. Will you stay on it in the future if you're advised to?'

'Maybe, if I think it will stop me having another breakdown.'

'This was not the first time, though, and the psychiatrists seem clear that you have a mental illness that may relapse without treatment.'

'Look, I didn't have a mental illness; I had a breakdown, all right. Don't make a meal out of it, man!' The fact is that there was considerable evidence of Kevin having developed a psychosis with the accompanying hallucinations, delusions and associated behaviour. Apparently his medication has had a hugely beneficial effect for there is no current residual evidence of any psychotic phenomena and the team are toying with the prospect of returning him to prison to continue his sentence.

'Okay, but I shouldn't have been there in the first place! If they hadn't put me there I wouldn't need to use their facilities.' Whilst this is undeniable, there's a striking consistency that he cannot grant other parties any credit and, when it comes to the brink of having to concede this, he'll sidestep the issue as he's managed here.

* * *

This is the tenor of our several sessions during which we barely touch on his index offence. We have not been able to progress much in the therapy since we are truly stuck at an early stage. This is not to say that the time is not spent profitably, for all that I am learning from Kevin is indispensable material and indicates just how problematic is his potential for making changes and adjustments that will help him in the future. The message is that Kevin developed a lifelong rigidity of thinking which is intolerant of what he perceives as external interference. Maintaining this has not been acquired through assertion and diplomacy but, rather, through an uncompromising and aggressive defence of his position. His personality can be described as having narcissistic traits so that he regards his accomplishments, and everything else, only on his own terms. This resonates through my weekly endeavours to engage him in therapy. If he is permitted to orate his life aspirations and achievements in an unthreatened monologue he is contented to attend the sessions. If I dare to confront him about any aspect of his story, stirring the possibility of having to reflect on himself, his calm defences tumble into a mild chagrin and contempt and I have to be concerned that he will totally disengage. This leaves me in the predicament of facilitating the relating of his story while trying to limit the impression that I'm an uncritical admirer – a view which he will surely hold. Though I'm coming to believe his toleration of anything more demanding is somewhat remote, at the very least he's managing some basic level of engagement. Besides, considering he has few reasonable relationships within the unit and, seemingly, little or none outside, he does not attempt to manipulate me for any special consideration or to play me off against the other staff or patients. Perhaps he has simply learned not to trust a soul! Even though I've found him to be a thoroughly likeable, courteous and articulate character with a sense of humour and a full beamed smile when he's in the mood, I've also gained a real sense of what little provocation he would need to descend from conviviality into an aroused, explosive combatant. It is a view shared by the rest of the team and, since I am about the only staff member he will work with, I am prompted to broach the subject of the index offence to discover if there's been any change here. Though an ironic term to use in the forensic field, I *have a stab* at approaching the issue. Kevin's steadfast stance has always been that his lad simply slipped on the wet bathroom floor, resulting in him banging his head as he fell – that neither Kevin nor his partner were present in the bathroom when the incident occurred and that Kevin found him on the floor, unconscious.

* * *

So during a forthcoming session I introduce the subject which he has studiously avoided and which I need to attempt to look at with him. After some preliminary entrée I eventually propose: 'Regarding the death of your son, Kevin, I cannot begin to imagine how difficult it must be for you to contemplate a different version of events to what you've admitted to over the years.'

'Well, I don't have to consider a different version of events,' in guarded understatement. 'I've said what happened. The Home Office can't accept my version because they, and the Police, and the Courts all work in unison. Why should they believe a black man! Good God, no, they couldn't do that!'

'But the Home Office can only be waiting for you to admit that you were directly involved – provided that's the truth, don't you think? And, if that *is* the truth...'

'The truth? Why don't they believe *me*? Why have they insisted all these years that I should have to own up to what they're demanding? What difference does it make now? Haven't I served my time? What does the legal system have to gain from holding onto me? Vindictiveness, that's all! They've had more than their pound of flesh. Over 20 years, man!' And that is the key, of course. It is the effrontery of not being believed, that the Law could oppose him, and that it's still not satisfied with the price he's paid – all on his own terms, though, unfortunately.

'Well, do you accept that there have to be prescribed limits on what individuals are permitted to do, and that they are limits which apply to everyone?'

'Of course. What a damn stupid question, if I may say!'

'The Law judged you to have gone beyond those limits; that you meted out your own justice.'

'I've had plenty of dealings with the Law in my time to realise that it's never taken my side! And so it proved to be in this case. Justice! Pah!' he responds, incensed with passion.

'Well, you know what was said in court about the circumstances of your son's death. Do you want to talk about that here, at all?' I return, quietly.

'What good would that do?' he flashes back.

'That's for you to decide in one sense, Kevin. I believe it would be most important for us not to avoid the subject. For myself, I would like to hear what happened in your own words.' He has become very quiet and looks away, clearly mulling over this prospect. He's still managing to sit out the session. To my surprise, the atmosphere becomes less tense and he actually seems to relax. He is looking away, far away beyond the window, and I sense an air of defeat and resignation mixed with his hostility. I yearn to spill out with evangelical fervour. 'The truth? Don't you see, Kevin? The truth will set you free, literally!' But I have come to understand how an admission of the truth will be more of a defeat than a victory for Kevin. Truth or no truth, over 20 years of imprisonment has been the cost that he has had to bear, and it has been his choice. Maybe he needed to be punished, to punish himself? Alternatively, whatever he did that night when his son died, he believed that he was doing the right thing even if the ultimate consequences were unintended. He has defended himself against guilt all these years and it has sustained him, permitted him the empowering affirmation of righteous indignation. And, whatever the legal niceties, there is his mental health that lies in the balance and he probably knows that as well as anyone.

One or two sessions later, Kevin made the following admission when I again broached the precise details of his son's death.

'It's all very straightforward. There's nothing much to say about it. My missus and me were watching the TV in the living room and we heard the boy playing about upstairs when he should have been going to sleep. I was angry with him and called him down the stairs. All I wanted to do was discipline him. That's my right as a father. I pushed him, but not that hard. I didn't hit him.' I'm stunned for a few moments, completely taken aback. Where do I go from here? I wait. Kevin is waiting. I sense that he will volunteer no more than the absolute minimum.

'You say you pushed him. Can you say exactly in what way?' I venture, as sensitively as possible.

'I pushed the lad backwards.' I look at him steadily. 'He struck his head against the bathroom wall, that's all.'

'*He* struck his head?' I pose, suggestively. He admitted to hitting his son's head against the wall, but only once. This did not tally with the post mortem evidence of the lad's several injuries which suggested more than one blow. Neither at this or further meetings did he elaborate on this. He had not purposely intended to hurt the boy, he said. The revelation was quite something – a breakthrough of some substance, after over 20 years of stolid denial. Okay, relative to the post-mortem results, there was still a minimisation of the act but there had been an essential admission of personal culpability and this would be a beginning for the Home Office, surely. I informed Kevin that it would be indispensable that I relay his description back to the team, to which he agreed. In turn, the Psychiatrist fed back the surprising submission to the Home Office and Kevin began the slow process of rehabilitation back into the community. It would have to be a slow progress. Firstly, arguably, his anger had been relatively contained within the controlled environments of the last 20 years and he had not really been tested by normal, everyday stressors. Then there was this situational avoidance of remaining aloof from company – staying out of potential conflict, most probably – which rather predisposed everyone to doubt his conflict-resolution skills since he didn't give himself the opportunity to display them much. Perhaps he had sufficient self-awareness to realise he did not have the requisite self-control, so better to stay out of harm's way. But these could be balanced with his maturation that had probably dampened his pugnacity. And, in the last analysis, what likelihood was there of a similar incident to his index offence recurring once back in society? His personality was characteristically inflammatory and invariably attached the blame for any breakdown in relations to other parties, rather than himself. There was some optimism, much reservation, but as to what else had changed, and how adaptable he would be, time would tell. For there was also the straightforward complication of having to adjust back into society after experiencing the restricted opportunities of a life sentenced prisoner.

It took but a short time before Kevin opted out of our sessions. I imagined he believed he had come to the end of any narrative he was prepared to share and most certainly wasn't going to tolerate any further exploration or introspection. *His* justification was that we were going too deep for him and he just wanted to be left alone.

* * *

At the commencement of my hospital experience in the '70s nurses hardly wrote any formal notes on patients. Today's contemporary, litigious environment predisposes them to write continually, following each shift, after each group session, and each individual session, relevant or not – just as long as their arses are covered. Notes take various forms and may have negative and positive connotations, comment on a client's improvement and activity, decompensation, riskiness or dangerousness. Relative to the latter, every member of staff, of high degree or low, has an indefatigable responsibility to inform the rest of the team of anything suggesting a potential or actual threat of seriously deteriorating mental state, abscondence, self harm, harm toward others, or fire risk, for example. It is a very uneven ball game with one side entrusted to make official observations on the other. Once an individual is suspected of having a mental disorder, and acquires a psychiatric diagnosis, certain rules enter staff-patient relations. There is an unavoidable necessity for the staff to retain professional distance between themselves and their patients. Social intercourse is skewed so that the professionals should only be elaborating on their personal lives to an appropriate, but limited, degree. This is never made absolutely explicit and the manner of its fulfilment varies from individual to individual, but it means that there is an inequality between the two parties. The professional can forego the element of unravelling his personal life since the focus is turned to unravelling the inner world and motivation of the client. Within the specialism of forensic mental health every aspect of the client's world is scrutinised for signs and symptoms of mental unwellness, risk and dangerousness. The resulting scenario within the medium security units therefore approximates to what the Sociologist, Michael Foucault, characterised as the "carceral archipelago". This described the Victorian prison network, which resembled a group of islands containing its incarcerated inhabitants, having every feature of their daily lives observed and adjudicated on by the authorities. The unpalatable, but necessary, truth is that forensic mental health demands a degree of surveillance and monitoring which is nothing less than an explicit form of social control, and of a far more intrusive nature than anything which pertained to the old asylum era. Hospitalisation is used to create security and safety, and to set boundaries within which therapeutic exploration, confrontation and risk taking can occur. In short, that these measures enable some control over clients' deviant propensities until such time as they can take back self-control. But these conditions for establishing a therapeutic framework have to apply to in-patient, out-patient and community settings.

Due to the nature of our clients' offending history we have a precise dilemma in the forensic mental health field which is not quite so prevalent in general mental health. This is because mental illness is not, of itself, generally considered to be criminogenic. That is, it does not causally generate criminal behaviour. However, there is definitive evidence that certain symptoms of mental disorder are causally related to violence and these focus on the content of certain delusions and hallucinations. It is safely predicted that violence is associated with a patient's unfounded beliefs: that they are being physically influenced by other forces or persons, or being poisoned; after having misidentified someone as a threatening agent; of being persecuted in some way; or of experiencing bodily sensations; or of hearing voices commanding them to enact some instruction. Each of these may be amplified by the exact content of the belief, ideas or sensations; the exact construction of the ideas; the degree of conviction with which they are held; and the degree to which the patient is disturbed and preoccupied by them.

In turn, there is a socially pathogenic context which contributes substantially to the incidence of mental disorder, quite distinct from any constitutional precipitators. Health and disease are no accidents of biology alone, and there is an incontrovertible body of evidence affirming that health inequalities are causally related to socio-economic inequalities. The more disadvantaged end of the class structure is correlated with general poor health, relative poverty, overcrowded living conditions and inner urban space, poorer working conditions, impoverished life opportunities and diet, unemployment, and generalised deprivation. Just as conclusively, it can precipitate a susceptibility to mental disorder. In turn, the risk of criminogenic symptoms is also raised. And lower socio-economic status, frequently accompanied by a pre morbid history of lawbreaking, is certainly what characterises the overwhelming majority of our forensic client group. In other words, clients may have acquired a forensic tally both prior to the onset of their mental disorder, coterminous with its onset, and post onset. Poor people have little to invest in society. They have less to lose, and may have a more limited range of economic, personal and social resources with which to respond to adversity, and be persuaded to become disaffected. Amongst these, some of the most important may be active resistance to authority, and actual violence.

Forensic mental health staff, while ostensibly health agents enabling people to come to terms with their mental illness, are also required to help the patients comprehend any associated dangerousness that might potentially threaten either the safety of themselves, their family, the staff, or members of the general public. To cover both poles in this relationship between mental illness and dangerousness there is a demand for scrupulous observation of any phenomena – comments, conversations, behaviour, reading and TV material, general interests or preoccupations, etc – that may cast light on the patients' deviant functioning. In short, the clients soon realise that to offer any hint of risk to other residents or staff, however close the relationship, is to risk raising the alarm, increasing personal scrutiny, changing/increasing their medication, intensifying the therapeutic work, and delaying their discharge. The clients have to make choices at every stage of their residency as to how much they can afford to expose to the staff or whether they are prepared to accept the more protracted consequences. All staff, of whatever discipline, attempt to manage this dilemma by openly admitting to the clients that it is their professional duty to share with colleagues any information which might reveal some potential risk or danger. Then the clients are not so likely to feel that they have been snitched upon or have their relationships jeopardised. For staff and patients engaging in individual therapy the stakes are even higher. The therapist and client have consecutive sessions of focused time, exploration and discovery. The unavoidable depth of relationship and objectives unearths a good deal of psychological material which, even though it has been excavated in a private setting, must enter into the professional melting-pot. The therapist must, necessarily, become a conduit for passing on a person's private thoughts and feelings. Since there is a vested interest in discovering any material pertinent to a forensic motivation, the rôle sometimes has the feel of a detective spilling the beans as a policing agency. The client spontaneously obliges with biographical background which the therapist may view as further evidence of potential dangerousness. It is a dilemma which becomes increasingly uncomfortable as the therapist and client struggle with the ambivalent dynamic around trust which must, of necessity, be enacted. For his or her part, the therapist can only justify the ongoing reporting back of a client's motivations and revelations on the basis that what is known by the whole team can help to develop a fuller picture about what the client has to learn to manage. In turn, that this will anticipate and prevent future crises and help determine what will need to be in place to help him/her cope more effectively.

Two standard practices are now performed by the Unit nursing staff, these days, in this respect. They both stemmed from Stan's work using the Cognitive Behavioural Therapy model and both are prepared programmes. One is to help educate clients about their specific disorder in what is called "illness awareness" which is performed in individual sessions. The second is an interpersonal programme of "early warning signs" which is designed to uncover those signals which will predispose a client's mental state to deteriorate so that, so warned, they may put in place certain thoughts or actions to prevent the slide into illness. Neither of these would have been remotely envisaged in the past.

During those ignorant days of the Mental Hospital the patients' delusions and hallucinations were of the order of psychological stigmata. They amounted to sensory and intellectual blemishes that marked their incumbents off from normal people (and staff). In themselves, they were sufficient to confer upon them the label of madness. That doesn't imply that this does not still persist. But at least such techniques as "illness awareness" and "early warning signs" that are used today, along with the collaborative format that accompanies them, are truly empowering for the staff – as well as the patients

353

– so that they are not completely impotent and do not have to be wholly reliant on medication.

In other respects, clinical strategies in mental health are both conflating and diverging. For example, Cognitive Behavioural Therapy is attaining the status of an orthodoxy based on its capacity to establish evidence of its efficacy in changing/improving clients' conduct. Overall, it is considered value for money: the aims of the therapy are modest – that is, focused on specific symptoms – it is time limited in terms of the requisite sessions; and the training of the therapists of shorter duration, and relatively inexpensive. In these respects – and this is not the place for an extensive discussion on the subject – it has given the elbow to more protracted, more broadly focused, evidence impoverished, and expensively trained, therapists operating in more traditional psychodynamic/psychoanalytic models, who trawl the unconscious depths. However, the current demand for evidence of therapeutic efficacy is bound to produce proof of efficacy in every therapeutic model in time.

But there are also welcome signs of divergence and unorthodoxy. Serious consideration is again being given to questioning orthodox interpretations of "psychiatric" phenomena. The mental health association MIND – the National Association for Mental Health – now publishes material which questions traditional symptoms and labels. Rather than stamping such phenomena with deleterious connotations a body of authors promotes a more positive perspective such that a client's "voices", for instance, can be made sense of, and should be accepted, rather than dismissed. They argue for a more accepting approach which encourages clients to try to make sense of their voices, thereby giving them credence, and enabling the "sufferers" to accommodate and live with them. Similarly, as in the days of the anti psychiatrists, the traditional psychiatric diagnoses are under attack for their distorting, meaningless and invalidating influence. Delusions and hallucinations should not be "cured" but should be viewed as extensions of mental activity occurring in the lives of normal people. This is exciting stuff which will make many uncomfortable, while some feel uplifted, but time will tell as to the impact on the psychiatric and political establishments.

Chapter Six
Policy, makes Practice,
makes Perfect

A NY SIGNIFICANT CHANGE TO PUBLIC SERVICES RIDES on a groundswell of momentum originating in social, professional and political development. Whether there are any determinate relations between the three elements is impossible to say but, intuitively, their inter-relationship integrates all three into a cumulative policy making agenda that is logically progressive. But, at some level, politics is meant to make policy, and policy is meant to give political direction to practice. The intention is that the resulting governmental drive, by invigorating further increments in voluntary, professionally mandatory, and statutory activity, so impacts on the service delivery to patients that it transforms both the practical and ideational landscapes for health. The succession of formal reviews, policies and legislation in the United Kingdom over recent years has tried to do just this – to fundamentally reorganise general, physical, and mental health care. It is useful to consider two main policy eras in relation to general health and mental health changes: the first being a Conservative Government era; the second a Labour administration. These initiatives, from both eras, conceivably fell into four broad areas – professional development (I'll stick with nursing), NHS reorganisation, mental health reorganisation, and patient status evolution. Each represented successive reversals to the mental health care appertaining to the hospital asylums.

The latter part of the Conservative era included a reorganisation of the NHS itself. The *Working for Patients (1989)* review delegated the responsibility for delivering healthcare so that NHS Trusts had more control over their own localised population needs and the associated service responses. From this launch, the **NHS and Community Care Act (1990)** advocated the development of health services within the Community and away from hospitals, and a greater collaboration between the health services, social services, and the independent sector. It promised that the mental health system would be more supportive, and based on preventative and crisis intervention strategies. Both the relocation of services and the legislative transformation were predicated on the evolving policy of closing psychiatric in-patient beds and the closure of the traditional asylums. Health service units could no longer take themselves for granted. In came service contracts and *service-purchasers* who sought out "value for money" *service providers*. These service providers' activities and health outcomes were rigorously evaluated on a competitive basis. Therefore, units had to be seen to be performing effectively at every level of service provision.

The reorganisation of mental health strategies, specifically, was also keeping pace with the changing health climate. One of the most prominent, at this time, was the introduction of the **Care Programme Approach (1990)**. Mental health provider units were to combine with Social Services in better coordinated "care programmes" between hospitals and the community to improve services for people with mental illnesses. So, for those accepted by specialist psychiatric services, that is, patients admitted to hospitals, these detailed aftercare programmes were to be in place prior to the patients' discharge. This was to ensure that patients were not left to drift unattended and unsupervised in the community, as was probably the case in the old hospital era. Introduced to ensure that the mental health services did not lose contact with former in-patients, the benefits were numerous. Any patient who was admitted to an in-patient facility was to be allocated a key worker – later renamed as a Care Coordinator – who would hold overall responsibility for coordinating the patient's care following discharge, geographical relocation, or involvement with other agencies such as the Police or Prison Services. Potentially, this meant that every patient had swift access to an ongoing relationship with a member of the mental health team so that any deterioration in mental state or other cause for concern could be rapidly assessed and acted upon. Continuity of information gathering and sharing was likely to be optimised. Any doubts about the necessity for this goal of keeping tabs on discharged patients were regularly media-fed with the often fatal repercussions of failures to do so. Patients who had been lost to a more rigorous monitoring, or whose mental status had deteriorated, but been underestimated, could resort to elaborately disturbed conduct, even committing homicides.

The year 1992 was a singular turning point for mental health management from all professional, political and public standpoints. At a general policy level from 1992 onwards, mental health was one of an inclusive group of five health targets given particular emphasis in the Department of Health's *'Health of the Nation'* drive. In the same year the Department of Health and the Home Office, in a joint enterprise, brought out the *Review of Health and Social Services for Mentally Disordered Offenders and Others requiring Similar Services*. This Reed Report, so-called because of its lead author's name, was the most in depth assessment of "forensic" mental health services to date. It examined the special issues emanating from various client groups: those with learning disabilities, brain injury, hearing impairment, drug and alcohol mis-users, sex offenders, potential suicides, children and adolescents, elderly people and women. It also argued for all agencies dealing with these classes of patients to develop guidelines for risk assessments and that these should be integral to the Care Programme Approach. As if a testing riposte to the very veracity of this document and strategy, the real life circumstances of mentally disordered offenders and the disjunction with actual mental health practice, revealed themselves in two singularly adverse incidents. They loomed like ironic clouds over the launch of the Reed Report that year. In one incident, Ben Silcock was mauled when the young schizophrenic, with many years of psychiatric treatment, jumped into the lions' enclosure at London Zoo. Arguably, it was the sheer ordinariness of the venue and its family orientated associations that alerted the media, public and political sensibilities. The most widely publicised adversity was the case of Christopher Clunis in the same year. Christopher Clunis, a psychiatric patient with chronic mental disabilities and years of in-patient admissions, fatally stabbed a member of the public, Jonathon Zito, while he waited for a train at Finsbury Park railway station. Again, the utter ordinariness of the situation, and the consequent vulnerability of Joe-Public, stunned the nation. Clunis' failing mental state had been grossly misjudged by his psychiatric services despite giving evidence of increasing dangerousness which should have been acted upon.

Yet further calamities were to erupt in the same year. Not only were the professionals deemed to have failed psychiatric patients in the somewhat fledgling Community Care programme, but they were exposed as continuing to do so within the more established institutions. The Ashworth Report constituted nothing short of a cataclysmic admonishment of high security mental health services as published under the mantle of a *Report of the Committee of Inquiry into Complaints about Ashworth Hospital (1992)*. The "ritualistic character of nursing practice" and "the continuation of traditional routines and programmes associated with the concept of the total institution" were just for starters in this catalogue of hellish revelations. It gave examples of the insular, contra-therapeutic thinking in identifying written care plans which, in the instance of managing a patient declaring suicidal ideas, proposed to "implement seclusion regime" as a first stage.

Thereafter, the indispensability of the Care Programme Approach was consolidated by the Department of Health's "Health of the Nation" *Building Bridges Report (1996)*. This invoked the requirement for inter-agency collaboration and coordinated care for severely mentally ill people in the community. The integrated association and networking of mental health services, social services, police, probation services, magistrates' courts, housing agencies, voluntary sector and patients' carers represented one of the signal departures from the original, one-horse hospital regime which operated exclusive of almost any other agency. That same year, probably the most infamous of cases in recent decades – the Russell family murders by Michael Stone – took place but it would be a full ten years before the Inquiry Report would publish its findings.

The third area of significant change that fundamentally reversed the former hospital regime was the development of the status of patients. This was intended to transform their situation from their historical reliance on the beneficence of individual practitioner propensities and aptitudes, or the abusing control of institutionalisation and some renegade practitioners. To begin with, as its very title suggested, the *Working for Patients (1989)* review proclaimed service users as the pinnacle focus of the NHS. Then the *Patients Charter (1991)* defined all health units in consumerist terms so that they should deliver services that conformed to predetermined standards, which were a public entitlement, and reflected patients' rights. The promise of such explicit health service ideals, within limited time schedules, had never been so illuminated! The *Disability Discrimination Acts (1995) and (2005)* ventured to protect the rights and equal status of all disabled people, including those with mental health problems, so that they were not disadvantaged by their various health conditions. They were to be supported in retaining their homes, to have access to banks and personal accounts, and to employment, transport and buildings access. More than this, all employers and service providers were to actively remove any organisational, interpersonal or physical obstacles that would prevent access to services by people with disabilities.

Nursing development played its part, too. From the document *A Vision for the Future (1993)*, mental health nurses were expected not only to respect the religious and cultural beliefs of their patients, but to acknowledge the associated influence these would have on the course of their illnesses and behaviour. The main impetus behind this was to give validation to the culturally diverse responses which different ethnic groups revealed during the course of mental illness which could be at some variance with the indigenous population. For instance, African-Caribbeans were often ascribed to be loud, frenetic, aggressive and drug fuelled, and research was beginning to show that these cultural characteristics were being aligned with violence and dangerousness, thus attracting disproportionate convictions for lawbreaking. Then came the wide-ranging review, *Working in Partnership (1994)*, the thrust of which demanded that mental health nursing should examine its practice relative to the needs of its service users. And, with a realisation that things had still not altered from the old hospital routines and rationales, it recommended that patients should not be expected to conform to the convenience of the service. One of its most potent recommendations was to target the implementation of Clinical Supervision. Instead of progressing through a career relatively unattended by superiors, as we old stagers had done in our early careers, each practitioner would be helped to advance their nursing practice and therapeutic skills, and identify their failings and prejudices, through the guidance of an experienced clinical supervisor.

* * *

So significant a political issue was it perceived to be that the Labour Party's 1997 election victory heralded a massive funding injection for health, including mental health, and a veritable deluge of legislation and official guidance. This could not have been conceived just for political goodwill or conviction. For 18 years, British voters had consigned the Labour Party to the arid wastes of parliamentary opposition and political impotence. Now that they had come in from the cold they wanted to remain basking in the warmth of the popular vote and political recovery and their initiatives would also benefit from the trials, errors and lessons of the earlier administration. The manner of carrying this out would rely on a conflation of factors: part political pragmatism and political ideology; part scepticism toward the competence of the professionals; and a necessary supervisory political tutelage. Pragmatically, there was no greater assurance of remaining adopted by the enfranchised public than sorting out the unlimited demands which were necessarily made of the NHS to meet the nation's health care needs. Ideologically, a quasi-Socialist "Third Way", enjoining private finance and the public purse, would ensure that the NHS was accessible to all, free at the point of delivery, and obliterate the internal market of the preceding Conservative era.

Government could not depend on the professional staff who were too preoccupied with the daily clinical and organisational functioning of services to be able to steer a strategic route for the future of the NHS. Hence the need for centralised Governmental intervention that would be disseminated through the various Ministries and Departmental bodies to produce a rationalising constructive programme of development. From the very first year of Labour's office the Department of Health went mad with a policy deluge!

The Labour administration elevated mental health to sit among one of three health priorities, along with cancer and heart disease. Altering the course of mental health management, the Labour administration sought to build on the principles of the previously mentioned *National Health Service and Community Care Act (1990)*, at the same time acknowledging that since 1990, 24,000 psychiatric beds had been closed and lost to the mental health services. Anecdotally, despite these intended changes in priorities, a good deal of Community Care had been described as amounting to an isolated bedsit, fortnightly or monthly visits by a nurse to administer an injection, and a place at a Day Hospital.

Within months of election, it produced a white paper of intent called *The New NHS Modern and Dependable (1997)* which epitomised the coming reforms by prioritising the needs of patients as its focus and the building of public confidence in the NHS as a public service. To effect this service transformation there would be a radical structural overhaul: the twin national resources of (i) National Service Frameworks, and (ii) National Institute of Clinical Excellence: and the localised systems of (iii) Clinical Governance and (iv)a Commission for Health Improvement, embedded in all the NHS Trusts. All these would become the statutory duty of Trusts to either directly implement or access. The following year these several strands were fleshed out in *A First Class Service: Quality in the NHS (1998)* in which the following strategies were to be institutionalised: the National Service Frameworks; the National Institute for Clinical Excellence; Clinical Governance; and the Commission for Health Improvement.

The National Service Frameworks would provide a range of forums where the Government would collaborate with professional groups, service users and their carers to draw up service models for specific service or client groups. The model was to be based on a systematic appraisal of need and service so that, in ascertaining from the best available evidence that something actually worked in practice, this "best practice" would be disseminated across the country to avoid unacceptable variations. With the accumulating demands on the NHS, the model would accumulate an evidence base of the clinical effectiveness of specific interventions and set national standards. To help supply some of the evidence to these Frameworks, an independent organisation called the National Institute for Clinical Excellence would arbitrate on the available evidence and produce authoritative clinical guidelines on good practice that promoted good health and prevented ill health. Its guidance would be subdivided into three areas: public health, health technologies (treatments), and clinical practice.

The NHS Trusts were to be made more accountable for their service delivery to a patient led service through the implementation of Clinical Governance. Each NHS facility was to incorporate an organisation-wide accountability for quality provision at every level of that particular service. Quality was not an aspiration, a target; it was now a statutory duty among all NHS bodies. Clinical Governance would be an engine for continuous improvement in clinical care and standards that would include: users, public and carer involvement, strategic planning, risk management, staff perform-ance, professional development, clinical effectiveness, information manage-ment, leadership and team working. All this activity would be monitored at the local Trust level through quality improvement activity which would involve, firstly, clinical audit and, secondly, practice that was based on evidence. This clinical audit would be an indispensable tool for reviewing patient care and care outcomes by measuring actual care against explicit criteria. Measuring the effectiveness of different features of a localised service against definitive quality based standards would be qualitatively different from the value free, open-ended exploration of research projects. In a logical progression, the search for quality demanded that any clinical, managerial or organisational practice should require evidence of its efficacy. And so was ushered in the strategy of seeking out the evidence base that would support the effectiveness of any given practice. Ultimately, the evidence base would discover the most appropriate health prevention strategies, treatments, and practices rather than waste time on less effective interventions. It would provide more consistent care, improve practitioners' status, and increase value for money. In turn, the findings would assist the process of implementing necessary change.

Lastly, the Commission for Health Improvement would be another inde-pendent, complementary body that would systematically monitor and check that all these preceding targets were being met in clinical practice. CHI was to become the performance regulator of the NHS so that, against specified performance indicators, each hospital unit could be ascribed a performance rating.

Since these bountiful arrangements applied to the entire Health Service the Government, presumably, felt it necessary to support these with specific arrangements for the Mental Health sector. Consequently, in the same year, ***Modernising Mental Health Services: safe, sound and supportive (1998)*** was assembled in order to raise expectations about the management of mental disorder. At first glance, this guidance seemed to extend the theme of user consumerism and libertarian policy making to the mental health client. Acknowledgement was made of the prevalence of mental illness in the general population, of its complexity, and that there was still far too much stigma attached to it. Reference was made for the need for society to be more inclusive of the mentally ill, to allow them their independence like anyone else, and that they should not be socially excluded. Advancing this, patient needs could not be fully appreciated unless the service users themselves were fully engaged and empowered within the services. Then, masked in the same libertarian ethos, the tone of the document veered toward the policing of certain psychiatric conditions. Accumulating concern was attached to those people with mental illnesses who had either been involved in serious harm toward others, or in the killing of other citizens. It categorically stated that there was a clear relationship between mental illness and violence and that Care in the Community had failed. In essence, it proposed that the only means of avoiding the adverse fallout from mental people with mental illness was to take every possible step to comprehend the wide-ranging needs of such clients so that the potential adversities could be anticipated and operations effectively accessed and implemented.

This anti libertarian tenor was indubitably predicated on an incident of almost unequalled horror from the year prior to Labour Party re-election and, therefore, very fresh in the shared political, public and professional memory – the Michael Stone affair, as alluded to earlier. The need for proactive, Governmental intervention in the face of professional failures from a number of State agencies was overwhelming. However, it was not until 2006 that the final Report on this so sad episode was finally published.

The adverse political agenda associated with people with mental illness was reinforced with the joint Home Office/Department of Health proposal *Managing Dangerous People with Severe Personality Disorder (1999)*. Its inaugural sentence in the Executive Summary encapsulated this adverse view: "the challenge to public safety...people with severe personality disorder... risk of serious offending". People with severe personality disorders were seriously anti-social, dangerous, and posed a high risk to society because of committing serious sexual or violent crimes, or arson. While the public safety was the key concern, crime reduction would be a corollary if these people were better managed, treated and given therapy.

The Department of Health managed to slip in more guidance with *The National Institute for Mental Health in England (2001)* again using the notion of social inclusion, that prioritised the needs of service users, their families and carers as the focus for mental health organisations. It proposed that this be yet another resource to assist in the reshaping of services and practices with a coordinated programme of research, service development and support that would also incorporate the work of all the foregoing agencies mentioned here. The service would be accessed through regional Mental Health Development Centres which would disseminate mental health knowledge and skills.

An example of the product of the NIMHE, above, was the policy entitled ***Personality disorder: no longer a diagnosis of exclusion (2003)***. So controversial was this minority that a dedicated infrastructure was to be inaugurated for those specifically diagnosed with antisocial personality disorder. Linked to this novel infrastructure would be a welcome requirement for targeted staff training and development, not least in evidence based treatment programmes. At last, proper competency-based training to enable those staff that were selected, not just nursing staff, to realise therapeutic expectations! To facilitate selection, selection procedures, attuned to appropriate personal characteristics and skills, would be preconditions for working in such units. Again, the awareness of the attritional effect of what was described as hostility, conflict, behavioural dyscontrol, self harm and resistance aroused by this client group, the need for emotional resilience and boundary setting from the staff members, and a willingness for staff to engage in their personal reflective insight, all pointed to a concerted Governmental attempt to get this one right! What was most illuminating, though, was the recognition of the indispensability of therapeutically trained clinical leaders. Clinical leaders rather than managers – hallelujah! It seemed that, for once, policy would reach right down to the quality of staff/patient interaction.

In the meantime, why not contrive a document or two for the nursing profession while they were at it? So the Department of Health duly launched ***Making a Difference: strengthening the nursing, midwifery and health visiting contribution to health and healthcare (1999)*** which set out strategies for nurses to enable them to be fit for practice relative to the plethora of advances swirling about them.

* * *

364

There was yet another group of legislative changes enacted in the immediate wake of the Labour government accession which drove a cart and horses through any lingering doubts about the primacy of an individual's citizenship rights, whether of a general political order or of health. The **Data Protection Act (1998)** provided for the regulation of information appertaining to any individual, and the conditions under which this was to be protected, disseminated, or disclosed. Such sensitive data included a subject's racial or ethnic origin; political and religious beliefs; trade union membership; physical, mental or sexual conditions; and offence background. Access to this sensitive information would be strictly controlled to prevent access from outside agencies, and would require the consent of the individual subject.

Virtually simultaneously, another generic enactment, the *Human Rights Act (1998)*, would reach down into every minute crevice of public and private life, safeguarding freedom of expression and thought, and prohibiting any discrimination or the abuse of individual rights. This must have added a good deal of the stimulus to the *NHS Plan (2000)* which acknowledged that the NHS had failed to keep abreast of societal changes and outlined a health service which would be designed around the patient. The user focus screams out of its subheadings: information to empower patients; strengthening patient choice; protection for patients; new patient advocacy service; rights of redress; patients' views; and patient representation throughout the NHS. Due to the high public expectations of NHS performance, for quality treatment and care, an update on progress in implementing the NHS Plan came in the *NHS Modernisation Agency (2003)*. Abrogating the "monolithic paternalism" of the old NHS and heralding innovative working practices, it included detailed areas for patient focused benchmarks that should constitute the "Essence of Care". Respect for patients as individuals, the privacy of patient information, and only sharing that information with other agencies with the client's consent, give a flavour of these.

If any further enhancement was needed it came in the shape of the *Equality Act (2006)* which combined all the major inequality issues in Great Britain under one legislative cloak to ensure protection across the variable fields of age, disability, gender, sexual orientation, gender reassignment, race, religion, and belief.

* * *

In the main, libertarian credentials informed Government health policy and legislation by the early millennium as it attempted to conflate the philosophical, social, professional and political trends of the times. Contrarily, there was more than a hint that one civilian class still deserved some exemption from general liberties – the mentally disordered. Believing that the ***Mental Health Act (1983)*** required updating to take account of current concerns, it disseminated the contents of a contemporary ***Mental Health Act***. The impending legislation met with the concerted criticisms of an alliance of mental health professionals who considered the political response to certain issues to be draconian. The concerted outcry derived from the proposed new powers to enforce medication on patients discharged from hospital if they should decline to continue with their treatment, and for the enforced hospitalisation of people diagnosed with personality disorders who were deemed to pose a threat either to themselves or others, even if they had not commissioned any violence. (Incidentally, these criticisms mirrored past concerns among sections of the criminological fraternity about the "net-widening" strategies within the criminal justice system which have subjected convicted people to a host of community restraints and sanctions as alternatives to their traditional imprisonment – electronic tagging, community curfews, community service punishment, and Probation monitoring, etc.) Eventually, the legislative overhaul of mental health culminated in the ***Mental Health Act (2007)*** which retained the provision of enforced treatment of patients, with the implementation of the Community Treatment Order.

Now, among the most contemporary debates – trumpeted by Professor Dinesh Bhugra, the incoming President of the Royal College of Psychiatrists, in 2008 – is the receding and parlous condition of acute in-patient services. He has enumerated the funding shortages, the concentration of the most highly disturbed clients, the stigmatisation, the impoverished environments, and dangerousness for both staff and patients that prevail within these facilities. No doubt some reversal of mental health policy will be effected when the service strains become overwhelming and in-patient provision will be consolidated again.

* * *

Sprinkled, from time to time, about this centralised bureaucracy have been the reports of Inquires into homicides perpetrated by patients with histories of mental disorder which have cropped up with uncomfortable regularity, and which significantly informed the more draconian impetus in the *Mental Health Act*. Every one of them has contained derogatory findings, and necessary recommendations, for all professional groups and agencies managing the mentally disordered, including the occupation of nursing.

Equally spontaneous and haphazard have been the voluminous publications by nurses themselves. With the burgeoning opportunities afforded by an explosion in professional publishing, nurses now contribute their own research papers, compose text books, and submit journal articles on current practices so that they enjoy an unprecedented ownership of their professional development, as well as the personal kudos that accompanies such ventures. Some of this is commissioned work, much derived from voluntarily submitted endeavour, but all permitting opportunities for the profession to contribute to its own destiny.

Lastly, some space should be given to the expansion of rôles, positions and service designations. In our earlier era, a nurse was a Student, then a Staff Nurse, then a Ward Charge Nurse or Sister, in a rigid hierarchy which gave only an indication of relative seniority and authority. Clinical expertise or focus was obfuscated. The contemporary professional scene is one of deliberate specialisation of purpose and function. A clinical nurse can be better identified as a Community Mental Health Nurse, a Cognitive Behavioural Nurse Therapist, or a Practitioner in an Early Intervention Psychosis Service, while those with a specifically managerial orientation have exclusively managerial titles, such as Ward Manager. Allied to these is the precise breakdown of purposes in the form of job descriptions.

* * *

What can be concluded from all this endeavour when in the making of this veritable Health Reformation, swathes of vanishing Rain Forest have been lopped and pulped in the process! How is it possible to measure what all this has achieved?

Firstly, there can be little hesitation in acknowledging that developments

367

in public and health policy, if not exactly making health practice, provide it with a significant strategic orientation. Indeed, if health occupations were capable of self-administered, strategic innovation there would be no need for governmental involvement. How progressively would mental health care have moved along if the old Mental Hospitals (nee Asylums) had not ceased to function? They would still be in operation now, and who knows how little would have changed? For sure, people with mental health difficulties would not be managed at their General Practitioners' surgeries but would be carted off to the local bin! Fortunately, liberal democratic politics has to have some level of dialectical relations with so-called public opinion, evolving ideas and values, and to act upon these. That's the theory!

Intended change may not be happening in practice or, at least, nowhere near what may be expected from policy refinements. Distinguishing between the structures and responsibilities of the various organisations that actively contribute their services to mental health, or monitor the work of others, made all the more confusing by the areas of overlap, could be described as some new art form. Practitioners, people who actively work in mental health (or any area of health), need time to systematically locate, study, and assimilate the policy development, particularly during the current Labour administration. In lieu of such, I would defy any general or mental health practitioner to admit to keeping pace with the constant precipitation of initiatives. There is no political bias intended when I admit to having found the policy evolution of the Labour era to be less containable due to its complexity, sophistication, and accelerating volume. Speaking for myself as a health worker, being on the receiving end of this persistent frenzy was like being deluged in a constantly precipitating reform-storm so that the inexorable momentum for innovation seemed to rise up like a menacing flood. There was such a sense of being swept away in defeated resignation that one option was to climb onto the terra firma of ignorance, avoidance and withdrawal, and just let the torrent pulsate below. And if that was speaking as someone in a fairly responsible position, who was senior and motivated, how did those colleagues at the coal face, with even less reflective time, deal with the policy deluge? I would venture that a huge amount of policy making, research findings, and nursing literature, including innovative clinical practices – all merge into a blur of rarefied abstraction totally lost to the average clinical practitioner, including myself.

Intended change may not be happening, in practice, for other reasons. No matter how well a job description or organisational rôle is formulated, this is only half of a potential professional capacity. The other potential is the individual who performs the tasks and position in question. The position maketh not the man – necessarily! Each relies on the other and, in turn, the organisation depends on both. Conversely, the person of the right calibre can have a huge influence on a service despite a limited authority and position because he/she has the competence to reach way beyond the confines of their limited designations. The characteristics of the individual, their motivation and intelligence, are as indispensable as ever. The difficult task of managerialism is to harvest the qualities of the individual, within the constraints of their explicit and scrupulous remit, for broader organisational results. To some extent control must be in tension with creativity.

Personally, the only areas of policy innovation not taken on board by fellow colleagues that frustrated me concerned clinical practice. Perhaps I was rather naïve in assuming that nurses would be drawn to developing their nursing and therapeutic skills. Even those with an obvious interest in and concern for their clients seemed content to operate at a surprisingly prosaic level of clinical practice. What were the predominating factors: lack of encouragement, or personal motivation, or professional endeavour, or plain intelligence or, alternatively, were they content with their lot and saw no need to strive to better themselves? Whatever the cause it was clear that many did not better themselves. Nursing care plans – that described the written planning around patients' needs – said as much about the limitations, as well as the credentials, of their authors. Nurses still have difficulty in generating cogent ideas to guide their everyday practice which is why there is still such a heavy reliance on the straightforward demands of the "shift" routines and waiting on patients' behaviour to dictate the practice agenda. I would not be alone in my disappointment. Once, when I was engaging in an audit of another medium secure facility, one of the Consultant Psychiatrists committed himself to remarking that his nurses' care plans were "puerile and vacuous". Criticism indeed!

There are some *must do* practices which are stringently carried forward. Such an example would be the mandatory Care Programme Approach which no one would let slip when it provides incontrovertible evidence of agencies' collaborative monitoring of clients and a sound protection when things go wrong.

From my experience, one of the most remarkable features of mental health practice has been the low take-up of clinical supervision by the average nurse. Of the many reasons people give for non-participation, my take on it is that because their practice remains solidly task orientated around organisational routines, they doubt the pertinence of submitting themselves to unnecessary scrutiny. Additionally, they also perceive the strategy as yet another means by which their superiors can monitor their behaviour and press out more productivity from their bones. Why offer themselves up to such vulnerability? In my own case, the facility of clinical supervision probably offered more opportunities for developing clinical competence than any other single professional initiative, though I count myself fortunate enough to have had a practising, and training, psychotherapist for the purpose during a rigorous psychotherapy training.

There is also ample proof that change neither covers the ground in a long, steady hike, nor in short sprints, and that behaviour, particularly institutional behaviour, cannot be altered by law alone. There are a couple of unavoidable conclusions for consideration. However well intentioned the centralised policy initiatives may be, if local managers do not provide time to relay their contents to practitioners, they will not be incorporated into practice. Innovations in clinical practice, especially, have to be both organisationally managed and individually supervised. The alternative is that, save for individual strivers, long established rituals, even today, remain far from touched, and change far from perfect.

* * *

With the advantage of retrospect, I have had time to re-evaluate my experiences in the field of mental disorder and mental health, and how my own life articulated with these. I am left with the confusing emotions of awe, trepidation and some satisfaction. Incontrovertibly, identifying and categorising citizens who deviate from normal mental health and devising the political and professional arrangements to manage their problems, while simultaneously safeguarding their personal rights and the rights of the general community, remains a problematic, philosophical issue. None of the arrangements remain constant indefinitely. The nineteenth and twentieth century asylum movement, if it could be called such, was a concentration of mental disorders that was inspired by a belief in social and institutional entitlement over its patients. Those of us who operationalised the movement could justify our work because of the protection afforded to patients, managing their accessibility to effect treatment, preventing further deterioration and an inevitable slide into poverty, and shielding them from society's condemnation. But the extent to which the county asylums, along with all subsequent arrangements, have effected favourable solutions to those stamped with the master label of mental illness remains open to speculation on a number of counts. Not the least of these is that there is always the theoretical and real possibility that the illnesses might have spontaneously remitted without medical interference. Also, the notion of psychiatric asylum has a perverse connotation since it frequently requires the exercise of power against individuals, against patient classes, in the event that those individuals do not volunteer compliance to medical prescription. Ironically, the fact that society believes it has the right to seize the mentally disordered means that, ultimately, there is no asylum for them in society. Even when discharged, there can still be a continuing legal right of seizure! The same applies with equal rigour to the situation appertaining to the current Community Treatment Order! It remains a conundrum as to whether, once a citizen has acquired the label of an enduring mental illness, and the economic and social repercussions that this has for them, there can be any such notion as "asylum" for them in society. Additionally, there are the critical ingredients of whether there is a potential for risk and dangerousness toward both the patients and the public so that the mentally disordered can never properly be freed from this stigmatisation.

The model into which I was trained and encultured was almost entirely an institutional one. Crucially, this predetermined the status of the patient category as necessarily excluded, dependent, submissive and passive recipients of paternalistic treatment strategies and management. It could not be said that we offered a state of "inviolable protection" for our patients. Hospital facilities will never again evoke the image of the staff centred commune that facilitated disproportionate rights, comforts and opportunities. At its worst, the system which explicitly sanctioned the control of one social group by another, also inadvertently facilitated physical and emotional neglect. When the nursing staff were known as Charge Nurses that was because it described their roles precisely. They were *in charge*. Every decision was sanctioned by them, and without them was nothing sanctioned! In their wake, all staff, not just nurses, ordered, controlled, delivered instructions, expected and ensured compliance, expected little resistance, and acted with relative impunity. In large part, patients were inmates, not exactly captive, but certainly socially, economically, geographically and politically marginalised. This was not wholly deterministic of what might seem the oppression of a minority, however. Manifestly, the system was well intentioned. Many, if not most, individual practitioners meant well. Many patients would have benefited. In one sense, at least, patients did have a degree of asylum – they were hidden from direct public admonishment and ridicule. But as long as this situation prevailed, mental patients would never be reacclimatised into their rightful place in the world.

It is tempting to believe that the progressive manoeuvres have been serendipitous for those who suffer with mental ill health. The contemporary psychiatric model is, in large part, the very flipside of the position that appertained when I entered the mental health services over three decades ago. The situation has evolved, and been reconstituted. The concept of mental disorder, per se, continues to be refined, elaborated, and redefined. The treatment technologies are a heavily subscribed university of discrete agencies, intrusions and ideologies. As the Community model has taken precedence over subsequent years, mental health care has assured patients that they have an inclusive, consumer orientated status of equal citizenship. We may still make reference to the *patient*, without defamation, but move freely between the enlightened nomenclature of *client, resident* and *service user* also. Mental health policy intends that the status of the mentally unwell steadily converges with that of other civilians. Even so, it has never been able to dispense with the necessity for some residual, institutional apparatus. Institutional reconstruction now accommodates the mentally disordered in the wings of local hospitals, community homes, or permits residential privacy. It also includes the newer species of forensic institution, diminutive in capacity, garnished with security technologies, and restrictive of patients' movements, in which a minority of more problematic patients is contained. Indeed, there is a strong argument that the widespread development of forensic in-patient services across the country, for patients who are difficult to manage or dangerous, actually represents a creeping forensic asylumisation. In most instances, these new institutions have been constructed within the grounds of the older asylum estates.

But if there are any lessons to be learned from the past, they must include all of the issues that were pertinent to the hospital/asylum era. The pertinence applies to staff attitudes, the community model, current in-patient establishments, and social prejudice. Just because policy has promoted liberty and a social valorisation of the mentally unwell, this cannot guarantee a translation into mainstream social acceptance. In practice, they are exposed to direct public ignorance and scepticism. The mentally unwell remain a disadvantaged constituency who are not fully integrated and remain stigmatised and marginalised. Professional staff acquire professional values and education which will militate against such prejudice but they are themselves still members of the wider society and will retain variable degrees of social distance and defamation toward their charges. There is huge professional and political pressure for the clients to accept prescribed medication, to have regular meetings with Care Coordinators, and to refrain from the use/abuse of recreational drugs. And in-patients are now regularly tested for illicit drug use via drug screening methods. Does all this detract from their human rights? Is it right that, for the sake of everyone else, they should abide by the rules that are fashioned to avoid inconvenient behaviour, and to safeguard the safety of the rest of the populace? Conversely, it is not so easy to disclaim this right if their psychological decline generates adverse symptoms and dangerous outcomes for others with whom they may come into contact. However, when they are vulnerable to such decline, they should be entitled to every accommodation and distraction that benefits each and every one of us.

Chapter Seven
Closures

I N THE TOWN IN WHICH I SPENT my earlier years, the five psychiatric hospitals in that vicinity doubtless acclimatised me to a degree of acceptance of such institutions and their residents. I have spoken of the variegated influences at large in the old hospital and this has not deterred me from speaking of the overall experience with fond nostalgia and sentimentality. It is not difficult for me to admit that when I commenced my work at a hospital asylum I projected onto it the image of an idealised, protective refuge from which I differentiated a broader world from which I had an expectation of being met with either opposition or indifference and there is every reason to believe that this expectation was ingrained from my childhood parenting pattern. But there was the issue of dysfunction and mental disorder that had trickled through the family which may have precipitated a degree of personal identification with matters psychological and psychiatric. The nursing rôle was empowering because, in the opportunity it gave for caring for others, it permitted me subconsciously to care for my own needs, too. Also, it conferred upon me the offices of authority and responsibility, and an adulthood for which my background had not prepared me. My choice of working with the difficult to manage and aggressive clients, then the dangerous, forensic clients, afforded an even greater empowerment as if I was resisting, and taking control of, those that threatened to harm and control others. Ultimately – me. The threat of killing had been verbalised in my family and my emotional allegiance had, essentially, been killed off, in any case. So perhaps I had had to resist those who threatened harm to others, and had been prepared to work in high security conditions to contain them, so as to insulate them from the opportunity to do so? Perhaps that fear was so predominant that I could not be satisfied with external measures of containment – hospitalisation, security technology, medication, forceful restraint – so that I felt resource to internal control was warranted? Had I elected for a psychotherapy training to effect, subconsciously, an internal management of particularly dangerous clients even though I manifestly had intended to improve their understanding and insight? Or had I attempted to defuse their dangerousness toward me, especially? Was there a deeper motivation for working with Kevin, an adult who had killed his child? Did the psychotherapy training allow me to control my own forceful resistance to opposition and indifference – ultimately, my own lethal potential? Could these retrospectives of my career trajectory be mere notional conjectures, or rhetorical confabulations, or profoundly subconscious truths?

* * *

I count myself fortunate to have been enabled to move away from the disadvantage and the restricting personal repertoire that dictated my early life. For this I have to thank the opportunities I had to internalise more nurturing and empathic individuals, and many positive life experiences which, together with that "irrepressible life force", came to make all the difference to my journey. Among the several historical footnotes left by the Conservative politician, Enoch Powell, was his view that every politician's career ends in failure. Does this not apply to most careers and the majority of folk? Ambition tends to level out for everyone so that they resign themselves to an eventual, inevitable plateau, with no further advancement, a failure to attain further aspirations, or where they reach their level of personal incompetence. After approximately 30 years of mental health work I resolved to withdraw from my career, prematurely, because I had failed to attain the position to which I had aspired after two attempts. The position of Nurse Consultant evaded me and opened up that frail wound of rejection so that I withdrew from trying to secure the position again. I had enjoyed a core profession of nursing and it had provided me with innumerable opportunities, knowledge, experiences and skills. In many respects, I suppose I no longer viewed myself as a nurse engaged, as I was, in more explicitly therapeutic work and rôles. Ironically, in my imagination at least, I had achieved that in which I might have expected to have been engaged when I first set out on that occupational journey in 1973. The rôles which I'd taken on over more recent years were somewhat independent ones as if I was preparing to break away. And, as the accompanying therapeutic road seemed to offer up other personal possibilities, there emerged a need for a new beginning while the nursing journey was all but at an end. I was releasing myself from the constraints of organisational life and its requisite conformity, avoidant of the deluge of policy impositions, and even more resistant to managerial interference and managerial supervision (quite distinct from clinical supervision). More saliently, I was loosening the ties with the institution, wanting to express my individuality, and yearning for a freedom of sorts. I tied up my career and left the secure unit, and the hospital estate, for the last time. Borrowing the oft quoted lines from T.S. Eliot's "*Little Gidding*", I could say:

> "What we call the beginning is often the end
> And to make an end is to make a beginning.
> The end is where we start from."

* * *

Within a year or so of my premature retirement and the end of my nursing career, the medium secure unit, itself, had been closed, transferred, and incorporated into another surviving hospital complex in a different location. It had lasted barely 20 years and would now deteriorate and be vandalised as was its progenitor, the old asylum. It will become no more than a relatively modern, architectural scrape with none of the surviving grandeur of its host. The entire estate is now closed off, being of no further practical use.

* * *

Much as the buddleia seed was carried fortuitously, indigenous and migrant staff, and fatalistic patients, had settled at the hospital as if carried by opportunistic winds. It would find some way of surviving, of moving on, as conditions so demanded, just as the hospital regime and staff were required to readjust to change and development. As the place became moribund, losing its potency and its control, it was as if the buddleia had been liberated to flourish abroad, just like the patients were let loose and became free to roam the community. I am confident the buddleia migrated once again, populating new vacancies, novel localities, needing no tending, no particular nourishment, accommodating any conditions without protection. Watch the ragamuffin buddleia play in every dirty crevice of the secure unit set on the site of the old orchard, sprouting another wreath around another institutional death, honouring its memories.

* * *

Not long afterward my mother died. No coincidence, but a resonance, all the same. There was much I had to forgive of her and much, no doubt, she had to reproach me for. But much is now reconciled.

* * *

ABOUT THE AUTHOR

Stephen Burrow was born in Surrey, where he commenced a Mental Health Nursing career in 1973 in days when mental illness was speedily hospitalised. The majority of this career was spent in the public sector forensic specialism, with varying spells in medium security mental health units and high security hospitals, as well as Prison Service Health Care. After qualifying as a Registered Mental Nurse in a Surrey mental hospital, he gained most of his professional training, and academic and professional development, in London: a first degree in Sociology from the London School of Economics, University of London; a General Nurse training, and a Practitioner training in Cognitive Analytic Therapy, from St. Thomas' Hospital, London; and positions of Honorary Lecturer and Honorary Researcher at the Institute of Psychiatry, London. A Masters Degree in Crime, Deviance and Social Policy was obtained from the University of Lancaster.

He spent time as an Editorial Board Advisor to two professional journals and has, himself, published a number of editorials, articles and book chapters. Two pieces of published research constituted a brief survey of the self-harming behaviour of Special Hospital patients, then, a multi-disciplinary study of the treatment and security needs of the same client group. He has longed to write more creatively about the machinations of the mental health organisations which he experienced, and not least, to convey his strong nostalgia for them.

Retiring early to the heart of Dorset, he now indulges his lifelong enthusiasm for the countryside, wildlife and rambling. He his devoted to his two daughters, Rachel and Heather.